Beyer, Peacock
locomotive builders to the world

ISBN 1 898432 05 8

Copyright Richard L Hills, April 1982

First printed April 1982
This impression printed July 1998

Printed and bound in Great Britain

Beyer, Peacock
locomotive builders to the world

RL HILLS
and
D PATRICK

Venture *publications*

Introduction to the original edition

The publication of this history was made possible by Beyer, Peacock & Co Ltd presenting its archives and the unique photographic record of its products to the then embryonic Manchester Museum of Science and Technology when Gorton Foundry was closed in 1966. One of the Directors, David Patrick, had always taken a keen interest in his Company's history and continued this after he retired. He was able to contribute personal recollections based on his own involvement both with the design of the locomotives and in the daily affairs of the firm. Sadly he passed away before this book could be published, but members of his family have continued to help in many ways, including the onerous task of proof reading.

Such a book as this has inevitably depended upon the help and advice of a great many people, too numerous to mention individually in a short introduction. There were, of course, other members of the Company who helped preserve the records and who have answered many queries and helped in other ways since the closure. The staff of the present North Western Museum of Science & Industry have helped seek out information, reproduced photographs, etc and of course many railway enthusiasts have contributed details and lent pictures of Beyer, Peacock locomotives at work all over the world. But mention must be made of Mrs Mumford, daughter of H. W. Garratt, who allowed me to go through her father's papers, to Mr R. Kirkcaldie, the penultimate Company Secretary, who contributed the account of the final years of the history and to Prof. Jack Simmons who drew my attention to the Robertson Papers in the National Library of Wales. Finally, without the Joint Committee of the Museum granting me three months leave of absence, the manuscript would never have been finished.

Of course it has been impossible to reproduce all the information and illustrations within a single volume, so much has had to be omitted. The aim has been to cover a broad spectrum of the Company activities and to give sources wherever possible so those who want more details can know where to find them. One problem has been to compare Beyer, Peacock's achievements and success, particularly on the economic side, with those of its rivals because this is the first time that a detailed account of a private locomotive building firm has been published. It is hoped that this will be not only a useful reference work but also an authoritative account of one of Britain's most famous engineering firms. I would like to give my very great thanks to all those who have contributed to this book, and helped to make it an outstanding record.

Richard L Hills
April 1982

Introduction to the third impression

This is a fitting moment to issue another reprint of this history of Beyer, Peacock, because, today, just over thirty years since the closure of Gorton Foundry, it is possible for people in Britain to travel behind an example of the most famous type of railway locomotive developed by this Company, the Garratt, on the newly reopened Welsh Highland Railway. Like these engines, and ordinary ones for example on the Isle of Man, this book has stood the test of time and I am delighted that it is being reprinted so it will become available to more railway enthusiasts and researchers. While there has been more information published about individual railway companies and locomotives, the history of Beyer, Peacock itself has not been investigated further and so the text has been left unaltered except for the addenda and corrigenda.

Richard L Hills
July 1998

Contents

Ex-Lancashire and Yorkshire Beyer, Peacock 0-6-0 No. **52044** pilots USATC No. **72** on an enthusiast's open day at Oakworth on the Worth Valley Railway in March 1977. [Photo Dr. L.A. Nixon]

In 1966, Beyer, Peacock & Co. Ltd. built its last locomotive and Gorton Foundry, its Manchester works,
closed its doors for ever. So ended a period of 112 years
during which this great Manchester company distinguished itself as designer and builder of locomotives for
railways all over the world. The total of over eight
thousand locomotives, most of them steam, ranged over
an enormous variety of types, from the tiny works shunters
of 18in gauge to the vast Beyer-Garratts, some of which
were the largest steam locomotives in the world outside
the United States of America. At the beginning of this
Company's history, railways were the dominant form of
transport, but from the beginning of the twentieth century
this position began to be challenged until, at the end of
this story, railways were contracting as a result of the
severe competition they were facing.

The Beyer, Peacock story commenced in 1854, when two
men, then working in the Manchester area, joined forces
and devoted their combined resources of capital and
know-how to the business of locomotive construction.
As both men had been concerned with railways practically
all their working lives, their experience went back to the
very early days of this industry. They were personal
friends through meeting each other in their previous work,
and their qualifications were happily complementary
and well suited to their new enterprise. They contrasted
markedly in personality and sprang from very different
backgrounds, but both had risen from humble beginnings.
These two men were Charles Frederick Beyer, then aged
41, and Richard Peacock, aged 34.

Charles Frederick Beyer, [*1813 - 1876*]

Beyer was born on 14 May 1813 (1) in Plauen, Saxony,
of parents who earned a meagre living as hand-loom
weavers. Charles was going to follow his parents in this
trade and was already bound in a three-year apprenticeship to a master-weaver when a lucky event occurred.
While still a lad, he had amused himself by making models
of buildings and had been encouraged in drawing by a
young architect, who had settled for a time in Plauen.
When a doctor called to attend a sick elder brother, his
eye was caught by a portrait drawing done by Charles,
which was framed and hung on the parlour wall. That
drawing, and others, were sent to the Kreishauptman,
or Chief District Officer, who forwarded them to Dresden
soliciting Charles Beyer's admission to the Polytechnic
School there. His father knew that he could not afford to
maintain his son in the capital, but agreed to terminate

the apprenticeship and allowed Charles to go because he
was afraid of offending the high official.

The State awarded the sum of 30 thalers annually to
each person entering the Polytechnic, but this did not
cover all the expenses, so Beyer had to exist on a pittance,
as no help could come from his family. At the end of six
months, he seriously contemplated returning home, but
one of his professors persuaded him to stay on. He was
able to supplement his meagre resources by doing a few
small jobs, such as keeping some of the time books.
His struggles at this period are best illustrated in his
own words:

> "A benevolent lady of Dresden was in the habit of
> giving, every Friday, a good dinner to the two or
> three pupils of the Polytechnic School who had
> distinguished themselves most during the pre-
> ceding week and I can still recall how eagerly I
> strove, week after week, to be one of the chosen
> few that I might not lose a meal which was almost
> necessary to my sustenance, so hardly was I
> obliged to live." (2)

He continued this struggle throughout the four-year
course and successfully completed his studies. During
that period, the whole of his expenses, including the fees
of 120 thalers, did not exceed 410 thalers, or about
£61 10.0, an incredibly small amount even at the then
value of money.

On the completion of his studies, he went to Chemnitz
to work in the machine shop of Herr Haubold, to whom,
twenty years later, he was to sell machine tools made at
Gorton Foundry. In his first year there, he received wages
the equivalent of 6 shillings a week, which were increased
in the following year to 9 shillings. His progress must have
been more than satisfactory for he received a grant of
300 thalers (£45) from the Saxon Government to visit
England for studying and reporting on improvements in
machinery, principally textile machinery, and cotton
spinning. After returning home, he made his report and
received an ex-gratia payment equivalent to some £10
from the mill-owners of Chemnitz, as well as a reward
from the Saxon Government. Although only 21, he was
offered posts of mill manager in both Chemnitz and
Dresden, but he refused them and, in 1834, left Germany
and returned to Manchester.

Through the growth of the by now wholly mechanised
cotton industry Manchester had become the engineering
centre of the world, so it was only natural that a young
technician should seek employment in the Mecca of his
trade. There was, however, probably another reason for

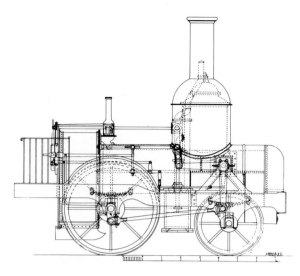

Roberts' first locomotive, the ''Experiment'', was delivered to the Liverpool & Manchester Railway in May, 1833. It was not a success, for it consumed 40 per cent. more coke than the other engines, the variable expansion valves did not work properly and the vertical cylinders made the engine ride roughly.

Richard Roberts, 1789-1864, the most versatile and prolific inventor of the nineteenth century.

selecting Manchester, although the accounts unfortunately are at variance over this point. On his earlier visit to England, Beyer definitely would have heard of, and some accounts say actually met, Richard Roberts, the man who had perfected the power loom, and had recently developed a successful self-acting spinning mule. When he returned to England, Beyer applied for work to John Sharp, a partner with his brothers Thomas and Chapman, and Richard Roberts, in the firm of Sharp Roberts & Co., but was apparently refused, possibly through fear of a xenophobic reaction if a foreigner was employed in the works. Beyer, on being offered a sovereign instead of a job, is reputed to have said somewhat indignantly, 'It is work that I want,' and such was the look of chagrin on his face that Sharp took the risk and offered him a subordinate position as an improver-draughtsman. Even if he had not met Roberts before, his work soon caught Roberts's attention, for he was a quick and natural draughtsman and was, in addition, a good mathematician.

Roberts' second design of engine was not much more successful. Three, including the ''Hibernia'', were delivered to the Dublin & Kingstown Railway in 1834 and, through their vertical cylinders, still rocked so badly that they bent the rails.

It was at Sharp Roberts that Beyer made his mark as a locomotive designer, and laid the foundations upon which he was to build so successfully in his own firm. In 1832, Roberts had designed for the Liverpool & Manchester Railway the **Experiment**, a locomotive with vertical cylinders which was not a success and which was hardly improved when built in its final form as the **Hibernia**.(3) An order for ten engines for the Grand Junction Railway was received in November 1835 (4) and it fell to Beyer's lot to carry out the design, under Roberts's supervision. These engines were built on orthodox lines as 2-2-2s, with 5ft diameter driving wheels, 12½ x 18in cylinders, and weighing 12½ tons. They proved to be the prototype for the range of Sharp 'singles' which made that Company famous. Soon Sharp Roberts began to rival the older firm of Robert Stephenson & Co., and gained a most distinguished reputation for the design and workmanship of its locomotives.(5)

Roberts had long been famous for his designs of machine tools and had been one of the first people to build a planing machine for metal. He recognised the need for improving the quality of workmanship in locomotives as they were being constructed at that time and used his engineering ability to produce high quality products. Not only were his frame structures stronger and the fastenings better, his bearing surfaces were better-proportioned, better finished and, wherever possible, machine-work was substituted for the hand-fitting employed by other manufacturers. (6) Roberts is credited with introducing the balancing of driving wheels as a regular feature, (7) plate framing with a sweeping curve over the driving axles to reduce the depth of the horn-plates for the carrying axles,(8) and also helping to develop 'lap' on the slide valves to lessen steam consumption.(9) Yet between 1832 and 1840, Roberts was extensively engaged in the perfecting and manufacture of his self-acting mule, (10) and must have left the locomotive side of the business largely to Beyer.

Beyer was soon made head of the Drawing Office, and when Roberts retired from the firm, in 1843, became the Chief Engineer and, later, Manager. He carried on the Roberts traditions, particularly with the use of machine tools. It is interesting to note that in about 1845 a cylinder split on a Sharp locomotive supplied to the order of James E. McConnell, then Locomotive Superintendent on the Birmingham & Gloucester Railway. A replacement arrived within three days 'which actually fitted in every particular, so that not a file had to be put upon it; showing the perfect manner in which they were got up'. (11) Beyer was responsible for introducing proper engineering drawings at Sharp Roberts in place of earlier rough off-hand chalk sketches and took his system (as well as some of the actual drawings and books) to his own firm. (12) To him is ascribed the introduction of solid inside frames running the full length of the engine, with the axle guards

One of the standard Sharp Brothers "Singles" of about 1847-8.

fire-welded on, (13) and also the improvement to the Stephenson disc regulator by placing it in the dome and operating it by a double lever and vertical links. (14)

Beyer is said to have been one of the first people to give the boiler freedom to expand, and did not fit any parts to it which would be affected by that expansion. This improvement was probably made shortly before 1850 because the Sharp Brothers drawings in the Science Museum, London, show locomotives with frames firmly riveted to extensions on the sides of their fireboxes, but, in 1851, a 2-2-2 well tank for the London & South Western Railway clearly had the boiler mounted with brackets attached to the sides of the firebox and resting on top of the main frames. (15) He also advocated a high centre line for the boiler to help ensure steady running for he argued that the problem was one of dynamics and not statics. The height of the centre of the boiler from the rails in locomotives built subsequently has proved that he was correct.

Around 1842, Beyer developed a design of tender which became a standard for British railways, with outside frames and axle-boxes, and the springs placed outside above the platforms.(16) Then in 1844 six particularly successful 0-6-0 'luggage' engines were built, four for the Sheffield, Ashton & Manchester Railway and two for the Manchester & Birmingham. On 3 October 1846, one of these hauled a train of 101 wagons, weighing 597 tons, from Longsight, near Manchester, to Crewe, covering the 29 miles at an average speed of 13.7 m.p.h. This was no mean feat for an engine which weighed only 24 tons, though that was enormous for those days. In June 1847, one of these engines ran 3,004 miles on the London & Birmingham Railway with a consumption of coke of 0.214lb. per ton per mile, while the next best engine burnt 0.38 lb. These performances were records for their time. (17)

From this it will be clear that Beyer's reputation as a designer of powerful and economical engines soon became well established. His designs were noted for their clean lines and well balanced proportions, and it is probable that these features, for which later British locomotives became renowned, were introduced to this country by a foreigner! (18) By the end of 1849, Beyer had helped to turn out 600 locomotives, most of them being 2-2-2 types.(19) He was well known in engineering circles, and there is a story that the decision to found the Institution of Mechanical Engineers was taken after an informal meeting of engineers at his home in Cecil Street, Manchester, in 1847. Even if this is not true he and Richard Peacock were certainly present at the gathering of engineers on the Lickey Incline, generally regarded as the birth of the Institution. (20) George Stephenson was elected its first President and Beyer one of the Vice-Presidents. Beyer was one of the first to read a paper to the Institution, and chose as his subject a 'Description of the Luggage Engine **Atlas** etc'; a little later he presented another paper 'On Boring and Fitting Up Cylinders for Locomotive Engines'. (21) He was naturalised in 1852 and elected to the Institution of Civil Engineers in 1854, but, in the meantime, his fortunes changed.

In 1842, John Sharp Senior died, so on Roberts's departure in the following year, the firm was continued by the sons, John and Thomas B. Sharp, and John Robinson and the name changed to Sharp Brothers. In the summer of 1852, C.P. Stewart became a partner and the name was changed to Sharp Stewart & Company. (22) Then Thomas B. Sharp retired. Whether Beyer felt that he ought to have been offered a partnership, or whether, as another story has it, he was refused the hand of one of the Misses Sharp, Beyer left his old firm and, after a few months travelling about England and the Continent, returned to Manchester and formed a partnership, with Richard Peacock, to make locomotives.

Richard Peacock, [1820 - 1889]

Richard Peacock, seven years younger than Beyer, was born on 9 April 1820, in Swaledale, Yorkshire, (23) the seventh son of Ralph Peacock, who was foreman of several leadmines in the area. His father, besides being a prominent member of the Wesleyan church, was something of a doctor-cum-chemist-cum-vet who helped both people

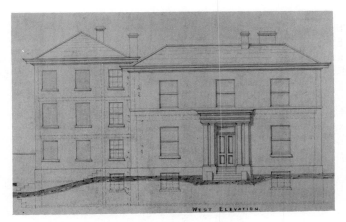

C.F. Beyer's house at Stanley Grove, Manchester. There were over twenty five rooms, with eight bedrooms [including those for the servants], one bathroom, breakfast, dining and drawing rooms, library and a beer cellar.

Richard Peacock's last portrait, 1888.

and cattle in their illnesses, and who also undertook the repair of clocks and musical instruments. In 1825 he took his son Richard to see the opening of the Stockton & Darlington Railway and, because the new railways offered excellent employment opportunities to people experienced in mining or tunnelling, he left Swaledale in 1830 to become Assistant Superintendent to the firm of Walker & Burgess, who were building Marsh Lane Tunnel, close to the Leeds terminal of the Leeds & Selby Railway.

This move gave Richard the opportunity to go to Leeds Grammar School for four years. He left when he was fourteen and became apprenticed to the Leeds firm of Fenton, Murray & Jackson (later E.B. Wilson & Co.).(24) This was a well established engineering firm, which had connections going back to the earliest days of steam railway locomotives, for Mathew Murray had helped build the rack engines for John Blenkinsop in 1812. When Richard Peacock joined, the Company was making locomotives for the Liverpool & Manchester and the Leeds & Selby railways. Peacock was placed under the direction of Richard Jackson, the active head of the firm, and so gained an insight into every branch of the business, but he devoted himself more particularly to the locomotive side. At the age of seventeen, he married a daughter of Mathew Murray.

At the age of eighteen, Richard Peacock was offered the post of Locomotive Superintendent on the Leeds & Selby Railway. This department had been mismanaged and several people had been tried but had failed to secure the confidence of the Directors. At first Peacock declined the offer because he felt that some of the older men would not take orders from anyone so young. Peter Clark, the General Manager, who had noticed Richard Peacock when visiting his father, assured him that he would undertake that part of the business, and so Peacock agreed to the appointment. In fact there was no difficulty with the men as soon as they saw that their new Superintendent knew more about the job than they did.

When the Leeds & Selby was taken over by the York & North Midland Railway, under the ruthless and unscrupulous Railway King, George Hudson, Peacock refused the offer to move to the locomotive works at York. So in 1840, he set off to London and presented himself to Daniel Gooch. (25) Gooch was in charge of the locomotive side of the Great Western Railway, which Brunel was then building. Here Peacock seems to have tried his hand at a variety of work, from superintending a gang of workmen to driving Brunel up and down the line.

In 1841, the Manchester & Sheffield Railway was nearing completion and Peacock applied for the position of No. 1 engine-man. (26) The letter inviting him to the interview was delayed, but he was given the post without even being seen and so moved north to Manchester, arriving there a week before the first locomotive. Very soon he assumed control of the locomotive department. The first workshops for this line were situated near Hyde in wooden huts, which became inadequate as the railway expanded and developed. Accordingly Peacock was asked to find another site. The place he chose was at that time well in the country, at the small village of Gorton, whose 2,000 inhabitants were mostly engaged in the hatting trade.

At Gorton, Peacock had the task of planning the new locomotive depot and railway workshops, and was particularly proud of a circular domed engine shed which he erected. In a paper given to the Institution of Mechanical Engineers, he gave his reasons for choosing the site:

"These works are erected at the first point from Manchester where the Railway and the land take the same level, viz. at Gorton, about two miles from Manchester, this being considered the best position from its being near the principal terminus of the Company's lines, and from the facility with which materials can be procured and workmen engaged: and though it is a terminal establishment, with the advantage of being situated near enough to a First-class Mechanical town to secure any that may be had therefrom, it is sufficiently far out of it to be clear of the heavy local taxes with which such establishments in all large towns are burdened." (27)

Peacock was responsible for changing Gorton and Openshaw into an important manufacturing area, for he persuaded Jack Ashbury to put his extensive carriage works there, and also Sir Joseph Whitworth to move his gun factory and machine tool shop from Manchester there. (28) The near-by Stockport branch of the Ashton Canal provided another form of transport, but, more important, it provided water for the steam engines driving these new works, a facility which Beyer and Peacock were to use when they set up their own factory.

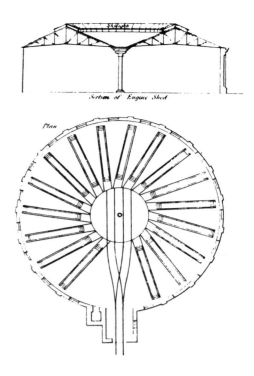

Peacock's circular engine shed at Gorton "Tank", completed in 1848, had a diameter of 150ft. With the main roof supporting column in the centre, the turntable had to have two tracks.

As early as 1841 the Manchester & Sheffield Railway ordered locomotives from Sharp Roberts (29) and regularly purchased Sharp locomotives thereafter. This may be how Peacock first met Beyer, and it is possible that they collaborated in 1844-6, when an 0-6-0 engine for the Manchester, Sheffield & Lincolnshire was the first to be fitted with a deep plate frame running the full length of the engine, (30) one of the most important improvements of this period. As he was concerned so much with the practical aspects of running railway locomotives, it was natural that Peacock would try to make improvements. In 1848 he held some comparative speed trials with engines of different makes and proportions, on the first eighteen miles out of Manchester of the Manchester, Sheffield & Lincolnshire Railway. (31) Then in 1850, he conducted a series of tests with the 0-6-0 Sharp goods engine **Sphynx** and established that it was better to place the orifice of the blast pipe just above the level of the boiler tubes and not at the base of the chimney, as was the practice up to that time. (32)

Peacock's part in the founding of the Institution of Mechanical Engineers has been mentioned already, (see p.10) and in 1849 he became a member of the Institution of Civil Engineers. It seems to have been Peacock who dissuaded Beyer from following his dreams of going to Oxford or Cambridge and convinced him that they could set up their own locomotive works. Accordingly he resigned his position with the Manchester, Sheffield & Lincolnshire Railway in 1854 and joined Beyer in the new venture. To the partnership Peacock brought an exceptional ability as an organiser of men, and competence in commercial matters, as well as valuable experience in locomotive operation and maintenance. He was a powerful, virile character, whose interests already included local public affairs and were to extend far beyond that in later years.

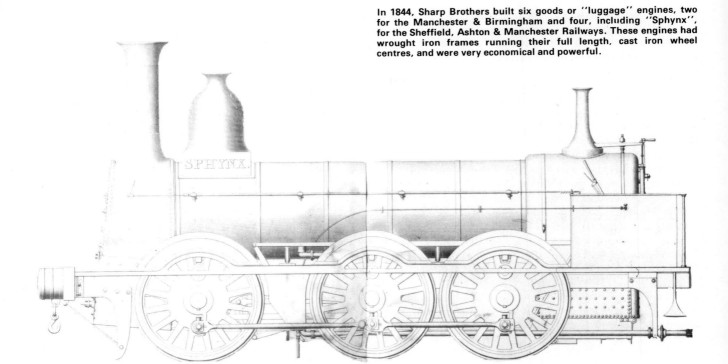

In 1844, Sharp Brothers built six goods or "luggage" engines, two for the Manchester & Birmingham and four, including "Sphynx", for the Sheffield, Ashton & Manchester Railways. These engines had wrought iron frames running their full length, cast iron wheel centres, and were very economical and powerful.

The Formation of Beyer, Peacock & Company

In the earliest years of railways, locomotives were practically all made by private builders, starting with the great pioneers, Mathew Murray of Leeds (1812) and George and Robert Stephenson of Newcastle-upon-Tyne (1823). They were soon followed by many others, including Charles Tayleur (forerunners of the Vulcan Foundry) of Newton-le-Willows (1830), Edward Bury of Liverpool (1830), R. & W. Hawthorn of Newcastle-upon-Tyne (1831), James Kitson of Leeds (1835), G. & J. Rennie of London (1838), Neilson & Mitchell of Glasgow (1843) to name but a few. In the Manchester area in 1854, the important manufacturers were W. Fairbairn & Sons (1839), B. Hick (1833), James Nasmyth (1839), Rothwell & Co. (1830) and, of course, Sharp Stewart & Co. (1833).

Meanwhile, the principal railway companies had established workshops where they were able not only to maintain and repair their own engines, but had the capacity to build new ones. For example, Crewe Works was originally built by the Grand Junction Railway and opened in 1843, turning out its first new locomotive in 1845. The London & South Western Railway was beginning to build some new locomotives at Nine Elms by 1845, and the Great Western Railway opened its famous works at Swindon in 1846. The works at Derby was originally built as a repair depot by the North Midland Railway, and did not build any new locomotives until 1851.(33) Other companies followed these examples, so the competition in the home market was intense, but in the overseas market, the era of railway development was only just beginning to blossom and opportunities were immense.

This was still the period of unlimited liability, which meant that the partners of a company were responsible for all its debts if the firm failed. Therefore it was a much more momentous decision to establish a partnership, and people tended to be involved in as few as possible. The foundation of an engineering firm needed quite a large capital sum to pay for the buildings and machinery before any products could be sold, and before there could be any income to help balance expenditure. Beyer had arrived in England twenty years earlier virtually penniless. Peacock could have had few savings when he moved to Manchester in 1841 and he was married with a family. It is amazing that they should have contemplated establishing their own firm to build locomotives using almost entirely their own resources. Yet this is what they proposed to do. From later figures, it seems that Beyer was willing and able to find £9,500, and Peacock was expected to contribute £5,500, but this money fell short of what they estimated they would require.

Therefore they had to borrow money from somewhere, and that source was Charles Geach. Geach was one of the founders of the Midland Bank, and had great business and financial acumen. He had an interest in the Park Gate Iron Company, which produced rails and axles for railways, was a director of the Manchester, Sheffield & Lincolnshire Railway, and was also the first Treasurer of the Institution of Mechanical Engineers, as well as being Member of Parliament for Coventry. (34) Thus he was well known to both Beyer and Peacock, and, with his help, they purchased twelve acres of land in Gorton on the other side of the railway line to Peacock's works for the Manchester, Sheffield & Lincolnshire Railway. Cows were grazing there on the first day of May 1854, but soon Beyer was relaxing on Saturday afternoons by cutting down the trees to make way for the new buildings.

A full account of the new works will be given in the next chapter. Here it will be noted merely that the buildings were sufficiently far advanced that summer for the first order undertaken, a cast iron drum for the Shrewsbury & Chester Railway, to be sent out on 10 November 1854. (35) But just at that moment disaster struck, for Charles Geach died on 1 November 1854, at the early age of 46.(36) His solicitors called in his loan, so in their predicament the partners turned to Henry Robertson.

Henry Robertson, [1816 - 1888]

The story goes that Robertson said he had no ready money and suggested that the partners should try Thomas Brassey, the great railway contractor. Brassey was unable to come in himself but thought so highly of the prospects of the new enterprise that he encouraged Robertson to go to some lengths to raise the capital and reverse his first decision. At this time Robertson was fully engaged with developing railways around Chester, and may have felt unable to devote sufficient time to the new company, for he was to be very involved in helping to run it.

Henry Robertson, 1816-1888.

Henry Robertson brought to the partnership a completely different type of experience with railways. He was born on 11 January 1816, at Banff in Scotland,(37) and was the youngest son of a family of eight. His father held an appointment in the Inland Revenue Administration, but he was not well off, and, if his son had failed to gain a scholarship, probably could not have supported him at Aberdeen University. Henry Robertson had received the degree of Master of Arts before he was twenty, when his father died and the family moved to Glasgow. There, as he no longer felt called to the Ministry, his original intended vocation, he followed his natural inclinations and began an engineering career.

He started work as a mining engineer in the collieries of Lanarkshire and later said that for months he never saw the sun except on the Sabbath. He hoped to start his own colliery on land owned by the Duke of Hamilton, but the Duke refused permission because he thought Robertson was far too young to assume so much responsibility. He therefore became a pupil with Robert Stephenson and helped to build some of the railway lines around Edinburgh and Glasgow. He was responsible, under Joseph Locke, for the actual levelling and setting out of that part of the West coast route over Shap Fell. (38) He acquired a little capital, and, more important, experience in handling contractors, when he obtained a contract for building some of the overline bridges on the Glasgow & Greenock Railway. About this time, he met Mathieson, a Glasgow contractor, through whom he obtained more work and also a recommendation that he should go on behalf of some Scottish bankers to report on the estates of the ironmaster, John Wilkinson, at Brymbo in North Wales.

John Wilkinson's will had been contested and the Brymbo estates were put up for auction by the Court of Chancery. Robertson reported so favourably that the Scottish bankers advanced him and some of his friends money to exploit them. That led Henry Robertson to move to the Chester and Shrewsbury areas from Glasgow in 1841, and he never returned to Scotland. Not only did he develop the Brymbo Iron & Steel Company and collieries in the Wrexham and Ruabon areas, but he realised the necessity for improved transport communications in that region and so helped to build most of the railways there. He was responsible for the lines between Chester, Wrexham and Shrewsbury; Shrewsbury and Hereford; Shrewsbury and Llandovery; Ruabon, Llangollen and Dolgelley; Bala and Ffestiniog and the Wrexham, Mold and Connah's Quay Railway.

Pale Hall, Llandderfel, between Corwen and Bala in North Wales, which Robertson had built for himself on the banks of the Dee.

He was responsible for designing the beautiful railway viaduct over the Ceiriog at Chirk, and the larger one over the Dee at Cefn. How he developed steel making at Brymbo, and his parliamentary career, must be passed over, for a full biography of this remarkable man cannot be included here. His death in 1888 prevented him being awarded a knighthood for his services to North Wales and the Chester area, so this honour was conferred on his son, Sir Henry Beyer Robertson.

Henry Robertson may have become known to Beyer either through his ironworks or by buying Sharp engines, in connection with his railway activities. The older Sharp brothers, Thomas and the John who originally offered Beyer employment, had bought iron from the Wilkinson who inherited the Brymbo estates from the famous John Wilkinson, (39) and it is possible that Sharp Roberts and Sharp Brothers continued to receive their iron from Brymbo. In 1846, Sharp Brothers supplied some 2-2-2 engines to the Chester & Shrewsbury Railway, the first of many orders for the lines with which Robertson was associated.(40) But there must have been a deeper relationship between the two even at this early stage. In 1853 Robertson was examining the state of the stock of the Shrewsbury & Birmingham Railway with "Mr. Dubbs, Mr. Beyer & Mr. Jeffreys and preparing affidavits". (41) Then in a letter dated 13 December 1854, before the formal agreement of their partnership was drawn up, Beyer wrote to Robertson:

"I am much obliged for your pleasing information respecting my God-daughter, May God preserve her and bless her. With kind regards to Mrs. Robertson, Yours truly, C. Beyer." (42)

Later Beyer was to buy an estate at Llantysilio, Llangollen, North Wales, close to where Robertson lived and which he left on his death to Roberton's eldest son, Sir Henry Beyer Robertson. These personal factors may be the reason why Beyer turned to Robertson when Geach's loan was withdrawn.

The New Company

The terms of this partnership have survived in the First Minute Book, and show that the original intentions of the founders were carried on until Gorton Foundry finally closed in 1966:

"Copy of the Memorandum of Terms of Partnership between Charles Frederick Beyer of 63 Cecil Street, Manchester, Richard Peacock of Gorton Villa, Openshaw, and Henry Robertson, Civil Engineer of Shrewsbury.

The Partnership to consist of the above named partners and to commence on the first day of January 1855 and to be for a term of FOURTEEN years from that date.

The Partnership to be carried on under the name of "Beyer, Peacock & Co."

The capital paid up to be £30,000 in equal shares of £10,000 by each partner subject to the provision in respect of the share of Richard Peacock as hereinafter provided.

The capital to be subject to be increased out of profits up to £90,000 with the sanction of TWO of the partners.

The Partnership to be allowed to borrow on mortgage £10,000 or an amount equal to one third of the capital at any time invested in the business exclusive of the borrowed money.

The business of the firm to be that of Mechanical Engineers and to be carried on at the premises at Gorton and to be confined chiefly to the manufacture of locomotive engines and other such light machines as the present works are adapted to make and no heavy machine work involving additional outlay of works is to be undertaken without the consent of all the Partners.

Charles Frederick Beyer and Richard Peacock to devote their entire time to the concern as Managers of the Works and to be paid for such Management a salary of £500 per annum each.

In the event of the death of one of the partners, the business shall be carried on to the end of the Partnership term by the surviving partners, the interest of the deceased partner remaining to his heirs, etc. etc. subject however to the right of the surviving partners to purchase the share of the deceased partner at a valuation to be decided upon by arbitration—such right to be exercised by the surviving partners within twelve months of the death of the deceased partner and the valuation to be completed without delay on either side.

With respect to the amount of the £10,000 to be paid by Richard Peacock, it is agreed that he shall pay £5,500 at the beginning of the partnership and the remaining £4,500 at the end of five years— viz. at the end of the year 1859 and up to that time he shall pay the interest payable by the firm on £4,500 of the £10,000 borrowed capital."

Sir Henry Beyer Robertson.

Full details about the financing of the firm in its early days have not been preserved, so it has been impossible to see how they managed to survive those first vital years and find the money to pay for capital equipment, materials and wages, until the first engines were sold. In the First Minute Book, there is a statement in January 1855, that the following amounts had been paid into the concern:

C.F. Beyer,	£9,524 10.0.
R. Peacock,	£5,500 0.0.
H. Robertson,	£4,000 0.0.

but this does not quite balance with a letter sent by Beyer to Robertson on 4 December 1854. From this letter, we can see the liabilities of the new Company just before serious production commenced:

"The total amount spent by us up to this day is £22,000, the amount paid up £15,000, making our total liabilities should we close the concern tomorrow, £6,500.

Our orders on hand amount to nearly £80,000 and to execute these in time and in an advantageous manner, it will be necessary to spend in tools £4,000 more.

The means required to conduct the business until it begins to bring returns and work itself will be as follows:-

Wanted immediately,	£2,000
" at Christmas	3,000
" by the 1st. of February (including £2,000 to pay for additional tools)	4,000
" by the 1st of March	2,000
" by the 1st April (including 2nd £2,000 for additional tools)	4,000
	£15,000
	(43)

For the first £5,000 needed before Christmas, Beyer and Robertson were going to find the money themselves, but they decided to take out a loan of £10,000 to help towards future financing. Orders at January 1855 stood at £73,445, so it seemed that the future of the new firm was assured.

2

Beyer, Peacock & Co. was started at a propitious time for, in spite of the Crimean War, it was a period of tremendous railway expansion, not only in Great Britain, but in Europe and elsewhere. Although Peacock had designed the workshops for the Manchester, Sheffield & Lincolnshire Railway, Beyer laid out Gorton Foundry. His note books show that he had begun to think about this as early as November 1853, and contain a drawing of a building made up of 12 bays, each 20 ft wide, flanked on either side by a foundry 16 ft wide, and a smithy with the same dimensions. There are further notes at varying dates for a grinding shop, boiler and smiths shops, etc., but the entry for 20 December 1853 is the most important.

"Build to begin with:

	yds	
Fitting Shops,		
a length of, say	54 x (3 x 16) =	2592 sq yds
Foundry,	40 x 16 =	640 sq yds
Smithy,	40 x 16 =	640 sq yds
Boiler shop,	40 x 16 =	640 sq yds
		4512 sq yds

This arrangement would put all the buildings in the same direction and have the advantage of having to cross only one yard to get to any of the shops."

(1)

Other pages contain notes for the construction of the shops, steam engines for driving machinery, line shaft dimensions, etc.

Beyer planned his works so well that he was able to start building in one corner of the twelve acres the partners had purchased, and gradually expand across the area so that, when Gorton Foundry closed in 1966, most of the original workshops were still standing. In 1856, Manchester was visited by one of the correspondents of **The Engineer** who went to Gorton and was very impressed with the layout and the buildings.

"I have lately had an opportunity of visiting an establishment which exhibits perhaps the best considered arrangements I have yet met with, for commencing the building of an engineer's workshop on a small, yet perfectly symmetrical plan, and which admits of almost unlimited extensions without in any way departing from the original arrangement of the nucleus. The establishment in question is that of Messrs. Beyer, Peacock and Co. of Gorton...

The buildings, being all of one storey, allow of their being lighted from the roof, and the effect is very cheerful and pleasant, while the additional

Gorton Foundry in 1856. The date of this, the earliest photograph of Gorton Foundry, is fixed by the four-coupled tank locomotive shown on the right of the picture, which was built for the Cannock Chase Colliery Company in 1856. A new boiler was delivered for this locomotive in 1912.

The nearest buildings on the left hand side were the fitting shops. The tall building was the erecting shop and then followed the machine shops. The low building to the left of the centre at the back contained the offices. The tall buildings at the back were part of Gorton "Tank" with the Manchester to Sheffield railway line hidden by the offices.

The buildings on the right-hand side, starting from right to left, include in order, the boiler shops, the smithy and forge, the pattern shops and stores.

advantage is gained of being able to cover the whole area of the workshop with tools, in place of confining them to the vicinity of the windows and side walls as is usually the case where the workshops are placed one over another and carried to any great height.''(2)

This layout, with the glazed roofs, gave Gorton Foundry very good working conditions, and avoided carrying parts of locomotives from one floor to another, as was necessary in the multi-storeyed buildings of some of the earlier manufacturers.

On Monday 13 May 1854, Beyer was able to write triumphantly in his note book, ''We remove this morning from our office, 13 Queen's Chambers, Market Street, Manchester, to our new offices at Gorton''. During the whole of that summer, building continued so that on 14 June, ''Peacock takes possession of his office''. (3) Many people were interested and called to see the design and buildings, including the following Locomotive Superintendents, Archibald Sturrock (Great Northern Railway), Joseph Armstrong (Shrewsbury & Chester Railway), and Matthew Kirtley (Midland Railway). Building had advanced far enough for the purchase of machine tools to equip the shops to begin in the middle of August, although some must have been ordered much earlier.

The Top Management

The three partners were already well known and respected in railway circles and indeed complemented each other in their technical skills. They co-operated closely in running their new company, through both formal meetings and by correspondence. In 1855 there were eleven partnership meetings and similar meetings were held roughly every couple of months until 1858, when the number began to decline, until there were none in 1862, nor indeed until after the end of the first partnership.(4) These men were willing to work very long hours and Robertson's diary for 1855 is typical of the strenuous life they led.

> ''Saturday, 10 February, 1855, Went by Express train from London to Manchester and out to Gorton at 5. Met Mr. Beyer and Mr. Peacock—held our meeting and walked into Manchester.
> Sunday, 11 February, 1855, With Mr. Beyer all day, walked to Longsight.'' (5)

At this particular meeting, not only was it recorded that Robertson had paid £3,000 to the credit of the firm but also that the account with the Manchester & Salford Bank was to be closed and instead an account opened with Messrs. Dixons & Wardell of Chester. (6) In fact Robertson seems to have taken over the role of Geach as financial adviser, for in December 1854, Beyer had written to him ''As to the loan of £10,000 I should much like you to find it, as it would keep our affairs in fewer hands'', (7) and the Chester firm of Haswell & Woodford became the Company accountants at least until Robertson's death in 1888. When the Knighton Railway in Radnorshire failed to make its regular payments of the interest due on the sum of £1,775 advanced to it to pay for its locomotive, Robertson at once turned to Beyer for advice.(8)

As well as the formal aspects of running the Company, there were informal social links binding the three partners together. Both Beyer and Peacock were invited for holidays to Robertson's estate at Crogen near Bala in North Wales at various times. Once at least Peacock had to decline the offer of a few days' shooting there through

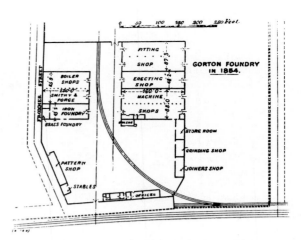

Plan of Gorton Foundry, September 1854.

The first erecting shop, built in 1854, in its original state before re-roofing in 1929. The roof lights gave much better lighting to the working areas than windows just in the walls. The locomotives were erected on the multi-gauge track in the centre which is probably a later addition when the building was refurbished to erect tram engines.

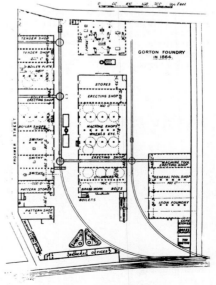

Plan of Gorton Foundry, 1864

pressure of work at Gorton, but both appreciated the gifts of game and grouse sent to them at Manchester. (9) Such periods of relaxation were very necessary for these two men, because not only were they responsible for supervising the work at Gorton Foundry, but were also travelling around Britain and overseas to secure orders and consult customers. To Beyer fell the task of coping with the mass of work involved in planning and building locomotives, and in the early years, he exercised close control over both Drawing Office and works; Peacock assumed responsibility for the commercial side of the business. Surviving letters show that Peacock was concerned with trying to obtain payment for locomotives delivered, sorting out the details of the financial balances of the partners, and advising on shareholdings in other concerns, etc.

As orders came in, there was a constant necessity for additions to the works to expand capacity. In the later part of 1855, a very large extension was made to the smithy and a new reservoir was constructed near Gorton Lane, so that by the end of October 1855, the capital outlay amounted to over £40,000. The number of orders continued to increase to such an extent that in 1857 the firm went through a management crisis. Peacock was ill at the beginning of that year, but it is not known whether this was the cause of the cryptic comments about him that appear in Beyer's letters to Robertson. Delivery dates were not being met, so it was decided that there ought

Henry Dübs, 1816-1876.

to be more assistance at the higher levels of management. Accordingly it was suggested that Henry Dübs should be considered as an Assistant Manager. He had been Works Manager at the Vulcan Foundry, Newton-le-Willows, since the early 1840's and it is possible that he was also being considered as the potential Manager of the locomotive works which Beyer, Peacock then was contemplating establishing at Vienna. (10) Beyer's letter to Robertson explains why more assistance was urgently necessary.

"I shall be glad to see Dübs. If we are to go ahead we shall have to do something. I have a letter here from Ireland since Thursday. I have not answered it because I do not know what to say. The Belgian Engine ought to be finished and is not yet begun. The two East Lancashire ought to be in hand in shops and are not likely to be touched in the drawing office for some time to come. - All want scheming - We have 3 sorts, nine coal boilers to make for Beattie. He expects us to deliver them, but does not know that we have not done as much yet as looked at his tracings. I might extend this list of short comings, but will close at this time... Peacock has not made his appearance yet." (11)

Dübs was appointed at the end of March 1857 at a salary of £500 per annum (the same as Beyer and Peacock) and an "additional sum of one half per cent upon the amount of work turned over on trade account or upon a minimum of £100,000 per annum".(12) These terms were for an initial period of two years but unfortunately things did not improve. That July Beyer wrote again to Robertson,

"I write to you to relief my mind. Everybody about this place or nearly everyone here seems to be at ease and to move at a speed to show that exertion is folly. Men and masters all alike. Four of the Venetian Engines were to be shipped last month and none of them is gone yet nor likely to go. Two only are finished.

Our correspondence consists chiefly of accounts. We receive many, very few go out and for none we receive payment.

This day we owe our bankers £8,409.11.6d.

Since my return from Ireland on the 19th I have seen but little of Peacock... Yesterday morning he did not appear and after dinner he just called to say that he was going off by the express to London on business of his own.

Owing to the Queen's visit our men's work this week will not be worth 2½ days.

The shop want work ere long, but Dübs is of a far more happy, easy temper than anyone and I do not see that scheming is likely or perceptibly to go any further.

Please do come and keep us right and assist me to make us stir". (13)

While the general position improved, Dübs did not remain long, for on 8 September 1857, he was given notice by Beyer, and had probably left by Christmas. The reasons for his dismissal remain obscure, since he was a competent engineer and was appointed Manager of Neilson's Hydepark Street Works in 1858, while in 1864 he established his own locomotive works in Glasgow. (14)

In the first weeks of 1859 prospects were so good that an earlier decision to curtail capital development was reversed, and it was determined to build a large new erecting shop with cranes, turntables, etc., and to move the forge to a separate shed on its own. (15) In 1860, the Company had over £10,000 in credit at the bank, and orders for 30 engines had been received at the beginning of that year. A partnership meeting in January 1861 recorded that 50 engines were on order and that the construction of the new erecting shed, already under way, was to be speeded up, as was that of the new forge, and that a tender shop was to be added.(16) During 1863, both

Crogen, Robertson's earlier house between Corwen and Bala where some of his descendants still live.

One of an order [178] for ten locomotives despatched in 1857 for the Lombardo & Venetian Railway. The simplicity and fewness of controls on the footplate should be compared with those of a Beyer-Garratt. There is a bracket with a square boss for an oil lamp so the level of water in the gauge glass could be checked at night.

Beyer and Peacock apologised to Robertson that they could not go to Crogen because they were so busy at Gorton. In 1864, Peacock wrote "We are almost pull'd out of the place for work & I care not how soon we get our additional shops to work".(17) These last extensions practically covered the whole of the land originally purchased by the partners. The business continued to expand, so that in July 1865 Beyer wrote from The Hague,

> "From ten o'clock till three today I have attended to business. We shall have to make 37 more engines for the Dutch State Rws. by June 1866 in addition to the orders we have and they talk about **50** more additional ones in 1866.
>
> I have also promised the Chairman of the Dutch East Indies Rws. (Island of Java) 2 Engines by the end of this year and he tells me he will require 22 more soon.
>
> How all these engines are to be made in the time I am not quite clear but we must set about it and do it. Our success is our trouble.
>
> If it please God to bring me back safe I will try to come to Crogen to talk to you about this."(18)

* * * * *

The Executive Team

Beyer seems to have had no difficulty in finding staff, although the working conditions at first may have been spartan, judging by his often quoted remark to Robertson, "I have no fear about getting men. As to space, spring is coming and we can work in the open air".(19) A few men left Sharp Stewart's and came to work for him, one of them being Thomas Molyneaux, who had been at Sharp Roberts from 1831 (20) Molyneaux was the first employee at Gorton Foundry, starting in June 1854, when he helped to cut down the trees on the site as a change from the Drawing Office, where he spent the rest of his working life; he retired in 1903, having given almost 50 years' devoted service to the Company. He purchased shares in the private company formed in 1883 (see p.71) and latterly was in charge of the buildings and plant. He died in 1906 at the age of 91.

During the earlier years it was a matter of crucial importance to Beyer to find the right men to assist him in the Drawing Office, where the designs of the locomotives were planned and developed. In his executive capacity, Beyer was Chief Engineer and had a preference for men of German origin, particularly from his own homeland of Saxony. This was partly because he attached the greatest importance to technical education, such as he himself had received in the Dresden Polytechnic, and at that time the British equivalent of technical schools—the Mechanics Institutes—had standards below those of the German polytechnics.

Right from the beginning there was quite a strong German element among the Company's staff, and most of the men selected were already known to Beyer. The first was Hermann Jaeger, a native of Beyer's home town in Saxony, who had been with Beyer at Sharp Bros. since 1847. (21) In September 1854 he came to Gorton Foundry as Technical Assistant to Beyer, just after the first buildings had been completed. He was the first to hold the title of Chief Draughtsman, to which position he was appointed in 1861, and which he relinquished in 1865 for health reasons, taking up some lighter duty assisting in the works management. Then there was Hermann Ludwig Lange (see Chap. 5 for further biographical details) and

his son Ernest F. Lange, who joined the Company in 1892 and was Steel Foundry Manager and Chief Metallurgist from 1899 until his death in 1932. Carl Heinrich Schobelt, born in Manchester, came from Sharp Stewart & Co. in 1888 as a leading draughtsman, and was Chief Draughtsman at the time of his death in 1927. Names of the draughtsmen in the first register, such as Schawbe, Heick, Baiver and Massadro, may indicate a German origin, as well as a few others who came in later years.

Whilst on the subject of draughtsmen, among the first was one Lancashire man called Timothy Fox who started work at Sharp Roberts as a rivet-lad. He moved to Gorton in January 1855 and remained there the rest of his life.(22) At this time, all important arrangement drawings were drawn and inked in on mounted Whatman paper and finally coloured. Timothy Fox was recognised as a master of this craft—so much so that in 1907 he was brought back, having just retired, to prepare a sectioned General Arrangement of a heavy 0-8-4 three cylinder tank engine built for the Great Central Railway (Order 9655) for display at the Franco-British Exhibition of 1908. This was afterwards presented to the Chief Mechanical Engineer and is now preserved in the North Western Museum of Science and Industry in Manchester. Incidentally, Harold Lane, the Works Manager at the time of the closure in 1966, was a grandson of Timothy Fox.

To undertake the construction of locomotives, men with a wide variety of skills had to be employed, working under the general supervision of the Works Manager. The first man to hold this position, John Nuttall, was appointed on 5 August 1854, but nothing else is recorded about him. His successor was Francis Holt (1825-93) who had served his apprenticeship at Sharp Roberts and became a foreman there. After various engineering jobs in this country and overseas, he was appointed Works Manager at Gorton in 1860 and held the post until 1871, when he went to R. & W. Hawthorn's at Newcastle-upon-Tyne. He was later Manager of the Derby Works of the Midland Railway.

By Christmas 1854, there were about 130 people on the books, a number which increased rapidly as the works grew, reaching 1,310 in 1864. The different types of craftsmen needed can be see in the First Wages Book (23) (see Appendix II). Unfortunately in August 1855, some of the categories of employees were transferred to other books which have since been lost, so from that date it is

Hermann Jaeger.

impossible to discover exactly what men were being employed. One important department is not included in these lists, for the forge was manned through some form of sub-contracting. A lump sum was given to the forgemaster,

so that what the bad workman lost, the good workman gained.

The anniversary of the firm's foundation was celebrated for some years afterwards by a day's sport and enter-

Beyer, Peacock Rules and Regulations, 1855.

Programme of Amusements to celebrate the opening of Gorton Foundry, January 1856.

who hired and paid his own men, but there is no indication about how many men had to share it. They began to be paid on 20 October 1854. The list finishes in August 1855 when the first locomotives had already been despatched. It reveals the extent of forging, smithing and manual fitting still necessary at that time in spite of the extensive use of machine tools pioneered by Roberts and Beyer.

Employment conditions appear to have been fairly typical of the period. Working hours were 6.00am. to 6.00pm., with an hour and a half for meals, and 6.00am. to 12.30pm. on Saturdays, making a working week of 57½ hours, by no means excessive for the mid-Victorian period. There was a series of fines for bad timekeeping. For instance, a workman arriving late in the morning lost a quarter of an hour's pay if he were over 6 minutes late, or an hour if he were 51 minutes late. Differences in wages between skilled and unskilled labour were very marked at this period, and, while skilled workmen received increased pay for working overtime, labourers did not.

A system of fines or stoppages for offences against works rules also existed, a feature of a great many firms at that time, (24) but at Beyer, Peacock the fines were small and only for fairly serious offences, like playing tricks with the timekeeping system, bringing liquor into the works except at meal times, being drunk, fighting and using bad language. None of the money was retained by the firm; all was applied for the benefit of the workmen,

tainment in the "Belle Vue" gardens. The one held on Wednesday 2 January 1856 was a gay affair, as its surviving "Programme of Amusements" shows. At 10.00am. the workmen were issued with tickets for Belle Vue, and at 11.00am. set out in procession to the gardens. At noon, the sports started with a 120 yards race for youths under 19. Prizes were very good, some winners receiving £2, the equivalent of a fortnight's wages to many of the men. After dinner at 2.00pm., the proceedings were resumed. There was a sack race in which "new sacks will be provided by Mr. Jennison, and all will be the same size". A football match was to round off the afternoon with "an unlimited number of players, the sides to be drawn for at the completion of the entries... to play which gets the most Goals in one hour, or if no Goal is obtained, the side who is nearest to a Goal to be Winner". All the winning teams received half-a-crown each. So far the day had been a wholly masculine occasion, but as the winter dusk fell, the nature of the revels changed, "Gentlemen will be allowed to introduce Ladies for Dancing at Five o'clock". (25)

In 1823, Robert Stephenson started his works at Newcastle-upon-Tyne with a pair of smith's bellows, anvils, vices and three lathes. In 1837, there were still no steam hammers or planing machines, and not a single crane. He had only one steam engine to drive all his machine tools, because most of the work was done by hand.(26) Beyer, of course, followed the Roberts tradition and used machine tools wherever possible, and from the outset was far in advance of most other manufacturers. Gorton Foundry was also better equipped than R. & W. Hawthorn's Works at Newcastle-upon-Tyne. (27) Thus in

NOTICE TO WORKMEN.

Workmen's attention is called to the 19th and 20th Rules, the violation of which has become a matter so serious that it is determined to take measures to put a stop to it, and NOTICE IS HEREBY GIVEN, that should any one be found

"Putting on his coat or making any other preparation of a similar character for leaving work before the bell rings, or stop working on Saturdays before the quarter past twelve bell rings for cleaning down, he will be fined One Shilling for every such offence,"

And the Foremen have strict instructions to see that such fines are enforced in accordance with the Rules

BEYER, PEACOCK & CO

Gorton Foundry.
January, 1866.

Notice to Workmen, January 1866.

the first Beyer, Peacock Company Assets Book, (28) there are over forty separate headings for the different machines installed to set up Gorton Foundry. Most of these headings date from its origin and, to show the complexity of establishing such a works, some of the more important headings are listed here.

1 Engines, Boilers and Shafting
2 Steam Hammers and Boilers
3 Lathes
4 Planing Machines
5 Drilling Machines
6 Boring, Shaping and Screw Cutting Machines
7 Key Grooving Engines and Slotting Machines
8 Punching, Shearing and Bar Cutting Engines
9 Dividing Machine, Wheel Cutting Engine and Pantograph
11 Riveting Machine
12 Hydraulic Press
13 Grinding Machinery
17 Cranes.
18 Weighing Machines, Railway and Turntables
19 Standard Gauges, Stocks, Taps and Dies and Surface Plates
20 to 24, Items for Smithy
25 One Peculiar Steel Yard for Testing Springs
28 Gas Fittings
29 and 30 Items for Pattern Makers
31 Stationery, Fittings and Office Utensils

34 Garden [deleted in 1866 as "not now worth much."]
38 Horses, Carts, Lurries, Harness and Stable Fittings.

A few details from some of the sections will show the extent of the works by 1860, when the first phase of its development may be considered as accomplished.

There were 4 boilers supplying 8 steam engines and a steam driven hydraulic pump. Some of the steam engines were built to a novel design, which was described by **The Engineer** in 1856:

"Another fundamental characteristic of Messrs. Beyer and Peacock's works is their very beautiful and ingenious system of wall engines... They consist of a pair of high pressure locomotive engines placed upright and connected by double cranked shaft...

The advantages of this form of engine for workshop's purposes are numerous and easily understood, in the first place they occupy scarcely a fourth of the space usually required; there is no flywheel to take up space or to call for heavy framework and foundations. The speed with which the engines can be driven obviates the necessity for intermediate gearing to get up the velocity required for driving shafts in tool shops. Notwithstanding the want of a flywheel and the immediate connexion of the engines to the driving shaft of the workshops, where the strain from occasional stoppages of the heaviest tools might be supposed to affect the uniformity of its motion, they work with remarkable steadiness. This is effected by the application of Pitcher's water governor which looks as if it had been expressly invented for the purpose of allowing a wall engine to be made.

It is a most amusing sight to watch the action of the engines and governor. The two engines resemble nothing so much as a couple of very lanky black cats making ineffectual efforts to scale the wall—one has just got halfway up when t'other pulls it down—and so they go on with a continual scramble, and tearing away with the speed of an express train, while Pitcher's queer little water governor seems continually on the point of bursting their sides with an hysterical giggle at the row going on above it''. (29)

These engines remained a feature of the works until they were replaced by electric motors, soon after 1900.

James Nasmyth supplied two boilers to work one steam hammer, rated at 50 cwt, and a smaller one at 15 cwt. These, together with two forge furnaces from which the waste heat passed to the boilers, cost £1,805. In addition, there were two compressed air hammers and another steam hammer.

Beyer, Peacock purchased or built itself over 58 lathes, ranging from special railway wheel turning lathes to an "Amateur Lathe with 6 in. Head Stocks". Two of the most interesting lathes were purchased from Richard Roberts in February 1854, before Gorton Foundry had been begun. Unfortunately, one of them, a special screw cutting lathe built by Roberts himself, has since been scrapped, but the other, built by Roberts in 1817, is now preserved in the Science Museum, London. Roberts was paid £240 for these machines, which shows that their quality must have been outstanding, because the price is higher than for other lathes which were new.

The list of manufacturers of these lathes reads like a directory of the machine tool industry. W. Collier supplied special locomotive wheel lathes; Sharp Stewart supplied a lathe with an 18 ft bed. J.S. Hulse, W. Kirk, W. Muir, J. Whitworth, T. Lewis, and Smith Beacock & Tannett, all supplied different types of lathes. James Nasmyth sent a ''self acting planing and shaping machine with nut apparatus'', as well as an ''ambidicator'' lathe.

[Top] Roberts' screw-cutting lathe, 1820. Lead screws with different pitches are stored under the bed.

[Lower] Roberts' back-geared slide lathe, 1817. The almost horizontal disc on the right had rings of teeth which were used for changing the speed of the shaft driving the slide rest to give different pitches for thread-cutting.

The name of T. Craven appears among the list of eleven planing machines although at this time, this famous firm was building only fairly small machine tools. It is interesting to note that Whitworth's was already selling its machine tools in certain standard sizes designated by letters, one such being a gear cutting machine now in the North Western Museum of Science and Industry. Colliers built the biggest planing machine which was capable of planing 24ft. long by 5ft. 6in. wide and 5ft. 6in. high. There were twenty-eight drilling machines, including radial arm varieties. Some tools could have been used in any engineering idustry, but others were specially adapted for the locomotive trade. Smith, Beacock & Tannett built a ''Strong machine for slotting the frame or horn plates of locomotive engines with 8 in stroke, bed 24 ft long to admit articles 4ft. wide''.

Top] An ordinary screw-cutting lathe built by Beyer, Peacock in 1854.

[Lower] A 7ft. wheel turning lathe built by Beyer, Peacock in 1854 still earning its keep in 1929.

An hydraulic press was used to force wheels on or off axles. For lifting, at first there were only shear legs, but in November 1854, Wren, Wren & Hopkinson installed a 10-ton travelling crane. By 1860, there were three or four travelling cranes about the works. The greatest capacity was a 20-ton travelling crane which may have been the one seen by the correspondent of **The Engineer**.

"In the foundry, there is a somewhat unusual arrangement of a travelling crane in place of the usual system of stationary cranes. I was told that, although at first opposed to it, the workmen have at length taken so kindly to it as to give it a decided preference over the old system". (30)

Indeed, as **The Engineer** commented, "The stock of tools is varied and complete, with all the most recent improvements of the best makers".

For manufacturing any precision engineering work, it is essential to have a good system of measurement with standard rulers, scales, gauges etc. The correspondent of **The Engineer** again commented on the high standard Beyer, Peacock had reached in this field, which was partly achieved by making all its own scales on one machine.

"Another fundamental article of this establishment is the dividing or graduating engine... the standard of which is derived from a very carefully cut screw made by Mr. Whitworth...

"The uses of an instrument of this sort in a locomotive factory are of very great importance. By means of the perfect measurement which can be obtained from it, marked upon wood or steel, the workmen can proceed to finish separate pieces of the same engine with thorough confidence that when they are brought together, the fit will be accurate.

"For the graduation of pattern makers' contraction scales and scales for drawings of all sizes, this instrument is particularly convenient.

Mr. Beyer showed me a series of scales which had been graduated by this tool for the use of his pattern makers, and certainly they looked very neat, the divisions being scored on the bevel edges of boxwood lathes."

The gauges, taps and dies came, as might be expected, from Joseph Whitworth. What seems surprising today is the great expense of gas light fittings. In the offices, £506 was spent under this heading, and at least £640 in the rest of the works. Colliers was paid £438 19s. 4d. for a large locomotive wheel lathe, and £455 0s. 0d. for its large planing machine, so the gas lighting must have been done very well.

With all this first rate equipment, together with a well planned layout, and the situation by the side of the Manchester, Sheffield & Lincolnshire Railway, Gorton Foundry must have been the most up-to-date locomotive works then in existence, and it is interesting to note that the greater part remained in use until the last steam engines were finished in 1958; some buildings still survive today, having been adapted for other industries.

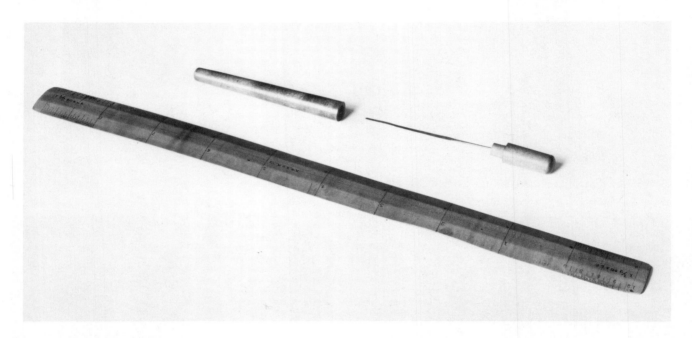

Beyer's feeler gauge and scale ruler.

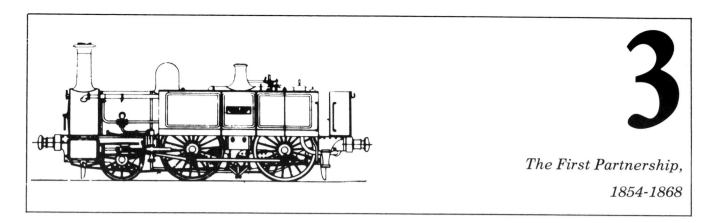

Beyer, Peacock & Co. was established chiefly for ''The manufacture of locomotive engines'', (1) and the success of Gorton Foundry depended upon securing sufficient orders to keep the flow of production steady. Bearing in mind the size of the home market available to independent manufacturers, overseas orders were vital to ensure that capacity at Gorton was filled. Up to the end of 1868, a total of 844 locomotives was built, of which 476, or roughly 56 per cent, were exported. In addition forty went to Ireland, where the first, a 2-4-0 tank, (Order 145) was for the Belfast & County Down Railway, which received its last, a 4-4-2 tank (Order 1425), in 1951. Some other countries also had long connections, with designs for India commencing in 1855. The first deliveries to Australia were

sent in 1859—five 2-2-2s (Order 354) and five 0-6-0s (Order 356) for the Victorian Railways—followed by thirteen 2-4-0s (Order 548 & 617) in 1861, which were among the first locomotives built at Gorton Foundry to have steel tyres.

[Heading] A 2-4-0 tank locomotive for the Belfast & County Down Railway [145] was the first locomotive Beyer, Peacock exported to Ireland in 1857.

Except for the spark arrestors on the chimney, these passenger and goods locomotives for the Victorian Railways in Australia are typical of the 1850 period. Compensating beams link the springs of all the axles on the passenger locomotive which gave a smoother ride. They were fitted with rubber pads on the hangers to dampen the shocks.

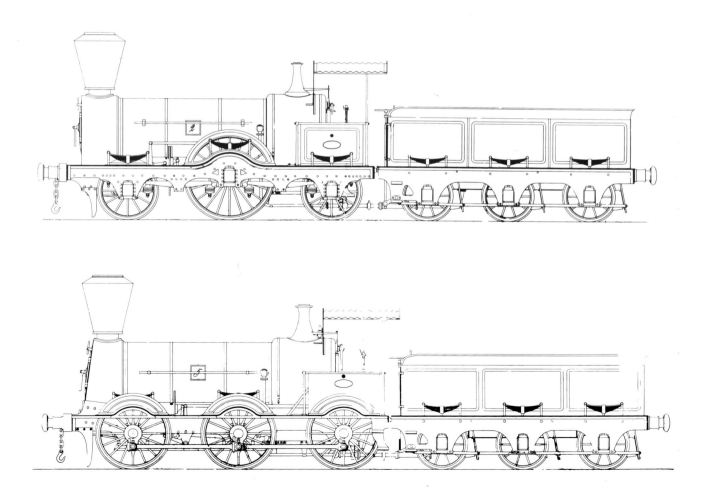

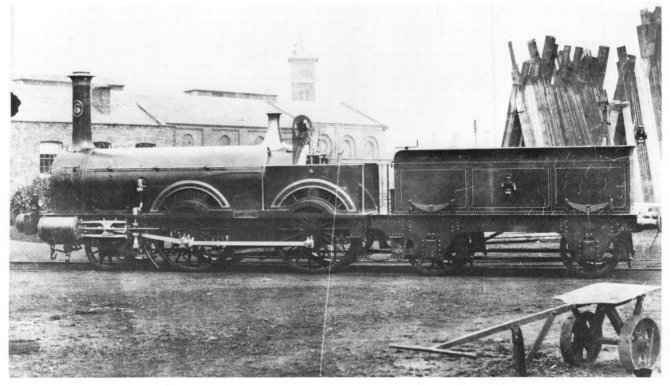

Beyer was no stranger to building locomotives for foreign railways, as the second design of engine with which he was concerned at Sharp Roberts, in 1836, was for the Munich & Augsburg Railway.(2) In 1855 he visited Hamburg and won an order from the Royal Swedish Railways (Order 97) (3) for six engines, which was the beginning of a long and successful connection with that country. In June 1857 he reported to his partners that he had been to Belfast to see the directors of the Belfast & County Down Railway,

> "to pacify them as to the delay with their engines and that he believed he had succeeded in doing so by promising the delivery of the engines by the end of August". (4)

A letter from the Berlin & Hamburg Railway suggests that he had been in Hamburg again in 1859, (5) while in 1863 he visited Holland, Germany and Sweden. (6) A

[Top] Order 548, finished for the Victorian Railways in 1861, had large coupled wheels because this was the time when four-coupled locomotives were gaining popularity for express passenger work through the introduction of steel tyres. What Beyer felt about fitting such a stark design of cab is not recorded.

[Lower] This 1856 photograph of the Royal Swedish Railways Order 97, was one of the earliest taken at Gorton and was made on a paper negative by the wax paper process. These Beyer, Peacock photographs are probably the oldest collection of industrial pictures in the world, intended as a commercial record and a sales adjunct.

similar trip two years later was far from the last he made to the Continent.(7) Peacock also travelled extensively. We know he visited Ireland in February 1863 and went to Belfast, (8) while his adventures in Holland that summer will be described later in this chapter. No doubt there were many other sales trips of which no records survive.

[Above] Four locomotives were supplied to the Shrewsbury & Hereford Railway [558] in 1861. The design is an almost standard 0-6-0 goods type with the rear axle behind the firebox.

[Below] ''Robertson'' was destined for the Broughton Colliery [254] at Wrexham in 1858. While the boiler pump driven off the crosshead was quite common practice, especially with inside cylinder engines, placing the eccentrics for the valve gear between the wheels and the frames was not.

Robertson also played his part in securing orders. The Brymbo Iron Company, Chester Station, the Shrewsbury & Hereford Railway, and other names which appear among the early orders, suggest that he persuaded companies in which he or his friends were interested to buy locomotives from his new firm. Sometimes he was able to secure orders himself, for example from the Broughton Colliery, Wrexham (Order 254), or as the following copy of one of his letters in 1858 to Mr. Barwell shows, from the Danube & Black Sea Railway.

"I am obliged by your letter and you may rely on it that the Engines we are to supply shall do us credit as well as the company—nothing that skill and good workmanship on our part can effect shall be spared to make the engines perfect. We are fully aware of the benefit to our manufacturers of sending out to a new country the most suitable and the best machines and we shall send out Engines that will be creditable to England when I trust not six but sixty engines alone shall be busily plying from Kestendjie along the shores of the Danube.

In terms of my original tender, we agree to accept payment for the Engines by 25 per cent in shares and the remainder in cash...

Dear Beyer, Above is the copy of my reply to Mr. Barwell—at once prepare the material for two six wheeled coupled engines... Happy New Year to you & Peacock and many of them." (9)

Normally orders were gained through competitive tender and Beyer, Peacock had to submit the lowest bid to beat other firms. One order was lost because Peacock was away.

"Peacock returned on Saturday morning and could not give a satisfactory explanation for his absence beyond the time B.P. & Co's business required... This morning he went to Birkenhead to see about the two Engines we had an inquiry for and returned at noon. The two Engines having been let on Saturday and it appears at fair prices. Had he returned on Wednesday, we might have got an order." (10)

Sometimes factors other than the lowest price might be taken in consideration when orders were placed. For example, this letter from the Manager's Office, General Railway Station, Chester, shows that delivery dates could be equally important.

"The Committee have agreed to take the engine according to your specification and price... but only on condition that it is delivered here on or before the 17th day of June 1856—being three months from the time you will receive this and that you will write binding yourself to pay the Committee a penalty of Two Pounds per day for every day the delivery is delayed beyond that date, a general strike of your hands being the only reservation to be made on your part.

"And I must beg of you to take notice that the penalty is not a mere form but that they will most certainly exact it if it is incurred...

"I may add that the Committee have had a lower tender and that the time alone has decided them." (11)

For the Madras Railway (Order 245), £25 per engine was to be deducted from the contract price for every week that the delivery was late—"the delivery of the first 8 engines by the time named is of especial importance to us owing to the seasons for landing them at Madras." (12)

* * * * *

Order 245 for the Madras Railway was another standard 0-6-0 goods locomotive with minor variations to the boiler fittings to suit the customer.

Design and Construction

Generally a steam locomotive was designed for a particular railway and often for a particular job on that railway, although standardisation was sought wherever possible. An engine to haul passengers would go faster than one to haul goods, while one used only for shunting would be smaller than either. A design with larger boiler and smaller wheels would be suggested for a mountainous country and the anticipated traffic would be taken into consideration too. This meant that the designers had to know the character of the lines, the gradients, climate, etc. Beyer, Peacock kept records of the rail gauges, loading gauges, gradient diagrams, etc. in its Drawing Office for most railways in the world.

In a study of locomotive history it is frequently difficult, if not impossible, to establish who was really responsible for the design of a particular type or class, since it has been customary down the years to attribute this officially to the Chief Mechanical Engineer of the railway concerned. For types designed and built in a railway's own works, this generally applied, but with those produced by private locomotive builders, the picture is far from clear, particularly with those built for overseas railways. This is a problem which starts with the very first locomotives built by Beyer, Peacock and continues to the end of its history, and now that the correspondence has been destroyed, it may never be possible to determine who designed what on any engine.

[Right] This 0-4-0 tank engine was designed as a standard small shunting locomotive for collieries, etc. Batches may well have been built for stock and so been available for quick sale.

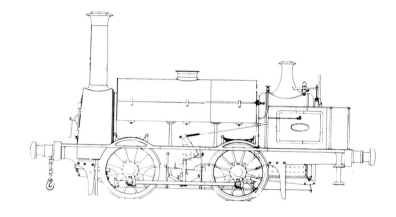

[Below] This 0-4-2 tender engine was the first type supplied to the Smyrna & Cassaba Railway [800] in 1864.

The designs for the first two types of locomotive built at Gorton Foundry were supplied by the customers and of course this sometimes happened with later orders too. On the other hand, Beyer, Peacock was sometimes given a free hand, as in the instance of an order (No. 920) for two tank engines for the Smyrna & Cassaba Railway.

> "(We desire) two more Locomotive Engines; they must be tank engines to work about ten miles of railway with a gradient of one in a hundred for about two miles; the traffic will be principally passengers: these are all the data Mr. Price gives, he leaves to you the power and general arrangement of the engines as he says you understand the matter and will do what is right." (13)

In addition to having its own local physical conditions, each railway tended to develop its own particular characteristics with the type of equipment it used and would also have its own rules and regulations. In the same way, each country developed codes of safety regulations, etc., which had to be followed in the design of its locomotives. This was pointed out to Beyer, Peacock in a letter from the Oppela & Tarnowitz Railway (Order 136).

> "I have only to draw your attention to the point that the Engines must be built according to Prussian Law; but which is easily done, in case your scheme should differ. To that effect I send you hereby an extract of all laws in the original language, and beg of you to get them translated and to act accordingly." (14)

This helps to explain why Beyer and Peacock so often went abroad, for then not only could they meet the managers and superintendents of the railways, but see the lines and conditions for themselves.

Once the design of a locomotive had been agreed, the private engine builders in this country faced one very grave disadvantage which they never really succeeded in overcoming. They had no way of testing a new design except by laying a short length of track in their own yard. Sometimes they were allowed to run trial trips on the lines outside their works, (15) but this was impossible if the gauges were different. Therefore great care had to be taken in the Drawing Office to see that the design was correct.

Beyer, Peacock was willing to include, when requested, features which it would not have put on its own designs. For example, the first engines it built, those for the Great Western, had main frames constructed from wood sandwiched between two plates of iron. This was an archaic design in 1855, but there is evidence that this type of locomotive rode more easily over the Great Western permanent way which was constructed with longitudinal bulks of timber.(16) Similar frames were fitted to engines built for the Victorian Railways (Order 354) in Australia, and again in 1861 on six 0-6-0s for the North Eastern Railway (Order 522). On three 0-4-0 engines for the Isabella Railway (Order 133) in Spain, Dodds reversing mechanism was fitted. This had wedges sliding along a

[Below] In addition to the Dodds reversing gear, these three locomotives for the Isabella Railway [133] had an unusual layout for the screw brake on the tender with an inclined shaft and handwheel. No brakes were fitted on the locomotive itself as was common then, but it was not so usual to fit pairs of brake blocks to each wheel on the tender.

[Foot] Order 522 for six locomotives for the North Eastern Railway in 1861. It was Beyer, Peacock's custom to give separate order numbers for engines and tenders.

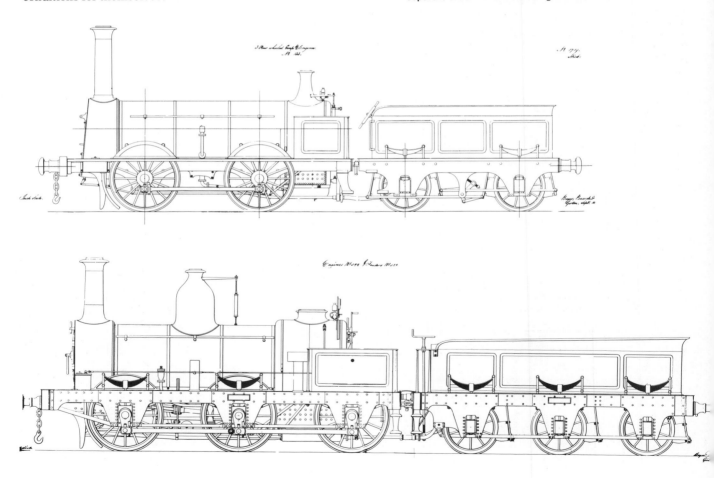

square portion of the axle to give forward, neutral and reverse positions as well as variable cut-off. (17) Normally, Stephenson's reversing gear was the standard type, but for the Belfast & County Down 2-4-0 tank (Order 145), Allan's link motion must have been specified. In later accounts, a royalty of £10 per locomotive had to be paid (see the accounts of the D. Luiz, p.38) whenever this valve gear was used during the lifetime of the patent.

This was the period when many locomotive superintendents were trying to burn coal by devising special types of fireboxes. The more important types were J.E. McConnell's (L.N.W.R.) which had twin fires placed side by side leading into a common combustion chamber; J.I.A. Cudworth's, (S.E.R.) which also had two fires side by side, but had a steeply sloping grate so that coal was fed in at the top where the gases were driven off, leaving it as coke to be burnt at the bottom, and J.H. Beattie's (L.S.W.R.) system, which had two fires, one behind the other, again feeding into a common combustion chamber. (18) On the Great Western locomotives, a boiler with double grate was specified with the two grates one behind the other separated by a middle feather filled with water. This appears to have been the standard type of boiler on that railway, even for burning coke.

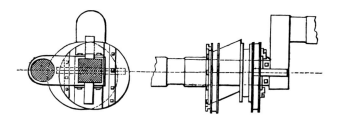

[Top] Dodds "wedge" reversing mechanism.

[Lower] Allan's "straight link" reversing mechanism.

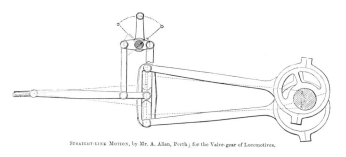

STRAIGHT-LINK MOTION, by Mr. A. Allan, Perth; for the Valve-gear of Locomotives.

Different types of coal burning boilers

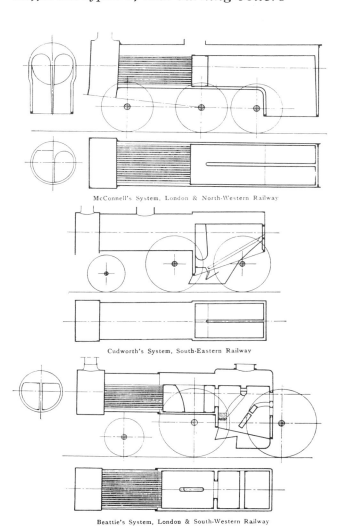

McConnell's System, London & North-Western Railway

Cudworth's System, South-Eastern Railway

Beattie's System, London & South-Western Railway

Beyer, Peacock came to a special agreement with Beattie (19) and built locomotives with his boilers for a number of railways. In 1858 the Midland Railway received two 0-6-0 goods engines (Order 247) fitted with Beattie's boiler and feed-water heating apparatus, to test against its own engines, on which Charles Markham and Matthew Kirtley were experimenting with brick arches. (20) By correctly proportioning the fireboxes, fitting brick arches, and admitting air through the fire door above the fire, but directing it by a deflector plate so it mixed thoroughly with the gases from the fire, they were able to solve the problem and their system became the standard method until the end of the steam locomotive.

The following letter sent by Mr. Patrick Stirling, then Locomotive Superintendent on the Glasgow & South Western Railway, to Joseph Beattie, ordering one of his special engines shows incidentally that Beyer, Peacock already had established a good reputation for its work.

> "I duly received your letter of the 30th March containing a copy of a tender supplied by Messrs. Beyer and Peacock for the construction of one of your Patent Locomotive Engines.
> I am authorised to accept your offer for the Engine in terms of the Tender supplied by Messrs B. & P. and from the reputation of that firm I am prepared to receive a first rate piece of mechanism. I hope no time will be lost in giving delivery of it as you must be well aware it is a matter of the greatest importance to us to have its powers tested and from the experience I have had of your patent Engine I am very sanguine of its complete success on our line. I suppose it will be unnecessary for me to communicate with the builders upon the subject and from their experience in making your Engines I should think they will not require much looking after." (21)

Beattie's patent fee for his boilers was £75. (22)

One of two goods engines supplied in **1858** to the Midland Railway [247] fitted with Beattie's coal-burning boiler and feed-water heating apparatus to test against their own engines fitted with brick arches in the firebox. Some of the steam exhausted from the cylinders was taken back to the tender to heat the water there, en route also being used to warm the boiler feed water further. The feed water was pumped into the boiler by a steam driven donkey pump with a flywheel, placed on the running boards of the engine.

Not only did Beyer, Peacock build the special boilers for Beattie, but at this period it was making many spares for the London & South Western Railway, of which he was the Locomotive Superintendent. Some of this work was done on a commission basis of 6¼ per cent discount, the only example in the Cost of Work books, so there must have been some special arrangement. The orders consisted mostly of axles and wheels, possibly because Beyer, Peacock had acquired a good reputation for its wheels.

> "They (Beyer, Peacock) understand the manufacture of Railway wheels so well that it will be sufficient for me to say that I require the present orders executing with wheels and axles of the very best workmanship and material." (23)

Before the days of steel castings, locomotive wheels, particularly the large size driving wheels, presented great manufacturing problems. Cast iron generally was considered too brittle, although Beyer did use it for the driving wheels of his 0-6-0 **Atlas** class "luggage" engines in 1846.(24) One practice was to make wheels with cast iron hubs poured round wrought iron spokes, with wrought iron tyres shrunk on wrought iron rims. In 1835, John Day developed a wheel made entirely from wrought iron parts welded together, and this was the type in which Beyer, Peacock specialised. (25) First each spoke was made individually, and then all the parts were fire-welded. Beyer designed a special forge for this work which was watched by the correspondent from **The Engineer**.

"The wedge-shaped ends of the arms [spokes], which when welded compose the nave of the wheel, have an angular groove swaged across them; so that when two of them are laid together a square hole is formed by the juxtaposition of the two annular grooves. When the wheel is bound together for the welding of the nave, square keys of green iron are driven into these holes or keyseats, and being more easily fused than the body of the nave, they form a sort of flux which greatly assists the operation of welding. I saw some finished wheels which had been forged in this way; and in looking at the bright surface inside the eye of the wheel, I could not observe the slightest trace of the numerous weldings which made up the mass of the nave." (26)

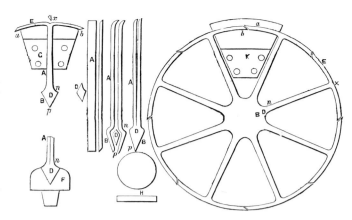

[Above] Day's solid wrought iron railway wheel, 1835.

[Below] Wrought iron wheel being forged at Gorton Foundry.

This, as can be imagined, was a very skilled job, and the difficulty of forging the hub, the individual spokes and then the rim of the 6 ft 6 in diameter driving wheel for an engine like the Great Western 2-2-2 can be well appreciated.

Beyer, Peacock was also noted for the high standard of its rivetting, and it used to countersink the holes slightly, which improved the joint. E.L. Ahrons commented on the quality of its rivetting because he had found hardly a rivet loose when he had to take twelve of its engines to pieces after thirty years service.(27)

Gorton Foundry was connected by rail to the Manchester, Sheffield & Lincolnshire Railway, so that standard gauge locomotives could be dispatched by rail to their destinations, an advantage which Sharp Stewart and W. Fairbairn did not have. Locomotives for overseas were shipped through Liverpool, London, Hull, and sometimes Newcastle-upon-Tyne. Engines of other gauges had to be taken to pieces and crated at Gorton. When the engines reached their destination, they had to be assembled and set to work. If the railway had no experienced fitters, this would be undertaken by a man from Beyer, Peacock, and this cost would be included usually in the original tender. Some railways had good workshops, but often the facilities were primitive in the extreme. In the early days, the local inhabitants might never before have seen such a marvel of advanced technology as a steam locomotive. After the engines had been assembled quite a few of the Beyer, Peacock engine erectors stayed with their charges, in lucrative posts, to run the locomotive sheds.

A letter from William Bradshaw, who was responsible for erecting the engines for the South Eastern of Portugal (including the **D.Luiz**), shows the trials and tribulations these men had to endure.

"I am glad to inform you that the **D. Luiz** and **Algarva** are both running very well. Mr. Price and Mr. Rose are both highly satisfied with the Engines. I should have had the last Engine running now but they kept me driving the **D. Luiz** up to Saturday night.

I expect to get steam up on Sunday in the **Guadiana**.

We had a bad misfortune on Monday night, the **Algarva** and **Ourique** had a pitch in, the Trailing end of the **Algarva's** Tender is badly broken, the Buffer plank, Sand boxes and pipes and Mud cocks on the Engine are gone.

The **Ourique** has her Buffer plank, Steam Chest Cover, Sand boxes and pipes and part of her

Platform smashed to pieces—the Valve Spindles badly bent and Glands and Bushes broken—I have taken off the **Guadiana** what I wanted and got the **Algarva** running the next day at 12 p.m.

Mr. Price has told me as soon as I have tried the last Engine I must take the dimensions of everything that is wanted for the Engine and Tender and come home and get them alright and come back to repair and put them both in running order and stop until the other Engines are here.

I expect to finish here on the 16th. I shall come home on the first Steamer from Lisbon after that date if nothing more occurs." (28)

The men chosen to erect these engines carried a great deal of responsibility, for on them, and on the quality of their work, depended the good name of Beyer, Peacock. They had to sort out the snags in new designs, often without much help from home because letters took so long. They also had to report on the performance of the engines so that later designs could be improved. One source of trouble on the Danube & Black Sea Railway however could not be ascribed to the erector:

"It appears our Engines have been worked with Sea water and the consequence is that not only the fire-boxes of the first six engines are done, but that the boiler shells are eaten away too." (29)

[Above] The South Eastern of Portugal received ''D. Maria Pia'' [627]
in 1862 at the same time as the ''D. Luiz''.

[Below] No. 8 ''Stockholm'' was supplied to the Swedish Government
Railway [370] in 1859. Boxes for sand were mounted on top of the
boiler.

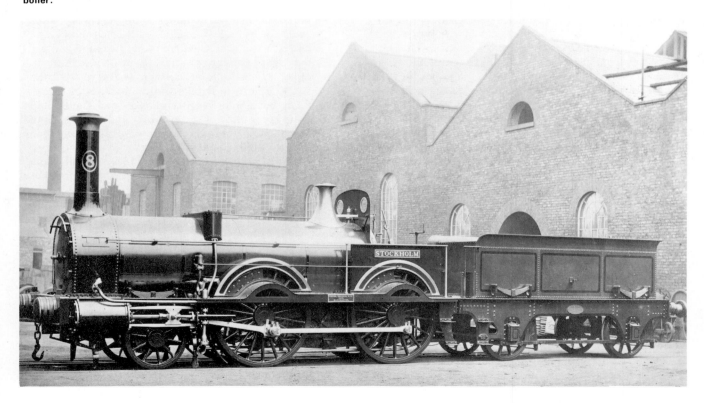

The Swedish Government Railway was satisfied with the first engines (Order 97) it had received and sent a testimonial on behalf of the erector, William Holmes:

> "I have hereby the pleasure to testify that Mr. William Holmes... who was sent to the place... on purpose to erect and put in good working order three Locomotive Engines with Tenders...
> May it be stated to the honour of the aforesaid William Holmes that he has with great activity skilfulness and good judgement attended to those Engines which have been under his charge and in full operation the last four months, and may it be stated to the knowledge of Messrs Beyer Peacock & Co., that these Engines in all points answer the purpose and give a perfect satisfaction." (30)

Another letter from Sweden also expresses satisfaction with these engines, but in addition points out various weaknesses in the design and suggests alterations:

> "Accept my sincere thanks for hospitality and all kindness under my last stay in England and in so poor state of health as I then was in, mercy has been with me and I am pretty well restored and am now in business again. Bathing in cold water has been the only thing beneficial to me, a medicine easily procured in this country six months in the year...
> "All are very satisfied with your Engines. I won't permit them to use them but sparily, I find them too good for their work of ballasting and don't like to see them run on the rails while the frost is still in the grounds. The road is not bad but very hard without elasticity. If it is from that cause or some other the rivets on both sides of the smoke box in the angle iron that join the cylindrical part have gone loose or the rivet heads broken. This is no particular case to one Engine but has happened to five Engines out of six. On the firebox sides all is right. It may come too much stiffness in the framing or the rings in the smokebox end of tubes, you know I don't like them, the fact is there. The screw of the **break** (sic) on the tender comes too low down so that it strikes the wooden balks that here are laid outside the rail on bridges, instead of being placed the inside as in England. I wish you could give me an idea how to alter this in the best manner." (31)

This letter underlines the difficulty of not being able to test new locomotives thoroughly in this country, where any faults could be rectified more easily.

Payment for Locomotives

Normally payment would be made in cash, partly during construction and the final amount upon delivery of the locomotive, but with export orders there could be a long interval between completion of the engine in Manchester and its entry into revenue earning service. Naturally Beyer, Peacock wanted payment as soon as it had finished building the engine, but the railway company wanted to know that the engine would be a success before it parted with its money. Therefore detailed arrangements for payment had to be drawn up in the contract. The terms agreed with the Zaragoza & Alsasua Railway for five 0-6-0 engines (Order 375) are quoted here:

> "The price of each Engine and its Tender shall be £2,300. In this price is included that of each Engine and its Tender delivered in Liverpool free of all expenses, and the mounting in Pamplona, but the transport between these two places is at the expense of Mr. Salamanca. The payment of the value of the five Engines shall be made up in the following manner, 20 per cent two months after the giving of the order, 20 per cent after the preceding one, provided that the firebox and boiler of all the Engines or the firebox and those of the tenders are finished, 20 per cent when the Engines are ready to be mounted in the premises of the Manufacturers, 30 per cent on delivery of the Engines in Liverpool and 10 per cent on their definitive reception." (32)

The terms for the next batch of engines (Order 498) were slightly different;

> "Payments in cash, on London, as follows:-
> 20 per cent two Months after the order is given—
> 75 per cent on the Engines being ready to leave our works, 5 per cent after each Engine has been put together and run a distance of 2,000 kilometres." (33)

It is interesting to note that Beyer, Peacock roughly covered its own costs before the engines left this country. With a selling price of £2,300 in each case, the engines cost £2,077 and £2,125 respectively, giving an 8 per cent profit after deduction of commission, packing, etc.

One of the more peculiar agreements (Order 128) was with Shelton Colliery & Iron Works (near Stoke, Staffordshire) who wished to see how its engine performed before finally purchasing it:

> "Referring to our conversation yesterday, I beg to request that you will send the locomotive engine to Etruria Station (where Lord Granville's Branch joins) as soon as possible. The conditions on which she is to be sent are as follows: We are to have her on trial for one week and if she does not suit us she is to be returned at the expiration of that time and Lord Granville is to pay the carriage both ways. If she suits us then Lord Granville is to pay for her £1,650, delivered at Etruria, one half down and the other half on the 4th March next." (34)

Some railways were unwilling, or unable, to pay cash for their locomotives and asked for deferred terms, or hire purchase instead. It is not known whether this was common practice, (35) but it occurs throughout the history of Beyer, Peacock, particularly with smaller railway companies like the Knighton Railway, the East & West Junction, Sligo, Leitrim & Northern Counties, etc. Another practice was to offer shares, often in part payment. The Danube & Black Sea Railway wanted to pay 25 per cent in shares, while, in 1857, Beyer wrote to Robertson asking his opinion, as a projector of railways, whether it would be safe to take payment from the Dundalk & Enniskillen Railway half in cash and half in Preference shares. (36) In the case of the Smyrna & Cassaba Railway which wanted to pay by Preference shares, Peacock's correspondence with Robertson shows that these shares were divided among the partners. (37) Once again it is not known how extensive this practice was, but lists of companies in which Robertson held shares suggest that it may have been fairly common, and it was, after all, a convenient way of paying the partners.

* * * * *

Profitability of the Partnership

These engines were sold through an agent, C. E. Balleras & Co., London, to the Zaragoza & Alsasua Railway [375] in 1860.

In the first **Cost of Work** book, there are accounts for forty-one orders for locomotives. Seven of these were built at small losses, while one broke even. In the second book, there were only two orders out of thirty-five which made a loss. The first order of all, that for the eight locomotives for the Great Western, was completed at about a 3 per cent. loss, but this was almost balanced by a 39¾ per cent. profit on two four-wheeled tank engines (Order 169) for the same company. The largest losses on locomotive orders were both of 14 per cent., on Order 415 for the Caledonian, and on Order 629 for the South Eastern of Portugal. The highest profit in this early period was 44½ per cent., on Order 545 for the Swedish Government, but this was comfortably exceeded in the eighteen sixties, an exceptional case being a profit of 86½ per cent. on Order 920 for two 2-4-0 tank engines for the Smyrna & Cassaba in 1865. The average profit on locomotive orders in these first two books was below 20 per cent., but the figures improve rapidly in later volumes.

On other orders, there was a much greater range of profits and losses. In the first book, 10 orders out of 171 were made at a loss, and in the second, 7 out of 94. Machine tools counted for ten of these, but in contrast, two portable cylinder boring machines for the Empress Elizabeth Railway were sold at a profit of 206¾ per cent. One of the largest losses was on two foot-drills for C.E. Balleras & Co., at 22¾ per cent., but the average rate of profit for the spares, or "duplicates", and tools was some 35 to 40 per cent. It has not been possible to determine how much of the workshop capacity at Gorton was filled by orders for "duplicate" parts, but this side of the business always represented a sizeable proportion of the turnover.

The evidence from the **Cost of Work** books suggests that there was a policy in the first few years of the Company's history of securing locomotive orders through tenders that covered costs and allowed a small margin of profit, while a higher rate of profit was made on the orders for spares. Few figures are available from other competitors in the locomotive building industry, but a similar policy was clearly being followed by R. & W. Hawthorn at a slightly later date. (38) It was essential to secure locomotive orders, for a satisfied railway company might order further similar locomotives from the same source, to reduce the subsequent costs of spares, etc. Just as important, an order for one locomotive would lead probably to additional orders for spares to keep it running and hence more work for Gorton Foundry.

Figures which show the performance of the firm during the fourteen years of the first partnership, have been drawn together from various sources, but the runs are incomplete and the accountancy methods totally different from those to which we are accustomed today. These show that even in 1856 Beyer, Peacock & Co. was beginning to make a profit on its trading, so that in the August of that year, the partners declared a modest dividend of £1,500, or £500 each. A similar dividend was declared at the end of that year and, early in 1857, there was for the first time a credit balance at the bank. (39) However, the later part of 1857 was not so profitable, for the locomotive side broke even on £12,000 worth of orders, and the profit of £6,327 obtained from manufacturing spares, etc., was swallowed up by capital expenditure. (40) Early in 1858, orders came in so rapidly and the financial position continued to improve so much that, at a meeting of the partners held on 19 May, it was resolved to pay a dividend of £1,000 on each one-third share, £500 then and £500 on 1 August. A further £1,000 was paid on 21 October, followed by a similar amount in February 1859. (41) The First Minute Book does not record another payment that year, but on 21 January 1860, it was resolved:

> "to declare and pay a dividend of £1,000 to each of the partners for the last half year and to continue to pay the same dividend half yearly, payable on the 24th. June and 31st. December, unless the financial position of the Company shall render it advisable to discontinue or alter this resolution."
>
> (42)

"Knighton" [460] was an extended version of order 99 for Chester General Station with a pair of trailing wheels added at the rear. This became the standard design from 1861 to 1879 when it was replaced by a six-coupled version.

With such dividends the firm was proving a very sound investment. Business continued to prosper so well that on 10 April 1863, it was recorded (unfortunately for later historians)

> "The partners mutually congratulated each other on the business having been carried on regularly and satisfactorily as to render more frequent recordings of the meetings of the Company unnecessary. At the same time it was thought proper to record that many meetings had taken place although the business transacted was not minuted." (43)

A profit of over £500,000 in fourteen years shows how well they did. (see Appendix I)

The First Orders

The first orders in the Order Books:-

1. Plate Bending Machine, Beyer, Peacock & Co.
2. One Dividing Machine, Beyer, Peacock & Co.
3. Two Wheel Fires, Beyer, Peacock & Co.
4. One Mineral Engine, John Horton, cylinders 14in. diameter x 18in. stroke. Wheels 3ft. 9in. diameter coupled. To be delivered January 30 /55.
5. Eight Passenger Engines, Great Western Railway.
6. Two 4ft. wheel turning lathes, Beyer, Peacock & Co. |October 1854|.
7. Seventy Wrought Iron Forgings, Beto Brassey Betts and Jackson
8. One 10in. Break Lathe, Shrewsbury & Birmingham Railway.
10. Two 10in. Break Lathes, Beyer, Peacock & Co.
12. Three Foundry Ladles, Beyer, Peacock & Co.
13. One Strap Pulley, Shrewsbury & Chester Railway.
14. One Centering Bench, Beyer, Peacock & Co. |November 1854|.
15. One 15 cwt. Air Furnace.
16. Eight Iron Squares for shop use.
17. One Lathe for turning wood, Beyer, Peacock & Co.
18. One Pair of Headstocks for a Centering Lathe, Beyer, Peacock & Co.
19. Two additional safety valves for steam hammer boilers.
20. One Compound Slide Rest for 2ft. Lathe |December 1854|.
22. Crane for wheel fire, Beyer, Peacock & Co.
23. One Cylinder Boring Machine, Beyer, Peacock & Co.
24. Two axles, Manchester, Sheffield & Lincolnshire.
25. Ten Passenger Engines, East India Railway.
27. Six Coupled Tank Engines, Bristol & Exeter Railway.
28. Four Straight Edges for the use of the Erecting Shop.

Cost of No. 629, One Express Passenger engine ''D.Luiz'' for Edward Price Esq., |Exhibition Engine|.

Particulars	Weight	Rate	Cost	Totals
Materials				
4 Low Moor Tyres from P.R.J. 3' 5" x 5¼" x 2¼"		9 6 0	37 4 0	
2 Low Moor Tyres from P.R.J. 6'7" x 5¼" x 2½"		22 15 0	45 10 0	
4 3'9" Wrought Iron Wheels	1 7 0 23	14 6	19 14 5	
2 7' Wrought Iron Wheels	1 17 1 8	14 6	27 1 2	
1 Crank Axle	1 3 2 0	30 0	35 5 0	
2 Straight Axles	15 3 4	11 0	8 13 8	
Boiler Plates, ''Low Moor''	3 7 2 23	35 4	119 13 7	
Angle Iron	1 1 2 6	10 0	10 15 3	
Frame Plates, ''Henry Sharp''	2 14 1 15	16 1½	43 17 0	
2 Forgings for Frames	1 7 2 0	30 0	41 5 0	
General Plates	4 9 1 22	10 10½	48 11 11	
Wrought Iron including all other forgings	6 1 3 16	12 10½	78 0 8	
Iron Castings	3 7 2 16	11 6	38 18 4	
8 Steel Slide Bars, ''A. Norton & Co.''	5 0 16	1 5 0	6 8 7	
Steel	1 1 18½	1 5 6	1 16 2	
6 Engine Springs	8 3 13	2 4 0	19 7 3	
Copper Plates, rate per lb.	1 9 3 18	1 0⅜	172 0 9	
Copper Stays, rate per lb.	9 0 7	1 0	51 0 3	
Brass Tubes |215| rate per lb.	2 4 1 6	10¾	222 5 2	
Brass Castings, rate per lb.	17 3 13	1 0½	104 4 5	
Brass Work, ''Clothing''			60 0 0	
Brass Work, ''Extra Clothing''			2 17 9	
Brass Work, ''Cocks''			15 2 6	
2 Spring Balances		@ 1 6 0	2 12 6	
1 Steam Indicator			2 5 0	
1 'No. 9' Injector			31 10 0	
Patent Royalties [Allan's Link Motion £10] and Miller's Pistons £3 4 0]			13 4 0	
Timber			8 12 0	
Gas, Coals, Coke, Rents & Taxes and Sundry Stores used in the shops			195 3 2	1,462 19 0
Materials Total				1,462 19 0

Wages					
Smiths	89 19 5	Grinding	7 0 6		
Fitting	115 18 6	Painting	14 1 11		
Turning	51 7 7	Joiners	3 5 10		
Erecting	68 12 8	Pattern Making	32 17 10		
Planing	33 9 7	Drawings	72 10 4		
Drilling	29 15 9	Brick Setting	2 6		
Boiler Making	85 16 9	Labouring	25 6 4		630 5 6

General Expenses including Foremen, Clerks and Jobbing Labourers,		116 1 0
Engine Total		2,209 5 6

	Weight	Totals
Carried forward, Engine total		£2,209 5 6
Tender total		500 5 7
Cost of Engine and Tender before leaving the works		2,709 11 1
Packing Account, Timber	21 14 8	
Sundries	5 7 8	
Wages	20 18 1	48 0 5
Carriage £36 13 7 and shipping charges £19 2 8		55 16 3
Mens expenses, Shipping £8 11 8, Wages £10 5 11 and General Expenses £1 18 6		20 16 1
Total		£2,834 3 10

Nos. 629 & 630 sold for	£2,500 0 0
Nos. 629 & 630 cost	£2,834 3 10
Loss	£334 3 10

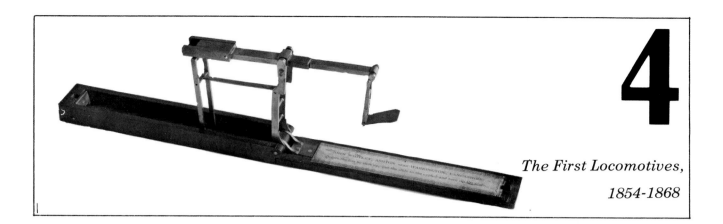

Once the buildings had been erected the immediate priority was to equip Gorton Foundry with suitable tools and equipment, and to this end some of the more specialised machine tools needed for constructing locomotives were built by the firm itself. Thus, at the very beginning, Beyer, Peacock started a tradition of building machine tools, which was continued up to final closure. Not surprisingly with the Roberts tradition behind them, Beyer and his successors were always looking for ways to improve their production methods, and Beyer himself patented a boring and drilling machine, in 1859.(1) Locomotive frames, or other articles to be drilled, could be secured to the bedplate and the three drilling heads manoeuvred above the work in such a way that it was easier to drill holes in straight lines.

The list of early orders shows that, right from the outset, Beyer, Peacock was willing to undertake general engineering work on a commercial basis; particularly so when its men and shops were not fully occupied with locomotive construction. The first orders of this type were completed in 1854, on 10 November it being recorded:

> "Send out the first work done at the Gorton Foundry, a 4ft. cast iron drum for the Shrewsbury and Chester Railway;"

and three days later

> "The first waggon loaded with Goods done entirely by us—forgings for the Canada Works, Birkenhead, leaves us this afternoon."(2)

In August 1854, the Manchester, Sheffield & Lincolnshire Railway ordered a lathe for turning and boring wheels, at a cost of £350, adding the admonition,

> "I have to remark that we have been induced to give you this order principally in consideration of the time of delivery, in which I trust you will be punctual."(3)

Other early orders were for a 10in. break lathe, a nut cutting machine, a plate bending machine, and a locomotive cylinder boring machine,(4) while the correspondent from the **The Engineer** noticed a couple of nut cutting machines, and a machine for reboring the cylinders of locomotives in situ. The reason why Beyer, Peacock built so many machine tools to equip its own works may have been to display them to potential customers. New railway lines, particularly those abroad, needed workshops to maintain their rolling stock and Beyer, Peacock could offer the tools as well as the locomotives.

In 1856, an order was received from the Swedish Government Railway for machine tools to set up workshops at Gothenburg and Malmö. Each workshop was to have a wheel turning lathe, two slide lathes and a hand turning lathe, a drill (''similar to the one in your works''), a planing machine, a shaping machine, smith's hearth, anvils, etc., hydraulic press, fitters' vices, Whitworth screwing apparatus, rolling mills for rails and templates.(5) Some of the order was sub-contracted to Cravens, Dunn, Hulse, Nasmyth, and Schiels.

There was a similar venture to equip the workshops at Vienna and Linz for the Empress Elizabeth Railway, and another for the Zaragoza & Alsasua Railway in Spain.(6) An earlier project, in 1856, to build a complete works for the manufacture of locomotives at Vienna came to nothing. This was surely being rather ambitious at a time when its own Company was barely established. The machine tool business continued to flourish until the slump of 1930, but it never achieved the prominence of the locomotive side, and generally concentrated on special tools for building or repairing locomotives.

[Heading] Beyer's sovereign balance.

A 4ft. wheel turning lathe built by Beyer, Peacock for its own use in 1854 and still being operated in 1929.

Gap bed or ''Break'' lathe built by Beyer, Peacock in 1854.

An axle-turning lathe built in 1864 with the drive in the centre so the bearing and journals at both ends could be machined simultaneously.

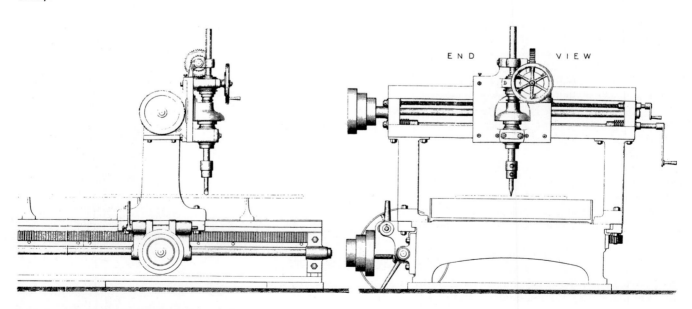

Beyer's patent boring and drilling machine, 1859.

The First Engines

The list of the first twenty-four orders received by Beyer, Peacock contains four for locomotives. Nothing is known about the Mineral Engine which John Horton appears to have ordered. Possibly it was cancelled when the Company realised that it could not meet the delivery date. Presumably the order (No. 27) for six engines for the Bristol & Exeter Railway, at £3,100 each, was also surrendered as it was not until 1862 that four 4-4-0 tanks (Order 606), the only 7ft. gauge engines ever built at Gorton, were finished for that railway.(7)

The first locomotive order to be completed was one of eight passenger engines for the Great Western Railway's standard gauge line between Birmingham and Shrewsbury (Order 5).(8) It is not known whether Peacock, who had worked under Sir Daniel Gooch, or Robertson, who had built the line where these engines were to work, helped to secure this order. The letter from Gooch placing it states quite clearly that they were to be built to the Great Western designs, which must have been a great help to a hard pressed Drawing Office.

> "The contract to be for 8 Engines and Tenders to be made strictly in accordance with the specification and drawings to be supplied to you by us. The price for each engine and tender to be Two Thousand Six Hundred and Sixty Pounds (£2,660).
> The delivery to be:
> 2 Engines and Tenders on the 24th June 1855
> 2 Engines and Tenders on the 22 July 1855
> 2 Engines and Tenders on the 19 August 1855
> 2 Engines and Tenders on the 16 Sept 1855''(9)

[Top] The first locomotive to be built at Gorton Foundry was one of an order [5] of eight to Gooch's designs for the Great Western Railway.

[Lower] 2-2-2 Tender Engine for the East India Railway [25] completed in 1856.

The Railway offered to pay a premium of £20 per week for each engine delivered early, which must have been a great incentive, but on 13 June 1855, Beyer wrote to Robertson:

> "I cannot tell you when the first engine will be finished. I work at it early and late and although we do not get on fast enough I believe everybody about the place does work and most of them hard too. My impression is we shall be three weeks if not four, before this first Engine will leave Gorton.''(10)

In fact, it was not until 21 July 1855 that the triumphant entry was made in the Minute Book:

> "The FIRST engine being one of eight ordered by the Gt. Western Railway Co. was sent off to Chester this date.''(11)

Presumably Beyer, Peacock never received a premium for early delivery, because the next engine was not despatched until 16 August, and the third on 20 August,(12) but the records are silent on this point. The order was made at a loss, the eight actually costing £23,373 13s. 8d., but selling for only £21,280.

At the same meeting which recorded the despatch of the first locomotive, it was resolved "to use every exertion to deliver the (East Indian) Engines at the earliest possible date''. In January 1854, James M. Rendel of the East Indian Railway had written to Richard Peacock:

"My Mr. Pole has made known to me your intention of joining Mr. Beyer in the establishment of a New Manufactory for Locomotive Engines and Tools. The present is a promising time for the commencement of such an undertaking, and I cordially wish you success.

"You will probably have heard that I have just given out a large order for Engines for this Company, distributing it among several makers: and in order to encourage your new firm I have recommended the Board to reserve Ten Engines for you. . . ''(13)

Beyer, Peacock agreed to build these engines (Order 25):

"In accordance with the Specification and Drawings issued by you, for the sum of Two Thousand Seven Hundred and Twenty Five Pounds (£2,725) for each Engine and Tender and also the duplicates mentioned in the said specification for the sum of Nine Hundred and Sixty Pounds (£960) each set... We will also agree to store the engines if necessary without charge.''(14)

The original delivery date of May 1855 was not kept, but the East Indian Railway appeared to be in no hurry, for delivery began in September and was completed in January 1856.(15) Beyer, Peacock received £29,293.15.0 for ten engines, which cost £27,873 17s. 2d. to build, thus making a profit of 9¼ per cent.

* * * * *

[Right] "Gardner", sent to the Fleetwood & West Riding Railway [128] in 1856, was the same design as that for Chester Station [99]. This photograph is the third surviving paper negative.

[Lower] No picture has survived of the first locomotives sent to Egypt, but they were similar to "Mohammed Said" [337] completed in 1859.

Beyer, Peacock's Own Designs

It was desirable that the new company should be able to offer its own designs of locomotives as soon as possible, for it was obviously more economical to have the drawings, patterns, flanging blocks, etc., prepared and ready for use time and time again, rather than building each batch of engines to a special design. The 0-4-0 tank engine sent to Chester Station (Order 99) became a standard design of shunting locomotive for collieries and other works. It was enlarged into a 0-4-2 for the Knighton Railway (Order 460) and continued to be built in that form until 1879 (see Appendix III). An early design that received high commendation was an 0-6-0 engine for the Egyptian Railways (Order 160), for it has been described as one of the best examples of the standard British goods engine. (16)

Another early standard design was based on the six 2-2-2 tender engines for the Edinburgh & Glasgow Railway, (Order 66). Some were so well built that they remained in service for over fifty years. The design had double frames, and the bearings for the carrying wheels were placed in the outer frames, to help secure steadier running, but the crank axle for the inside cylinders was made as short and rigid as possible by having its bearings on the inner frames. These inner frames ran the full length of the locomotive, with the boiler mounted on expansion brackets on top of them, as was Beyer's practice at this time. In 1856 these engines were seen in course of construction by the correspondent from **The Engineer**, who commented:

> "In the fitting up shop I observed a considerable number of engines in various stages of completion; one fine-looking fellow had just received his last coat of paint, and was looking as spruce and gay as a schoolboy about to leave his companions, in their shabby ferruginous coats, looking wistfully and admiringly at his jaunty holiday appearance. This fine gentleman was bound for the 'north countree', for the Edinburgh and Glasgow Railway, where I have no doubt he will soon have the shine taken out of him. . .
>
> "I was a great deal amused at some photographic 'likenesses' of locomotives which Mr. Beyer showed me; one in particular which he humorously declared to be like a cow in the dark!"(17)

This Edinburgh & Glasgow 2-2-2 [66] is the earliest photograph taken at Gorton Foundry by James Mudd, who was noted equally for his portraits and landscapes. He took this one using an early wet plate process on a glass plate slightly smaller than the 15in. x 12in. size on which he standardised later. The offices are in the background.

One of these engines was the first locomotive to be photographed at Gorton Foundry, and from then on a maker's photograph was taken of most types. Beyer, who had experimented earlier with the Daguerreotype process, was quick to realise the potential of Fox Talbot's negative and positive process as an advertising medium.

At the International Exhibition of 1862, Beyer, Peacock displayed various products, one of which was a lathe for turning railway wheels and axles,

> "a very first-rate and most excellent tool in all respects",(18)

weighing no less than 28 tons. Another machine tool was one of Beyer's patent three-head vertical drilling machines, but of much greater importance was the D. Luiz, which was awarded a medal, a 2-2-2 locomotive (Order 629) for the South Eastern of Portugal, similar to those for the Edinburgh & Glasgow Railway. Obviously it would have been manufactured very carefully, and this may account for it costing £2,834 3s. 10d. compared with a selling price £2,500—a loss of £334 3s. 10d. The expenses of displaying it at the Exhibition would have been considered and met, by the Company as advertising costs. The building costs are given to show the standard practice for every order at Gorton Foundry. (see page 38).

In the official Record of the Exhibition, the D. Luiz is described as

> "a most excellent example of good proportions, arrangement and workmanship"(19)

but it also won admiration from the ordinary public as well. (20)

> "Amongst other objects of special admiration which have come under our notice is one to which we think attention may be drawn. A locomotive

The South Eastern Railway of Portugal 2-2-2 [629] was awarded a medal at the 1862 International Exhibition held in London. This engine is now preserved in Portugal.

[Above] The medal awarded at the 1862 International Exhibition.

engine is, perhaps, hardly what one would examine from an aesthetic point of view; but there is a huge one, standing just on the threshold of one of the eighteen penny refreshment rooms, which is so graceful in its outlines as to arrest the attention of even people hurrying to their dinners. . . The beauty of form of this engine, (the **D. Luiz**) its flowing lines, and harmonious proportions, in which strength and beauty are so completely reconciled, arrest the attention even of the most careless observer; but the engineering draughtsmen, both English and foreign, are never tired of expatiating its manifold excellences. The wheels alone are models of iron work; but the whole machine indicates in a most gratifying manner how naturally and rapidly the taste for the beautiful is rising out of the aptitude for the useful amongst that great race, the bold blacksmiths of England.''

The design of the **D. Luiz** is mentioned in many of the standard accounts of steam engines and railway locomotives, including a very full account given by Clark in 1879 (21), because it was held in such high esteem. It certainly marks the point when Beyer, Peacock was well established, with a good reputation and a number of sound locomotive designs of its own.

In 1915, R.H. Burnett, then Vice-President of the Institution of Locomotive Engineers, commented that this engine was still at work in 1908 after 46 year's service, for in that year the Portuguese authorities had asked if Beyer, Peacock(22)

> ''could suggest a modification of the leading axle, either by bogie or otherwise, to adapt the engine for running at high speed round 300 metre curves of one of their recent extensions, the engine having been designed for 500 metre curves.

> ''The proposal did not eventuate in any alteration to the engine, as it would have necessitated new cylinders and other expensive alterations, but the interesting fact is that in the course of the correspondence the Portuguese railway autorities said, 'The engine is very old indeed, **but in good order;** we have yet the **same boiler**' ie after 46 years use.''

Here was a design where the handsome exterior was not secured at the expense of utility or quality, and it is fitting that the engine is now permanently preserved.

The Dutch State Engines

In 1862, six 2-4-0 engines were built for the West Midland Railway (Order 619), which were a development of the Edinburgh & Glasgow 2-2-2s, and similar ones were built as yet another Beyer, Peacock standard design. Locomotives of this type were sold to Holland. On his Continental tour of 1863, Beyer stopped twice at The Hague to try to win some orders. The Dutch Chambers had voted that the Government should build 500 miles (800 kilometres) of railway and Beyer met Brouwer von Hagendorp, who was responsible for ordering the locomotives and rolling stock. Beyer asked Robertson to meet von Hagendorp in England, if possible at Manchester, where he intended going, for the Dutch business was very important, and he feared the competition of Borsig of Berlin. It would seem that by the time Beyer, Peacock was

founded, German engineering firms were supplying most of the needs of their own country, and were beginning to look for orders beyond their own borders. By calling again in Holland on his return from Sweden, Beyer was able to confirm the order for four 2-2-2 engines, but he was very worried lest anything should go wrong when von Hagendorp visited Gorton Foundry.(23)

[Top] The photograph shows one of six locomotives sent to the West Midland Railway [619] in 1862. This design became one of Beyer, Peacock's standard 2-4-0 passenger types which was sold to many other railways including the Dutch State.

[Foot] "Blixten" was supplied to the Swedish Government Railway in 1862 as part of Order 768. It was another standard Beyer, Peacock Design, based on Order 750, and was the type Beyer, Peacock sold to the Dutch State Railways to open their first line in 1863.

At the beginning of August 1863, von Hagendorp visited Gorton and gave the official order for

> "four Swedish engines and a conditional order for four more of the West Midland Class with four 6ft. driving wheels". (24)

Speedy delivery must have been required because the Company records suggest that four 2-2-2s, part of an order for Sweden, were diverted to Holland (Order 750) and that the other four were of the standard 2-4-0 design being built for stock in the hope that somebody would purchase them. In this way, the first of the 2-2-2's was dispatched on 12 September and two more on the 17th. It was arranged that Peacock should go to Holland and supervise their erection.(25) He sent Beyer an account of the opening of the first stretch of the Dutch State Railways:

> "On my arrival here, I found one of the Engines had arrived, but the second did not arrive until Wednesday night.

> On Wednesday we took an empty train of carriages over the new line to Tilburg and the Engine performed very well, except a little priming. I had her well washed out however at night, and determined to use her for the Opening train on Thursday the 1st instant .

> "On Wednesday evening most of the Directors of the Rolling Stock Co. arrived here, including the Chairman, Mr. Froulie—and as they stayed at this hotel, I had a good opportunity of making their acquaintance. All gave me a warm welcome and expressed themselves well pleased with the punctuality we had shewed in the delivery of the Engines, and also with their beautiful appearance. I found out however that they were very anxious about everything being done well on the opening day, and the Chairman particularly pressed upon me that the Engines should perform well, and as I had seen enough on the Wednesday to satisfy myself that—barring accidents—the engine was alright, I spoke somewhat confidently of what we should be able to do.

> "On Thursday morning a special Train arrived from the Hague with the Prime Minister 'Thorbeck' and several of the Members of Parliament, and along with Mr. Brouwer de Hagendorp, Mr. Waldorp, etc. etc. and we prepared to start the Opening Trip at 12 o'clock, the engine being covered with Flags, Wreaths of flowers and all kinds of gay devices. The second Engine having arrived the night before, we started it as a pilot, a quarter of an hour before the train, and at a few minutes past twelve, we left Breda with 12 well filled carriages, and as the Chairman had given me special charge of the running, I made the Company's driver into the fireman, and myself driver, and I am glad to say the engine did her duty well, and very satisfactory. Well on arriving at Tilburg a large procession was formed, and the Minister and Officials had a lunch in the Town Hall, to which the Chairman would make me go; that over—we started our return journey at ½ past 2, and we made the return trip (16 miles) in thirty minutes exactly, including one rather long stoppage. This was considered so good, that the Prime Minister came to look at the Engine and after my being introduced to him, he congratulated me very warmly on the performance of the Engine, and tendered me his personal thanks for having come from England to assist in this—the first Opening of their State Railways. After this came dining and feasting for the rest of the day and I do believe if I could have eat and drank Gold, they would have supplied me with it in abundance.

> "I thanked God for the position he had pleased to allow B.P. & Co. to take and I think the impression made will be attended with all the future success we could wish in this country."(26)

Peacock's concluding words were to prove true, because his company was to supply over 600 engines to the Dutch State Railways. This first engine remained in service for over fifty years, covering 950,000 miles,

The standard Dutch State Railways [838] 2-4-0 locomotives had inside frames only with inside cylinders. This became a very popular type.

Inclined Outside Cylinder Engines

Also in 1862, Beyer, Peacock supplied eight 4-4-0 tank engines (Order 626) and forty one 2-4-0 tender engines (Order 621) to the Tudela & Bilbao Railway in Spain, the largest single order received up to that date. The design of these engines was evolved in collaboration with Thomas Hunt, who left his position as, in effect, Works Manager at Crewe, to become the first Locomotive Superintendent of the Tudela & Bilbao Railway.(27) His first designs for this railway were a 4-4-0 bogie tank engine built by W. Fairbairn, based on the "Crewe" 2-4-0 with double frames and inclined cylinders. In the order that Beyer, Peacock received, many of the "Crewe" details, such as the castellated chimney, were retained, but considerable changes were made, including the abandonment of the outside main frames. As many parts as possible of the tender and tank engines had to be the same, including the complete boiler and firebox, cylinders, motion, wheels, connecting rods and other details. The cylinders remained steeply inclined, but the fixed front carrying wheels were replaced by "Bissel bogies". The design of bogies was then in its infancy, and the earliest ones gave little guidance to the engine. Bissel patented a design in 1857(28) which had a pivot set a little to the rear of the truck, while the engine rested on the inclined planes on the truck itself, so that the truck would return to the centre line after passing round a curve, and also help to guide the engine round the curve. Hunt took a leading part in the design of these engines, even to signing the General Arrangement drawing. For Beyer, Peacock this order was very profitable, for the tank engines cost £1,914 8s. 10d. each and were sold at £2,850, a profit of 48.87 per cent.; the tender engines made 44.25 per cent. profit. The design also proved to be the basis of many other successful engines.

In a letter to Robertson of 21 January 1863, Beyer said on the subject of speed of manufacture:

> "Mr. Fowler asked us yesterday how soon we could make him 6 Engines for the Metropolitan, and to which we replied by June Next. . . If time is of great importance we can make them as fast as anybody."(29)

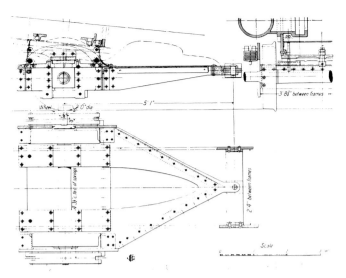

[Above] Diagram of the "Bissel" truck used on the Isle of Man locomotives.

In February, Beyer again wrote to Robertson saying they could deliver

> "Any kind of engine provided they are our scheme in 3½ months, that is as fast as any engine can be made".(30)

In 1862 the Vulcan Foundry had built six broad gauge 2-4-0 condensing tank engines, which were the first of their type to be put into service.(31) The condensing apparatus, however, was not a success, because the vacuum produced when the steam was shut off drew the water from the tanks into the cylinders. These engines were the property of the Great Western Railway, which had agreed to operate the Metropolitan Railway, which had been laid with mixed gauge track. On 18 July 1863, the Great Western gave notice that it would cease its operations in September, but in fact stopped on 10 August.

[Below] The order for 41 of these 2-4-0 passenger engines for the Tudela & Bilbao Railway [621] was the largest Beyer, Peacock had received up to 1862. It also formed the basis of many later designs. An interesting detail is that the smokebox was held together by bolts and not rivets.

[Above] The Tudela & Bilbao Railway [626] tank engine designed by H.L. Lange in collaboration with T. Hunt was a most important type because so many later Beyer, Peacock engines were derived from it.

[Below] The world's first successful condensing locomotives were built by Beyer, Peacock for the Metropolitan Railway [773] in 1864. The exhaust steam from the cylinders could be diverted by valves on the side of the smokebox either up the chimney in the usual way or along the large pipe beside the boiler into the watertanks on the side of the locomotive.

The Metropolitan was able to hire locomotives and rolling stock from the Great Northern and London & North Western Railways, and carry on with its services, but sometime before this Fowler must have been in touch with either Robertson or Beyer, for Beyer wrote on 10 August,

> "I have not yet looked at Mr. Fowler's Metropolitan Engines but intend to make a beginning tomorrow".(32)

Beyer hoped to finish the design for the Metropolitan engines by early September and see Fowler to settle the contract, but the first scheme was not approved, and at the beginning of October a special messenger took a new one down to London by the night mail.

> "The engines got longer than the first design by 6ft. and I added for it £50 to our previous price."(33)

But this one must have been rejected too, for four days later Beyer wrote to Robertson:

> "Since my return from London, we have been making another scheme for Mr. Fowler agreeable to his suggestion when at Gorton. The thing is a mistake, but I do think it incourteous to give him my opinion in writing. I am obliged to go again to London tonight to see him tomorrow morning before the board meeting. I begin to wish we were without this job which to do right ought to have more consideration and time than is given to it."(34)

Beyer met Fowler and persuaded him that the earliest scheme was preferable and, later that day, 7 October, Fowler was authorised by a special committee of the Metropolitan Railway to accept Beyer, Peacock's tender for eighteen engines, at a cost of £2,600 each.

The design of the Metropolitan locomotives was the first important one with which H.L. Lange was closely associated, and was based on the Tudela & Bilbao tank engines. R.H. Burnett, who had been sent to Spain in charge of erection of the Tudela engines, was also associated with them and helped Lange to make experiments with the condensing apparatus. He went to London to erect the engines and Fowler offered him the post of Locomotive Superintendent of the Metropolitan Railway, which he accepted and held until 1872, when he returned to Gorton Foundry as Works Manager.

The engines (Order 773) were fitted with valves in the exhaust pipes, which directed used steam either through the blast pipe in the usual way or, when working in tunnels, through pipes into the tops of the water tanks on each side of the locomotive. The tanks were filled to a predetermined level so that the exhaust pipe terminated above the level of the water and blew some of the steam across the surface of the water. Inside the end of the exhaust pipe was a smaller pipe, concentric with it, protruding into the water, so that steam was forced down through it, which caused the water to be agitated and absorb the heat evenly. After every trip round the Inner Circle, the water in the tanks had to be changed to keep it cool enough.

Deliveries did not start until 20 June 1864, but the design proved to be extremely sound and satisfactory, for Beyer, Peacock built no less than one hundred and forty-eight of them for railways in Britain between 1864 and 1886, while five non-condensing ones went to the Rhenish Railways in 1871 (Order 2640). On the Metropolitan and District Railways one hundred and twenty were in use, while the London & North Western, Midland and London & South Western Railways had the rest

among them. The original Metropolitan No.1, **Jupiter**, ran 632,145 miles before being re-boilered in 1887, and when it was broken up in 1897 had 1,050,000 to its credit. The original No.7 **Orion**, was sold to the Mersey Railway in 1925, and withdrawn from service in 1939.

In 1928, an exhibition of past and present rolling stock was held to mark the Diamond Jubilee (1868-1928) of the Metropolitan District Railway, and amongst the exhibits was one of these locomotives, it being the sole survivor of the fifty-six that comprised the full complement of the District Railway at the close of steam working. Metropolitan Railway No.23, which went into service in 1866, and had 82 years of operation before being retired in 1948, is preserved by London Transport as an historic relic.

Norwegian Government Railways

The design of the Tudela engines, with their sloping cylinders, was adapted for many other types and gauges. One of these adaptations was for the then very narrow gauge of 3ft. 6in. on the Norwegian railways. The story starts in 1862 when the Norwegian Government constructed a 3ft. 6in. line from Grundsett to Hamar, a distance of 24 miles. In 1864, a second line, 30 miles long, was opened from Trondheim to Stören and in that year the Government was building a further 56 miles. It was the intention to use this gauge for future railways which would have no connection with the main railways, which were being built to the 4ft. 8½in. gauge, the same as in Sweden.

In 1858, Robert Stephenson & Co. had submitted a quotation of £1,160 for a small tank engine, cylinders 10in. diameter x 18in. stroke, while Slaughter, Gruning & Co. of Bristol quoted £1,020 for a six-wheeled goods engine, and £920 for a four-wheeled tank engine.(35) The Grundsett line was worked by tank engines built by Stephenson, while Slaughter, Gruning built those for the Trondheim line, and had supplied a couple more in 1864 for the newly projected lines. It was against this background that in 1865 Beyer, Peacock entered the contest to supply new engines.

The Engineer of the Norwegian Government Railways was Carl Pihl. It is evident from the correspondence that Beyer and Pihl must have known each other quite well, and later in 1868 Pihl was to write and ask when he would see Beyer that summer,

> "You half promised that if all was well, then you would come over this year, and now as we are fairly in it, I ask, **when shall we see you?**
> "I should like though to know a little beforehand, in order to prevent the repetition of last year's extraordinary occurrence, when we travelled most of Northern Europe in quest of each other before I luckily intercepted you on the open sea."(36)

Pihl had been in England in the spring of 1865 and wished to have more information about the designs of his new engines before he left for Norway. He was certain that many more lines with narrow gauges would be built and had been given a copy of Tyler's report on the Ffestiniog Railway which had just introduced steam engines on a 2ft. gauge. In 1859 Beyer, Peacock had built two 0-4-0 tank engines for the Hudiksvall & Forssa Railway (Order 294), at a price of £1,100, on which it lost £30 per engine. It never built any more engines for this line, which had a gauge of 4ft., and had never built any locomotives as small as those ordered by Carl Pihl.

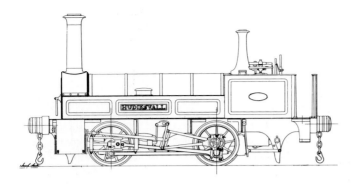

"Hudiksvall", one of two four foot gauge engines supplied in 1859 to the Hudiksvall & Forssa Railway [294]. The outside Allan straight link valve gear was rare on any Beyer, Peacock locomotive.

The tender from Beyer, Peacock quoting a price of £1,420 per locomotive has not survived, but Pihl's reaction to it has:

"Being fully aware of the difficult task you have had in producing the new design of the locomotive in question and being equally convinced of the excellency of the arrangements and quality of workmanship which we have to expect from you, the price which I had expected was nevertheless considerably exceeded by the price you quote. Of course there is from my side no question of bargaining to obtain a price lower than that which the work is entitled to as little as from your side to obtain one which is not fairly represented by the work you supply,—but yet in comparing your last mentioned price (£1,420) with that in your former tender and with those we have paid Rob. Stephenson & Co.—not to mention to Slaughter,—viz £1,213 & £1,124 respectively—I am here placed in a somewhat difficult position. . .

"Of course I expect your price to be higher than Stephenson on account of the bogie and the Steel Tyres. . .

"Now, my dear Beyer, you will understand me when I request you to go through the estimate again with a view to bring it lower, and if that can not be—point out for me some general reason for so large a plus to the prices demanded at an earlier period by yourself as well as other firms."

(20 July 1865)

Beyer had no intention of haggling, nor of reducing his standards. He believed that the good reputation of his firm and the high quality of his products would sell his locomotives. Accordingly he replied:

"I have been spending nearly a fortnight in Holland. . . Our price for your narrow gauge engines appears high compared with our tender for engines (£1,200) in November 6th. 1858. At that time we were in the wrong and would have lost money. . .

"We never take into account the trouble we may have in designing the engine required, and if I was longer in doing it than you expected, it was because I wished to satisfy myself in all points before writing to you. I should like to make you engines that will fulfil your expectations, but I should be sorry to make them at any price should I not succeed in their doing so."

(9 August 1865)

By agreeing not to send a man to help erect the engines, Beyer, Peacock won the order for these engines (Order 2000) at £1,400 each. They actually cost £1,256, including transport to the docks, so Beyer, Peacock made a profit of 11.37 per cent., considerably below the average at that period, but a healthy profit none the less.

Having reached this agreement, Pihl immediately began to ask for modifications. He asked for the position of the brake screw and reversing levers to be altered, the firebox door to be the sliding and not swinging type, the awning or cab, to be made larger and broader, provision to be made for head and tail lamps, the reversing lever to be a combined screw and lever type, the central coupling buffer to be the latest modification and spark catchers fitted in the chimney. Then he queried the basic design of the engine:

"I venture to remark on the construction proper of the Engine, and I need not tell you that when I make the following remarks, it is merely to ease my mind by drawing your renewed attention to them, not wishing to bring about any change in your design, which might not be approved by you."

(21 September 1865)

He queried whether the inclination of the cylinders and the position of the Bissel truck were conducive to steady running. Then he wondered whether the flanges on the wheels were going to tear up the track on bends, because the angles on the slides or inclines which guided the Bissel truck were too steep, but he realised his suggestions might alter the balance of the engine

"as the whole balancing of your Engine is perfect, you may perhaps think this counterbalance all the inconvenience".

The height of the boiler was queried because it was greater than on any other engine he had at that time

"tho I knew your decided opinions on this matter".

One wonders what Beyer felt about being asked almost to redesign his engine, but he managed to meet Pihl on most points, although he would not change the inclination of the cylinders, nor the layout of the Bissel truck, which did prove to be very successful in operation.(37) He discovered a mistake, for he had put the springs for the rear wheels on the driving platform, so he changed them to underneath, and sent Pihl a drawing to show the effects of a high boiler on the stability of the engine (letter 6 November 1865). Pihl wrote again (letter 8 November 1865) as he was still worried about the centre of gravity of a high boiler and there, as far as can be seen from the surviving correspondence, the matter was left, and there also Beyer must have left all progress on these two engines. Knowing that Beyer had claimed to be able to build an engine in three and a half months, we might reasonably expect to find that the engines would have been completed some time in March. So it was a somewhat anxious Pihl who wrote inquiring when the engines would be delivered, because he had heard that they might not be ready until about July, by which time the lines would be ready for opening (letter 21 March 1866). Unfortunately Beyer's reply is lost, only a pencilled comment "say end of August", but Pihl's feelings on receipt of that information can well be imagined:

"In relying on your high reputation, as well as the strong assurances of punctuality of the firm received as well from Colonel Beyer as from Tattie, I felt no necessity in the present order for Engines to make stipulations providing against nonfulfil-

The original design of the 2-4-0 tank engine for the 3ft. 6in. gauge Norwegian Government Railways [2000]. It became the prototype for many similar ones sent all over the world.

ment of order to the stated time. The matter is really in a much worse state than I think you can conceive and I only intend by this few lines to make my best appeal to you not only as part of the firm but also as a friend, to do your utmost to mend matters, so as to relieve me at the same time of as much responsibility as possible.''

(23 May 1866)

Silence then descends until George Gregory, Beyer, Peacock's erector, wrote from Norway on 23 September 1866:

"We were out on a trial trip some hours last Sunday the 16th. instant with No.2 Engine which gave general satisfaction. . . On Wednesday we had a trial trip with No.3 Engine for some hours and like No.2 they are satisfied with it. On Friday we went some 28 miles up the Country to meet Mr. Pihl with No.3 Engine and bring him to Drammen. During the journey he seemed quite satisfied with the engine.

"On Saturday we were out again over the same ground. . . having Mr. Pihl and a few Directors and their ladies with us. . . The Design of the Engines and her performance on the two occasions he was much pleased with. I heard him tell one of the Directors that the Engines worked excellently, in fact all parties seem much pleased with them.''

Pihl wrote a few days later expressing his satisfaction both regarding their construction and performance (letter 26 September 1866). He had found that the engines rode very steadily, both on the straight and round curves, and that the bogie acted perfectly, but he wanted to draw Beyer's attention to one or two details in the design. Not content with these first demonstrations, Pihl ordered that his new engines be tested against the one they had been using for ballasting and held a trial on a stretch of line 7 miles long, which included an incline of 1 in 100. A second trial was held on another 1 in 100 incline, which had a curve of 900ft. radius near the top. Both the Beyer,

Peacock engines took less time with the same load than the other engine and Pihl was later able to confirm the good impression he had of Beyer's design:

"I have purposely delayed writing to you until I could speak from experience as to the working of our small engines.

"It is with much pleasure I can corroborate the first report which I sent your firm by your foreman 'Gregory' of their successful trial.

"They have all along behaved well, perfectly steady & satisfactorily and are gaining favour every day. I trust you will feel yourself in some measure repaid for the trouble they have given you.

"There are though a few points I would wish to name to you.''

(1 November 1866)

Beyer did his best to reply to the problems which Pihl raised and pointed out that the priming might have been due to overfilling the boiler, because his firm positioned the gauge glass in a slightly different position from some others. He concluded:

"I took considerable pains to get your Engines into shape, but they pleased me when they were finished.

To hear from you that they perform satisfactorily pays for any little anxiety they may have given me. I do not trouble myself about the future but prefer living from day to day; still I do cherish a wish to see your Northern countries again and if God will I too hope to pay you a visit next summer.''

(no date)

Twenty-seven engines of this class were built for the Norwegian Government Railways, and some were adapted to be coupled up to a special carriage containing water tanks, to extend the distance they could travel,(38) a feature later used on many Garratt locomotives. Four similar ones were built for Seligmann & Haarbleecher (Orders 2512 & 2903) and one for McLean Bros & Rigg (Order 6191). The Norwegian Government ordered six of a slightly lighter design (Order 2232), while the basic design continued to be developed for other railways, with variations such as extended wheel arrangements, so it proved to be a very successful and popular type. Years later R.H. Burnett praised these engines highly:

"But for my part I never could feel admiration for mere size in a locomotive. I have always thought that the tank engines with the 'Bissel' bogie, that Beyer designed for the 3ft. 6in. gauge of the Norwegian railways. . . were as deserving of admiration for their general design and their suitability for the conditions they were required to meet as any locomotive that has ever been designed since then up to the present time."(39)

This was high praise indeed, coming as it did in 1916, fifty years after they had been designed.

Roskva and train photographed in Norway in 1868.

The variation supplied to Seligmann & Haarbleecher [2512] for work in South America.

5

The Second Partnership, 1869-1882

A meeting of the partners was called for 17 February 1869, because it was realised that their original agreement had expired at the end of 1868. It was resolved to renew the partnership for a period of seven years on almost the same terms as the original one, except that Beyer and Peacock were to receive salaries of £1,000 per annum, instead of £500, and were to be paid a percentage of the profits, in proportions to be agreed. They also no longer had to "devote their whole time" to the firm. At this meeting the partners decided to divide a payment of £10,000 between themselves, and add £5,000 to the amount of each of the partner's capital. This agreement would have run until the end of 1875, and may have been renewed again, which would have carried the partnership up to the beginning of 1883, when it was changed into a private limited company, but no records have survived to show what happended in these last seven years.(1)

Charles Frederick Beyer died on 2 June 1876, at the age of sixty-three, after a period of failing health. He was a man of prodigious energy who never spared himself. To quote from one of his obituary notices:-

"The great specialities of Mr. Beyer, by which he so rapidly became a leader in his business, were mainly three leading characteristics developed from natural talent, by high education, and good mechanical training, altogether constituting one who excelled in mechanical construction, delighted in beauty of form or outline, and gloried in simplicity of parts. These harmonising to a degree rarely to be found in any one man, and applied as they were to the construction of locomotive engines, together with a sound knowledge of shop work, coupled with that experience which Mr. Peacock was able to bring to bear were to result favourably."(2)

He had a profound influence on the construction of locomotives at that time, and the legend of his ideas persisted at Gorton Foundry long after his death—indeed traces of them could still be detected in Drawing Office practice as recently as 1925. Tales of how he would spend hours in elaborating a dainty curve, or improving the shape of a part, without sacrificing efficiency, circulated for years afterwards. His personality impressed itself deeply on all who worked with him, and he strove at all times towards perfection in matters great and small to do with the Company's products.

It is difficult to know how Beyer and his partners found time for all their many interests. Beyer, unlike Peacock and Robertson, never seems to have cared much for politics; perhaps after his industrial, educational and religious activities, he had no time to master the intricasies of English national or local government. This did not imply that he was unwilling to assume public responsibility, for, towards the end of his life, he became a magistrate. His personal friends included many prominent engineers of the day such as Richard Roberts, George Stephenson, James E. McConnell, John Ramsbottom, Daniel Gooch, and Joseph Beattie, to name but a few— while many others were pupils trained at Gorton Foundry in both Drawing Office and works during his lifetime, for example, R.H. Burnett, Gilbert (later Sir) Claughton, and Gustav Lentz.

Beyer was always keenly interested in technical discoveries. His patent for a drilling machine has been mentioned already, and in 1863 he developed a new type of safety valve which would open more fully when the required steam pressure had been reached.(3) He supported Bessemer in his quest for better, cheaper steel, and in 1863 was one of the promoters of the Lancashire Steel Company, which erected one of the earliest Bessemer steel plants on land adjoining Gorton Foundry. The plant ceased operations there in 1878 and the site, bounded by Bessemer Street, was then purchased by Beyer, Peacock for extensions.

[Heading] Pender sectioned for display at Liverpool Road Station, Manchester.

The last photograph taken of C. F. Beyer.

Beyer and his partners had taken great financial risks when they founded the Company in 1854, but a glance at the figures will show that they were amply rewarded, for by the end of 1876 the profits had reached somewhere around the million pound level. Beyer's own private wealth gradually increased and he gave generous donations for various purposes from about 1860 onwards. Improved facilities for technical education was a matter in which he had always been keenly interested, being very conscious of the fact that England was then lagging well behind his native Germany. He was a member of the Manchester Mechanics' Institute from 1847 onwards, and gave it some assistance, but was more interested in the development of Owens College. (4) As early as 1860, he was an acquaintance of the Principal, Professor Greenwood, and was an advocate of moving the College from the original Quay Street site. He made many large contributions not only to the general funds of the College, but the Departments of Engineering, Physics and Law also benefited, and in 1868 he helped to found a Chair of Engineering. Beyer did not believe that science was the be-all and end-all of education, but he was convinced that the life of any great educational institution could be at its best only when both arts and sciences were studied within the same walls by scholars who intermingled in their daily lives.

Before his death, the one-time German student, who had once consented to work for three farthings an hour, had become immensely wealthy. While he bequeathed his Denbighshire estate to his godson, Henry Beyer Robertson, the residue of his fortune, amounting to over £104,000, was left to Owens College, his intention being to endow professorships in science. His trustees found that this was impracticable at the then state of development of the College, and wisely decided to modify the form, though not the nature of the bequest. The major part of this vast sum, the largest donation in comparable monetary terms which the University has ever received, was applied to building the Beyer Laboratories, in the main University quadrangle, which were opened in 1888 and, even though the University of Manchester is now a vast modern complex, still stand as a proud memorial to a great Manchester engineer.

Second to Beyer's munificence as a patron of education was his generosity to the Church of England, of which he was devout member. Through the development of the various engineering works, the population of Gorton increased by leaps and bounds. Houses for employees sprang up close to the works and appropriately two streets were named "Beyer Street" and "Peacock Street". In 1865 Beyer bore the cost of building St. Mark's Day School in Gorton, and in addition helped towards building the church of the same name. Its consecration was an occasion for the partners to come together, because Robertson was invited to bring Mrs. Robertson and their family, and Peacock had volunteered to bring his.(5) In 1871 Beyer contributed £1,000 towards the rebuilding of the old parish church of Gorton, St. James, and in the end seems in fact to have provided all the money needed for this project and the reconstruction of its rectory as well, while among his last bequests was £10,000 towards the building of the new church of All Saints, in Gorton. He also helped to extend the church at Llantysilio, where he had his Denbighshire estate, and by his will augmented the stipend there. It was there that he died and was buried in the churchyard, where his grave can still be seen.

Llantysilio Hall as rebuilt by Beyer, the centre of his Denbighshire estates.

The Beyer Laboratories at Manchester University.

St. James's Church, Gorton.

He ignored all requests that he should spare himself as his health deteriorated and his work became more burdensome. He always endeavoured to use his wealth and position wisely, and to carry out the words which he had written in his diary on his fiftieth birthday, "Have mercy upon me, O Lord, and grant that the goods Thou hast entrusted to my keeping may bear fruit to thy Honour and Glory, through Jesus Christ." (6)

Beyer's plain red granite tomb at Llantisilio Church.

On Beyer's death it was necessary to value the assets of Gorton Foundry so that his share could be deducted. Documents showing this have survived in the Robertson Papers, together with a comparison of another firm which, although not directly named, must be Sharp Stewart from the pencilled initials "S.S. & Co." The figures were taken to the end of December 1876, to show what had been produced in the previous ten years and the valuation at that date:(7)

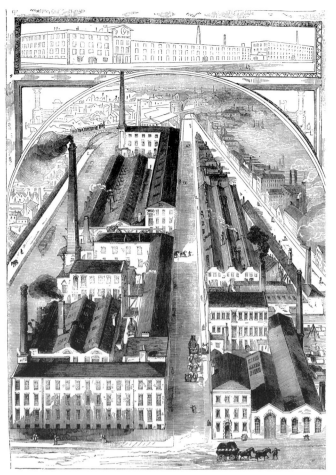

This picture of Sharp Stewart's Atlas Works in Manchester, drawn soon after 1855, shows the multi-storeyed buildings on the cramped site hemmed in by the Rochdale Canal on the left and Oxford Street in front. The Manchester, South Junction & Altrincham Railway, the nearest line, runs on a viaduct in the background.

	B.P. & Co.	S.S. & Co.
No. of Engines delivered	928	901
No. of extra Boilers	103	
No. of extra Tenders	76	
Total Deliveries	£2,779,901	£2,810,818
Net Amount of Profits	£ 608,670	£ 569,270

Total Assets as per books

	B.P. & Co.	S.S. & Co.
Land & Buildings	£ 61,345.15. 7	£ 84,476.18.11
Stationary Engines, fixed plant etc.	£156,361.14. 3	£ 87,129.18. 7
Working balance,	£132,095. 5.10	£189,840. 9. 0
Deduct sundry creditors,		£ 16,617.12. 5
Total Assets as per book	£349,811.15. 8	£344,829.14. 1

The figures quoted above do not show that towards the end of this period, Beyer, Peacock was generally building more locomotives each year than Sharp Stewart. Sharp Stewart was confined in a city centre site, which must have hindered it considerably as the size of locomotives increased, while Beyer, Peacock had room to expand on adjacent land. This was obviously one of the reasons for Sharp Stewart moving to Glasgow in 1888. Then it will be noticed from the figures quoted above that, while the site value was greater in the case of Sharp Stewart, reflecting the higher value of land in the city, its stock of stationary engines and other fixed plant was very much lower. Beyer had continued to follow the Roberts tradition of developing machine tools to replace manual work wherever possible. Between 1869 and the end of 1876 Beyer, Peacock's profits amounted to approximately £483,547, which gives a total figure of around £1,061,731 from the start of the Company; not a bad result on an original capital expenditure of around £30,000.

Following Beyer's death in 1876, Hermann L. Lange became Chief Engineer and Joint Manager, responsible mainly for all the technical work of the Company. Through his appointment as Chief Draughtsman in 1865, he was the best equipped to carry out Beyer's very positive ideas on locomotive design during and beyond his patron's lifetime. There seem to have been one or two Chief Draughtsmen during the ensuing years to 1890, but Lange continued to hold this post in effect if not in name. The other important change at this time was that Richard Peacock's son, Ralph, was appointed, at the age of 38, assistant to his father.

The Works Manager at the time Beyer died was Robert H. Burnett (1838-1916), who had trained as a pupil at Gorton Foundry, and was then sent out by the Company to introduce the engines delivered to the Tudela & Bilbao Railway in 1862-63. His part in the development of the "Metropolitan" tank engines has been described already and he returned to Gorton as Works Manager from 1872 to 1877, when he resigned and went to Australia the following year as Chief Mechanical Engineer of the New South Wales Government Railways. New South Wales was already a customer of Beyer, Peacock and no doubt Burnett helped to strengthen the relationship. In 1882, he came home to London and established himself as a consultant. He was an engineer of very high ability, and his reason for resigning as Works Manager may have been that, with Lange promoted to Chief Engineer and Joint Manager, and Ralph Peacock brought into the management, his prospects of advancement appeared remote. Later, at an age at which many would have retired, his services as a consulting engineer were secured by Beyer, Peacock alone, and he eventually became London Representative, dying in 1916 while still in the Company s service. His successor as Works Manager was Charles Holt, brother of Frank Holt, Burnett's predecessor.

One of the most important influences on locomotive design in this period was the introduction of steel. It started with steel tyres, particularly for the driving wheels, and one of the first orders on which Beyer, Peacock used them was for the five 0-4-2 tank engines supplied to the North London Railway (Order 428) in 1860. Two or three years after that, steel tyres, although costing at first twice as much as wrought iron, became the accepted practice because they had a much longer life. The weight on the driving axles tended to squash and deform the softer wrought iron,(8) so that with the introduction of steel tyres running on steel rails, weights on the axles could be increased, leading to larger, heavier locomotives. Then because the steel tyres did not wear so quickly, all the driving wheels remained closer to their original size for much longer and did not need re-turning so frequently. This was particularly important on high-speed passenger engines with coupled wheels because, with wheels of slightly different diameters through wear, enormous strains were imposed on the coupling rods. Therefore this was the period when the four-coupled express engine became accepted generally.

Gradually other parts of the locomotives began to be made from steel too. Moving parts subject to high wear were the first and in 1861 the 2-4-0 tender engines supplied to the Victorian Railways (Order 548) had steel cross-head slides as well as steel tyres. Twenty years later, the 0-6-0 engines ordered by the Great Southern & Western

R. H. Burnett, 1838-1916.

Railway of Ireland (Order 3970), then the most powerful goods engines in that country,(9) had in addition cast steel horn blocks, and axles made of steel, including the inside crank axle. By 1882, both the boilers and main frames were being made from steel plates. Steel used in the main frames gave a stronger construction which did not flex so much.(10) The tensile strength of steel was greater than wrought iron,(11) so that its use in boilers enabled higher steam pressures to be used, and more powerful engines built. In fact, D.K. Clark, writing in 1860, confidently expected that all boilers would soon be built from steel,(12) but twenty years later wrought iron was still popular, partly through its greater corrosion resisting properties.

Another important feature affecting locomotive design was the introduction of continuous brakes on trains, and brakes on locomotives themselves. In 1875, the famous trials of different braking systems were held at Newark and, in 1878, an Act was passed in Parliament requiring railway companies to report to the Board of Trade what action they were taking in this matter, but it was not until 1882 that another Act was introduced requiring all railway companies in Great Britain to adopt some form of continuous brake.(13) Beyer, Peacock had to understand all the various types of brakes then being developed, because it could find itself supplying locomotives to railways on which any of the existing braking methods might be in use.

[Top] Other unusual features at the time besides the steel for the tyres on these 0-4-2 saddle tank engines for the North London Railway [428] in 1860 were screw reversing mechanism and the springs for the Salter safety valves placed on either side of the dome.

[Above] The 0-6-0 goods engines built in 1881 for the Great Southern & Western Railway of Ireland [3970] were a slightly modified version of this design [2045] which originated in 1867.

[Right] Splasher detail showing the curved maker's plate.

[Above] One of the first batch of 2-4-0 well tanks built in 1863 by Beyer, Peacock for Joseph Beattie and the London & South Western Railway [649], complete with coal-fired boiler, feed water heating apparatus, etc. The outer springs under the ends of the leading axle as well as those on top inside the frames can be seen clearly.

[Right] Beyer, Peacock Progressive Number 1414 [order 3141] of 1874 still at work on the Bodmin & Wadebridge line in 1957.
[J. R. Walker]

The Locomotives Produced

From the end of 1868 to the end of 1882, 1,382 locomotives were produced at Gorton Foundry, of which approximately 60 per cent. were exported. The greatest number built in any one year was one hundred and thirty-one but the average was around the hundred mark, although there were slumps in 1869 and 1879, with only sixty-seven and sixty-three built respectively. At home, the largest customer was the London & South Western Railway, which received one hundred and twenty locomotives. These included the last twenty of its 2-4-0 well tanks. The design had originated in 1863 and continued to be built until 1875 when Beyer, Peacock had constructed a total of eighty-two. Few tank engines of their size were more successful. The weight was well distributed, and they had remarkable acceleration, even with well-filled suburban trains of twenty or twenty-two carriages. Their leading axles had four springs, the two outside ones being carried under the lower crosshead guide bars, which helped to keep them steady and prevent rolling. In 1892, **The Engineer** featured an article about them (14) in which it was pointed out that the majority of the sixty then running had been neither rebuilt nor reboilered. Also it was claimed that this type would soon become a matter of history, but in fact one of them survived for many years, working on the Bodmin and Wadebridge line in Cornwall, hauling the china clay wagons until the end of the steam era.

Beattie continued to use his patent boiler and feed water heating apparatus on most of his engines for the London & South Western Railway, for the Order 3097, in 1875, for six of the "Metropolitan" tanks had both these fitted. Fifty-six 0-6-0 goods engines were built for the London & South Western in this period, but Beattie had retired when twenty-four handsome 4-4-0 passenger engines (Orders 3767 & 3921) were delivered during 1879/1880 to the designs of W. Adams, and the Beyer, Peacock association finished in 1882 with the construction of twelve 4-4-2 tank engines (Order 6205), also to his designs.

Ninety-six engines were constructed for the Midland Railway, including another six "Metropolitan" tanks, but the bulk of the remainder was an order for thirty 0-6-0 goods engines in 1876 (Order 3350), and a further fifty in 1882 (Order 6210). This last order was preceded in 1881 by an order for fifty 0-6-0s for the Lancashire & Yorkshire Railway (Order 3950), which was the largest single order Beyer, Peacock had ever received. Unfor-

[Above] The London & South Western Railway [3097] version of the "Metropolitan" tanks, complete with feed water apparatus and therefore not fully condensing.

[Below] The Adams 4-4-0 tender locomotives built at Gorton for the London & South Western Railway [3767], which were fitted with W. C. Church & Co. patent valves, a single guide bar for the cross head, unusual at that time, and one lever that worked the brakes on both driving wheels.

[Foot] The Adams 4-4-2 tank for the London & South Western Railway [6205]. One of this type, but not built by Beyer, Peacock, is still running on the Bluebell Railway in Sussex.

[Above] Few Beyer, Peacock features can be detected on these 0-6-0 for the Lancashire & Yorkshire Railway [3950] built in 1881. Even the maker's name plate on the centre wheel splasher is an unusual shape.

[Below] The original South Australian [3713] version of the 0-6-4 tank engine design which also formed the basis for all the locomotives on the Sligo, Leitrim & Northern Counties Railway in Ireland, but those for Ireland were not fitted with cowcatchers.

[Foot] South Australian K67 of 1885 [scrapped 1936] hauling a mixed train at Sutherlands on the now abandoned Euduna Morgan line.
[H. Williams Collection, Australia].

tunately, such large orders were extremely rare, and more typical were the orders for one or two engines at a time, which were received from Ireland. A total of fifty locomotives was sent there, including the first couple of 0-6-4 tank engines for the Sligo, Leitrim & Northern Counties Railway (Order 6160) in 1882. The company remained faithful to Beyer, Peacock for the rest of its existence, with engines of this wheelbase, receiving the last ones in 1951. Its engines were never numbered, but were known by their individual names.

The Sligo, Leitrim 0-6-4 tank engines were a slight modification of a design with the same wheel arrangement originally built for the South Australian Government Railways (Order 3713) in 1878.(15) Both railways were 5ft 3in. gauge and up to 1884 eighteen of these engines had been sent to Australia. The extra width of this gauge allowed designers more space for accommodating inside cylinders, and valve gear, which were the fashion on many railways for a very long time. The wider gauge was more expensive to build, however, with the result that in Ireland feeder lines were constructed to the 3ft gauge, and in South Australia to 3ft 6in. For the South Australian narrow gauge lines, a 2-6-0 tender engine was developed in 1875 from the Norwegian Government Railways 3ft.6in. 2-4-0 tank and a total of seventy-five was built from then up to 1886. Many more were built in Australia itself, and it became a classic type, used on most of the 3ft 6in. gauge lines on that continent.

[Above] A South Australian Railways 4-4-0 built in 1881 which worked for over fifty years.   [H. Williams Col.]

[Right] The first of many 2-6-0 tender engines built for the Australian 3ft. 6in. gauge railways [3591 of 1875].

[Below] South Australian No. Wx 34 of 1879 [scrapped 1929], with mixed train on the Western section before it was converted to broad gauge in 1924.
[Wallaroo Museum Collection, Australia].

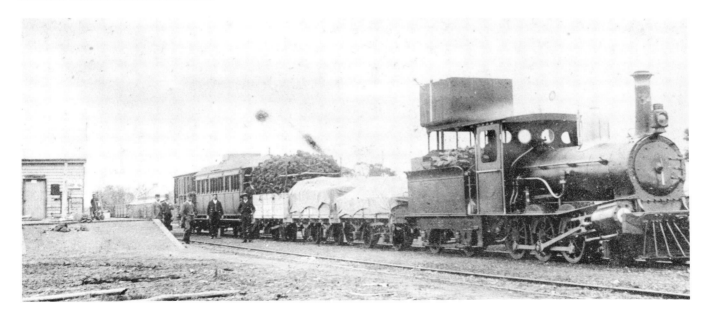

[Top] No. 1 ''Sutherland'' of the Isle of Man Railway [2965] now preserved at the Port Erin museum.

[Above] Isle of Man Railway No. 3 ''Pender'' [2965] of 1873 on Pickfords low loader at Douglas Station in September 1979, ready to begin the journey home to Manchester for preservation at the North Western Museum of Science & Industry. During its working life, the engine has been altered with a new boiler, different cab front, larger side tanks, etc.   [R. L. Hills]

[Below] 0-6-0 tank engine for the Ballymena & Larne Railway [3560]. The bellows of the Smith vacuum brake can be seen behind the steps into the cab.

For the 3ft gauge lines, Beyer, Peacock narrowed the same 2-4-0 tank engine and in 1873 supplied three to the Isle of Man Railway, which had the smallest gauge it had yet catered for. This type formed the backbone of the island's transport system for many decades, the final one being produced in 1926 (Order 144). The Isle of Man Railway celebrated its centenary with one section of the line being run as a tourist attraction, with these locomotives in steam; some are still operating regularly every summer. In 1877 the Ballymena & Larne Railway received a similar engine (Order 3525) and another one the following year (Order 3714), but this company needed something more powerful and so had two 0-6-0 tank engines in 1877 (Order 3560) and a 2-6-0 tank in 1880 (Order 3897), which was evolved from the Norwegian design with a similar pony truck, inclined cylinders, but with a saddle tank, a unique type for an Irish narrow gauge railway.(16)

The valuable connection with the Dutch State Railways continued to bear fruit with the delivery of one hundred and sixty-five locomotives. The original ''West Midland'' type was modified in 1865 by having only inside frames. The cylinders remained inside, but power was increased by raising the boiler pressure. Between then and 1872, seventy-four engines of this class were constructed, and in 1871 two similar ones were sent to the Malines & Terneuzen Railway (Order 2554), in Belgium. An order for another two engines of the same type for this latter railway (Order 2792) was noteworthy, for they were the first to be constructed in Britain with Belpaire fireboxes.(17)

Between 1872 and 1879, the Dutch State Railways tried a 2-4-0 with inside frames, but outside cylinders (Order 2848). A total of fifty was built, but they did not ride as smoothly as had been expected, so the Dutch railway authorities formed a strong preference for inside cylinders for their passenger engines, and no more were built with outside cylinders until after the turn of the century. Between 1880 and 1895 no fewer than one hundred and seventy-eight 2-4-0's were supplied to a new and elegant design (Order 3878), for which Hermann Lange was responsible at Gorton. It was a much more powerful type

This engine should be compared with the 2-6-0 tender type for the South Australian Railways for this one for the Ballymena & Larne Railway [3897] is the same basic design but has sprouted a saddle tank, vacuum brake, and different safety valves.

The last of the Dutch State Railways [2722] inside cylinder, inside framed engines built in 1872.

[Below] These locomotives for the Malines & Terneuzen Railway [2792] were the first to be built in Britain with Belpaire fireboxes in 1871. It was not until 1891 that the Belpaire firebox was actually used on a British railway [see Chapter 7]. These engines were also fitted with Beatties "smoke-consuming" appliance, a combustion chamber filled with fire-bricks but this did not work very well.

[Foot] Capable of over 70 mph, Lange's outside framed 2-4-0 for the Dutch State Railways [3878] was amongst the fastest locomotives of that day. One of these engines can be seen in the Railway Museum at Utrecht.

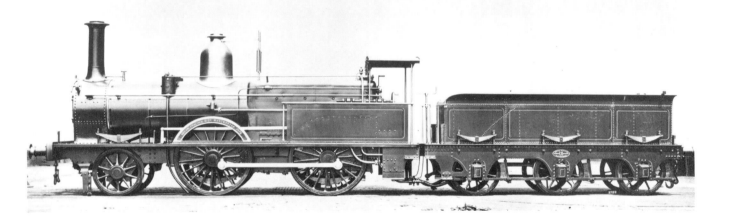

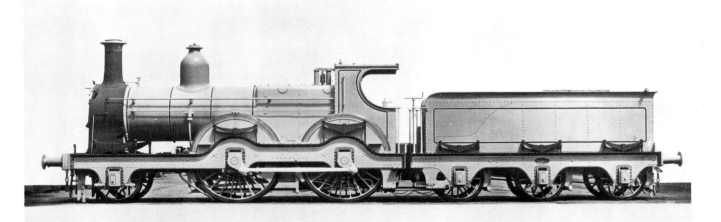

[Above] Dutch State Railways outside
cylinder 2-4-0 in service c. 1930.

[Right] The Dutch State Railways [2848]
2-4-0 type modified with outside
cylinders.

[Below] Dutch State Railways outside
framed 2-4-0 No. 1439 at Zwolle, August
1936.   [J. R. Walker]

with inside cylinders, double frames and a large Belpaire firebox. The advantages of this arrangement were that large cylinders with easy steam passages and exhaust ports could be used, together with large bearing surfaces. The trailing axle could be placed under the firebox without danger to the bearings from the heat, so that a good weight distribution could be achieved. With their 7ft diameter driving wheels they were designed to haul the Flushing-North Germany fast trains, which weighed over 200 tons, at an average speed of 60 miles an hour, but they were often used on goods trains, for they proved to be just as economical as the engines specially designed for goods work.(18) In 1892, one of these engines was built as a two-cylinder compound, and fitted with Walschaert's valve gear in place of the usual Stephenson design (Order 7468). These engines were highly regarded, for they were a good, simple, straightforward design, comparing favourably with other high-speed engines of that period.

The cost of the Dutch State Railways 2-4-0 locomotives are given below. Although the designs became heavier,

Dutch State Railways outside framed 2-4-0 No. 1381 at Zwolle, August 1936.
[J. R. Walker].

Date	Order	No.	Cost	Sold for	Profit	Notes
1863	761	4	£1,874	£2,450	30 5/8%	Double Frame "West Midland" design
1865	838	2	£1,969	£2,400	21 7/8%	Single inside frames, inside cylinders
1865	856	6	£1,837	£2,400	30½ %	
1865	945	15	£1,848	£2,450	32½ %	
1865	974	12	£1,848	£2,450	32½ %	
1866	982	31	£1,816	£2,450	34¾ %	
1871	2554	2	£1,753	£2,350	33 7/8%	
1871	2672	2	£1,753	£2,350	33 7/8%	
1872	2722	4	£1,800	£2,350	30½ %	
1872	2848	10	£2,286	£2,600	13¾ %	Outside cylinders, single inside frames.
1873	3013	10	£2,480	£3,000	20 7/8%	
1874	3046	10	£2,499	£3,100	24	
1877	3476	10	£2,152	£2,775	28¾ %	
1878	3614	8	£2,023	£2,700	33¼ %	
1879	3776	2	£2,085	£2,550	22¼ %	
1880	3878	7	£2,348	£2,622	9 7/8%	New design with double frames, inside cylinders & Belpaire firebox.
1880	3945	10	£2,374	£2,760	16½ %	
1881	6074	10	£2,359	£2,750	16½ %	
1882	6150	10	£2,307	£2,750	19¼ %	
1883	6333	18	£2,167	£2,630	21⅓ %	
1884	6424	17	£2,118	£2,583	21 7/8%	
1885	6640	5	£2,102	£2,530	20 3/8%	
1886	6727	10	£2,057	£2,510	22%	[19]

and features such as automatic brakes were added, the prices remained remarkably stable during the twenty-year period for which figures have survived.

In addition to these passenger engines, goods and shunting engines were also sold to Holland, and there was another connection through the Dutch with what is now Indonesia, where a further twenty locomotives were sent.

Another important customer was the New South Wales Government Railways. The first locomotive (Order 779), which had inclined outside cylinders, was sent there in 1865, and between 1869 and 1882 a hundred and twenty-five more were purchased, including fifty-one during the years R.H. Burnett was their Chief Mechanical Engineer. Between 1881 and 1883, seventy 2-6-0's (Order 6063) were built for this railway.

Sweden too took a great many locomotives, for besides the forty-seven purchased by the Swedish Government Railway, another sixty-three went to other railways in that country. This was also the period of brief flirtation with Eastern Europe, and the 5ft gauge lines of Russia and Finland. It started in 1865 with twenty 0-6-0's sent to the Dünaburg & Witebsk Railway, in what is now Latvia (Order 844), and in the period of the second partnership to 1880 a further seventy-five engines of different types

were sent to the Tamboff & Saratoff, Moscow & Kursk, and Grand Russian Railways in Russia, as well as to railways in Finland. The engines supplied to the Grand Russian (Order 2453) were the first with eight-coupled wheels to be built at Gorton Foundry. This was also the time when Beyer managed to obtain some orders from his native Germany. Although Sharp Roberts had exported many to that country, Beyer, Peacock sent none until in 1867 two went to the Berlin & Hamburg Railway (Order 2057). These were followed in 1871 by five "Metropolitan" tanks to the Rhenische Railway (Order 2640). In 1872 twenty-five engines were sent to the Bergisch Markisch Railway (Order 2904) in Alsace, and there were two orders for each from the Berlin & Potsdam—for eight engines (Orders 2900 & 3119)—and the Cologne & Minden—for fifty engines (Orders 3028 & 3131). This was the final fling, because no more were ever exported to Germany, although Beyer, Peacock did collaborate later with German locomotive builders over the Garratt engines. More success was to follow the delivery beween 1875 and 1880 of twenty-seven 2-6-0's (Order 3355) to the Cape Government, for they were the first orders from Southern Africa, an area which was to become so important in the later history of the company.

[Above] This 2-4-0 for the New South Wales Government Railways [779] built in 1865 is another early Beyer, Peacock design with inclined cylinders and Bissel pony truck. It was fitted with an injector for supplying the boiler with water but the side of the firebox was not the best place to fit the non-return clack valve.

[Below] This layout of horizontal cylinders set between the pony truck and the main driving wheels with large boiler above was used on many other railways at home and abroad as well as this one built for the New South Wales Government Railways [6063] in 1881.

[Below] The typical Beyer, Peacock chimney contrasts strongly with the continental features of the cab on these twenty engines supplied to the Cologne & Minden Railway [3131] in 1874.

66

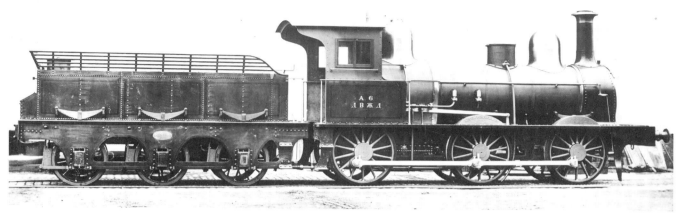

[Above] A Beyer, Peacock standard 0-6-0 goods type, dressed up to suit the requirements of the customer, in this case the Dünaburg & Witebsk Railway [844] of Latvia in 1865.

[Below] Outside valve gear of the Stephenson or Allan types, although popular on the Continent, was rarely used by Beyer, Peacock, one suspects because it looked clumsy, a fault in Beyer's eyes. These engines for the Grand Russian Railway [2453] had four domes on the top of the boiler. The one in the cab housed the safety valves; the next one contained sand. Inside the large one, the steam pipe collected the steam and took it to the one beside the chimney where the regulator was situated.

[Below] A small start, for this little 2-6-0 for the Cape Government Railway [3355] in 1875 was the forerunner of the massive Beyer-Garratt locomotives in South Africa.

[Left] It might have been expected that a somewhat grander design would have been the first that Beyer sent from his own works to his native Germany than this 0-4-2 saddle tank for the Berlin & Hamburg Railway [2057] in 1867.

[Below] The long-boilered 0-6-0 goods engine, with the firebox overhanging the rear axle remained popular on the Continent until the mid 1870s. The same design was supplied to the Bergisch, Markisch [2904] in 1872 and the Cologne & Minden Railways [3028] in 1873.

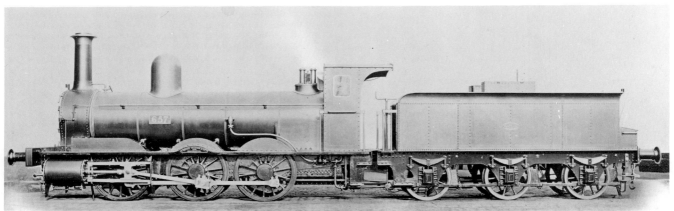

The ledgers for the costs of building the locomotives have survived for the period 1855 to 1886, but there is nothing to show how these figures were determined, or how the selling price was decided. The initial order for a type of locomotive cost more because drawings, patterns, flanging blocks, etc. had to be made, and this was usually reflected in the selling price. In repeat orders, however, it is not always clear from the **Cost of Work Book** what changes may have been made in the design, such as enlarged cabs or watertanks. The construction of the engines was based more and more on detailed specifications agreed with the customer, which might vary for different purchasers of the same type of locomotive. Orders 6511 and 6515, for 4-4-0 condensing tank engines for the Metropolitan, and Metropolitan District Railways respectively, show wide variations in prices for iron from different places, as well as different numbers of tubes in the boilers, etc. For two railway companies working so closely in association with each other, it seems extraordinary that one should have vacuum brake and the other the Westinghouse.

Selected Costs for Order 6511, Metropolitan Railway, per engine.

Boiler Plates, Bowling Iron Co.,	£ 64.14. 9½
Frame Plates, Parkgate Iron Co.	21. 9. 9
General Plates	55. 9. 8
Wrought Iron including all other forgings,	103.11.10½
Crank Pins, Jno. Brown & Co.	12. 2. 4
Copper Plates,	108.19. 1
Brass Tubes (800, 10′ 9½″ x 2″ x 11 & 13 W.G.)	118. 6.10
No. 10 Injectors, Gresham & Craven,	9.10. 0
Vacuum Brake supplied by the R.way Co free of charge.	

Selected Costs for Order 6515, Metropolitan District Railway, per engine.

Boiler Plates, Low Moor,	£ 106. 0. 8¾
Frame Plates, Farnley Iron Co.	31.12. 8
General Plates,	59.16. 9½
Wrought Iron including all other forgings,	96. 3. 2½
Crank Pins, J. Whitworth & Co.	6. 6.11½
Copper Plates	98.13.11¼
Brass Tubes (984, 10′ 9″ x 2″ x 10 & 12 W.G.)	140.11. 6
No. 8 Friedmanns Injector,	6.15. 0
Westinghouse brake work,	47.10. 0

(20)

Year	Order	No.	Cost	Sold for	Profit	Company
1864	773	18	£2,217	£2,679	20¾%	Metropolitan
1866	2001	5	£2,128	£2,679	25 7/8%	Metropolitan
1868	2090	5	£2,004	£2,675	33 3/8%	Metropolitan
1868	2090	5	£1,971	£2,600	31 7/8%	Midland
1868	2290	5	£1,961	£2,675	36 3/8%	Metropolitan
1868	2290	1	£1,927	£2,500	29¾%	Midland
1869	2336	6	£1,949	£2,600	33¼%	Metropolitan
1870	2383	5	£1,934	£2,545	31½%	Metropolitan
1871	2640	5	£2,111	£2,350	9¾%	Rhenische
1871	2661	24	£1,761	£2,280	29 3/8%	Metropolitan District
1871	2704	7	£1,734	£2,330	34¼%	London & North Western
1872	2816	9	£1,982	£2,330	17½%	London & North Western
1875	3097	6	£2,392	£3,160	33 3/8%	London & South Western
1876	3419	6	£2,319	£2,625	13¼%	Metropolitan District
1879	3808	5	£1,734	£1,923	10 7/8%	Metropolitan
1880	3894	7	£1,669	£1,950	16¾%	Metropolitan
1880	3894	3	£1,669	£1,950	16¾%	South Eastern
1881	6033	6	£1,916	£2,193	14½%	Metropolitan District
1883	6277	6	£1,969	£2,290	16¼%	Metropolitan District
1884	6511	5	£1,758	£2,150	22¼%	Metropolitan
1884	6515	6	£1,930	£2,400	24¼%	Metropolitan District
1885	6648	2	£1,921	£2,200	14¼%	Metropolitan
1886	6784	6	£1,878	£2,200	17.14%	Metropolitan District

The selling price usually included delivery charges within this country. For locomotives sent overseas, packing at Gorton and erection at the destination were included in the price. Sometimes delivery to the port, loading, and possibly unloading at the other end were included, but the actual shipping was paid for by the customer. The prices of the ''Metropolitan'' tank engines are shown above to show the trends over a run of orders which spanned twenty years, and involved seven different companies, and, of course, minor variations in design. The differences between selling prices to the Metropolitan and Midland Railway, for locomotives of the same Order (2090 and 2290), suggests that Beyer, Peacock adapted its charges to what it thought it could get from its customers, and did not have a fixed price. The engines were virtually identical for both companies, but were delivered to King's Cross and Derby respectively. The difference in delivery charges was nowhere near as great as Beyer, Peacock's difference in selling prices.

Improved machine tools and other methods of manufacture helped to reduce costs, so that most prices fell during this period. There was, however, a sudden rise between 1872 and 1875, accounted for by the effects of the Franco-Prussian War, after which costs and prices fell again. The 0-6-0 tender engines ordered by the Gefle Dala Railway in Sweden, and the 0-6-0 goods engines ordered by the Dutch State Railways show these trends.

These figures emphasize the importance of securing long runs of orders. Not only did the cost to the railway company come down over the years, but Beyer, Peacock's profits rose. The figures show the remarkable stability in prices during the Victorian era compared with today, in spite of the fantastic investment in all sorts of industrial development.

Year	Order	No.	Cost	Sold for	Profit		Year	Order	No.	Cost	Sold for	Profit
Gefle Dala Railway							Dutch State Railways					
1860	418	1	£2,258	£2,560	13 5/16%		1865	913	2	£2,247	£2,800	24½%
1862	603	2	£1,899	£2,500	31½%		1865	947	2	£2,124	£2,800	31¾%
1863	731	1	£1,828	£2,428	32¾%		1870	2503	4	£1,898	£2,800	47½%
1864	783	2	£1,814	£2,400	32¼%		1870	2557	6	£1,923	£2,700	40½%
1866	2007	2	£1,778	£2,400	34 7/8%		1871	2719	6	£1,960	£2,650	35¼%
1869	2321	3	£1,636	£2,300	40½%		1875	3218	10	£2,466	£3,050	23 5/8%
1871	2643	2	£1,595	£2,150	34 5/8%		1877	3528	6	£2,224	£2,700	21 3/8%
1873	2970	3	£1,975	£2,600	31½%		1878	3675	10	£1,975	£2,630	33%
1875	3286	1	£2,036	£2,500	22¾%							[21]

[Below] This 0-6-0 [603] of 1862 was one of the many long-boilered good engines sent to the Gefle Dala Railway from 1860 until 1875.

The Profitability of the Partnership

The figures given in the various tables to show the profitability of the partnership have to be regarded with caution. The value of the "Deliveries of Completed Work" are generally the same in all the surviving papers. However, the "Cost of Completed Work" consisted of materials and wages, and seems to have covered the staff in the Drawing Office as well as in the works, but it did not cover the forge or the iron and brass foundries. Generally the costs could be divided into two-thirds materials and one-third wages. In the half-yearly accounts submitted to the partners, a gross profit was obtained by subtracting the "Cost of Completed Work" from the "Deliveries of Completed Work", but then a second profit figure was obtained by adding or subtracting the forge and foundry figures. To further complicate the issue, managerial and other expenses were then deducted, but fees from apprentices and other income were added to give a third profit figure. Unfortunately the profit figures in three different documents in the Robertson Papers do not agree, so the figures given in the tables have been drawn from the longest runs, which appear the most authoritative. The figures do at least show that Gorton Foundry turned out more locomotives in its second period of fourteen years, at a slightly greater rate of profit, averaging £48,594 per annum, compared with £41,298

before. If the figure of £680,317 for the second period is added to £578,184 for the first, a total profit of £1,258,501 is obtained for the entire period of the partnerships.

It is difficult to relate this to either the Capital Account (because that has not survived to show what was credited to each partner) or to the Capital Assets, because there was no form of depreciation until the very end of the partnership. In 1869, we do know that the partners had a capital of £180,000, on which the profit returned them 21.45 per cent. (22) In that year the accountants, Haswell & Woodford, tried to introduce a system of depreciation, and tried again in 1872. Items remained on the Capital Assets at their full purchase price until they were sold and then that price, even if it were only the scrap value, was credited to the account. It was not until 1878 that an allowance began to be made for depreciation which was at the rate of 5 per cent. per annum, except for boilers, which were depreciated at 10 per cent. Even then, the original value of all the equipment was the one sent to Robertson in the half-yearly returns up to his death in 1888. Whatever may be the difficulties with the figures, they do show that the partnership yielded a very handsome return on the capital the three partners had invested in it.

Gorton Foundry in about **1870**, looking north towards the Drawing Office. On either side of the tall chimney are boiler houses with water tanks on top, from where steam was supplied to the rest of the works.

6

The Private Limited Company,
1883-1902

By the Act of 1856, the partnership under which Beyer, Peacock & Co. was founded could have been replaced by registration as a limited liability company, but the partners evidently saw no need to make such a change. Beyer's death did not alter the situation, since the agreement provided that if one of the three died the other two could carry on. However, the two survivors were getting older, and had sons whom they wished to enter the family business. There were as well certain senior employees who would have liked to take a financial interest, so in 1883 the partnership was sold to a private limited company: Beyer, Peacock & Co. Ltd. Those having business relations with Beyer, Peacock were informed of the change in a letter dated 31 May 1883, but by this time, the change was almost complete.(1) All applications for shares had to be received by 29 May, but the limited company was actually incorporated on 26 April, preparations for the change having started towards the end of 1882.(2)

In order to effect the sale of their partnership, Richard Peacock and Henry Robertson had first to determine a valuation of the entire works, equipment, stocks, orders in hand, etc. At first the capital assets were valued at the amount recorded in the partnership accounts, which at the end of 1882 stood at £251,230. Stores, work in hand, cash, debts, etc., were valued at £175,625, so the total sum, after various credits for profits, and deductions for bills outstanding, came to £402,002. It was therefore proposed to establish the new company with a nominal capital of £425,000, in 21,250 shares, so that the partners would receive £300,000 in paid up shares and £102,000 in cash, or cash and shares, as payment. The capital assets, however, had never contained any allowance for depreciation, and, in spite of £22,000 having been spent on new equipment in the previous four years, it was obvious that the concern was being overvalued.

By the middle of March agreement must have been reached, for the business had been valued at £307,332. The share capital to pay the partners and provide money for running the new company was reduced to 17,500 shares of £20 each. The partners were to be paid £250,000 in 12,500 shares, and the remaining £57,332 in cash. The shares and cash were to be equally divided between the two, so each received the equivalent of £153,666 for their twenty-eight years of endeavour.

There were more applications for the remaining 5,000 shares than could be allocated, so the issue was oversubscribed. In August 1883, Richard Peacock held 7,250 shares and his son Ralph 1,214. Henry Robertson had 5,000 and his son, Henry Beyer Robertson, 150, so the

Certificate of Incorporation
OF
BEYER, PEACOCK, AND COMPANY,
LIMITED.

I **Hereby Certify** that BEYER, PEACOCK, AND COMPANY, LIMITED, is this day incorporated under the Companies Acts, 1862 to 1880, and that this Company is Limited.

Given under my hand, at London, this twenty-sixth day of April, one thousand eight hundred and eighty-three.

W. H. COUSINS,
Registrar of Joint Stock Companies.

Fee, £41. 5s.

Certificate of Incorporation of Beyer, Peacock & Co. Ltd.

[Heading] Two centenarian Beyer, Peacock locomotives in Portugal.
[C. P. Friel]

new firm remained under the control of the families of the original partners. H.L. Lange had 501 shares and the Company Secretary, E.L. Webb, 600. Haswell, the Accountant, had 25, Charles Holt, Works Manager, 20, and various other foremen had five each, including the first employee, Thomas Molyneaux. The Directors of the new company were: the two surviving partners, with Richard Peacock as Chairman, Ralph Peacock, John Ramsbottom (the "Father of the modern locomotive", with 500 shares) and George Henry Wilson (with 250 shares).(3) There were in all 42 shareholders, covering a wide variety of people.

The next six years saw little change in the organisation of the Company, until the death of Henry Robertson in March 1888 at the age of 72.(4) H.L. Lange became a Director in that year, to replace Robertson, but continued as Chief Engineer and Joint Manager. Greater changes were to follow a year later, on the death, in March 1889, of Richard Peacock, at the age of 68.(5)

Richard Peacock 1820-1889

Richard Peacock

Details of the part played by Richard Peacock in the management of the Company during the thirty-five busy years since it was founded are somewhat sparse, but the success of the partnership and then of the early days of the limited company, bears witness to his commercial skill. One of the best portraits shows him when about to leave on a sales trip to Russia, and dressed ready to face the rigours of their winter. In contrast to the serious disposition and bachelor life of Beyer, Richard Peacock was an extrovert, who found pleasure and interest in many activities in addition to his devotion to the prosperity of Beyer, Peacock. Twice married, he was survived by four children, of whom his eldest son Ralph was already a Director. He took a strong interest in local affairs, being President of the Gorton and Openshaw Mechanics Institute from its inception, and was later President of the Manchester Steam Users Association. In 1861, in conjunction with the Rev. G.H. Wells, Peacock founded the Gorton Savings Bank, and continued as President until the growth of other deposit banks ended its period of usefulness. In 1880, he was President of the Royal Manchester Institution.

As a magistrate, he frequently sat at the weekly Petty Sessions held in Gorton Town Hall. He had a specially weak spot for any of his big forgemen who might happen to appear before him, through having indulged rather too well. Liquor was not allowed in the works, but this did not apply to the forgemen, for theirs was a thirsty job. They always had the privilege of bringing beer onto the premises, but Hoy, the General Manager in 1903, tried to stop this practice, and offered the men free barley water instead. This was turned down and the beer concession continued to the end of steam locomotive construction. It is interesting to note that in the very early days of the Company the forgemen were supplied with free oatmeal, which was taken with water, presumably as a thirst quencher.

[Above] Letter sent out by Beyer, Peacock & Co. on 31 May, 1883.

[Below] Brookfield Unitarian Church.

Like Beyer, Richard Peacock was a generous patron of church-building. Though a Wesleyan in his early days, he became a Unitarian soon after he had moved to Manchester. The Unitarian chapel at Gorton was small and in need of rebuilding, so, having first in 1863 borne the chief burden in the building of new schools for the chapel, he completed his gift in 1869 and 1870 by paying for the building of the new Brookfield church, at a cost of £12,000. In 1876, he gave a further sum to be spent on its embellishment, which he intended to be a token of gratitude for the sparing of the life of one of his daughters during a dangerous illness.

He took little part in politics until towards the end of his life. When Gorton was created a parliamentary division in 1885, he was eventually persuaded to accept nomination as a Liberal. He won the election of that year with 5,300 votes to 3,552, but had to defend the seat in the following year. He was returned again, but the onset of illness prevented his taking an active part in political affairs in the few years that remained to him.

In Manchester affairs, he was a staunch supporter of his friend Daniel Adamson, head of a famous engineering company in Hyde, promoting the Manchester Ship Canal. The first important meeting was called by Adamson on 27 June 1882, and a fund was launched for the purpose of covering parliamentary expenses. Peacock and eight other subscribers each guaranteed £200; further additional promises brought the total to £11,450. Peacock was one of the first Provisional Directors of the Manchester Ship Canal Company and, in the absence of Adamson, acted as Deputy Chairman. The Parliamentary Bill was passed in 1885, but Peacock did not live to see the canal completed, in 1894.

His dry humour is illustrated by a story he told at a meeting during the long campaign for the Canal Bill, which was bitterly opposed by various parties. In reply to a speaker who said the Canal would cost too much, he said that he was reminded of a man who wanted to buy a dog and meeting a person with one to sell, he said, ''What dost tha want for thi dog?'' ''Five pun,'' was the reply. ''That's a hell of a price, ain't it?'' ''Aye'', said the man, ''but it's a hell of a dog!'' Peacock delivered this story in all fullness. The first sensation of the audience was surprise at its bluntness and then everyone present roared with laughter except the tale-teller. Richard Peacock was as solid as one of his own anvils.

Peacock's part in the founding of the Locomotive Manufacturers' Association will be told later in this chapter, so to round off this brief biography, it is fitting to conclude with Gorton Hall, the house which he built for himself, about a mile from the works. It was a large and comfortable residence in beautiful grounds, which contained well-equipped stables and dairy premises. Happy in his home life, no role became him better than that of bountiful master and generous host. The Hall was a veritable museum of art treasures, testifying to a cultured and discriminating taste, but it did not survive into the twentieth century, such was the pace of urban development. Its creator died on 3 March 1889 after a lingering illness, in the home he had created. On his memorial tablet was inscribed:

> ''He was a man of sterling qualities, a kind and unostentatious friend to the poor and needy, and a generous supporter of all agencies for the elevation of the people''.(6)

[Above] Gorton Hall.

[Below] Richard Peacock's tomb at the west end of Brookfield Church.

Following Richard Peacock's death, his son Ralph, then aged 51, and generally known at Gorton as ''Colonel Peacock'' through the commission he held in the Lancashire Artillery Volunteer Regiment, became Managing Director, with Lange as Joint Manager and Chief Engineer. Lange's increasing responsibilities led to the revival of the office of Chief Draughtsman in 1890, and the man appointed was Robert Ramsbottom Lister, who started as an apprentice in 1869, and had been in the Drawing Office from 1872 to 1880. After a period as Assistant Works Manager, Lister went to the Broughton Copper Company as Works Manager, before returning to Gorton Foundry in 1890, at the age of 36, to take charge of the Drawing Office. It must have appeared that this team of men in their prime would be likely to control the Company's activities for a long time to come, since, in 1890, Ralph Peacock was 52, Lange was 53 and Lister only 36. However, the unexpected happened — Lange died suddenly in 1892, when only 55.

Hermann Ludwig Lange, 1837-1892

Hermann Ludwig Lange

Hermann Ludwig Lange was one of the outstanding figures in Beyer, Peacock history.(7) He was born on 10 May 1837, at Plauen in Vogtland, Saxony, and was thus a fellow townsman of Beyer. He finished his school career at the age of seventeen with every distinction but, instead of proceeding straight to a polytechnic, was sent by his father to be an apprentice at the works of F.A. Eggels, in Berlin. He remained there from April 1855 to July 1858, and gained experience of stationary engines, waterwheels and turbines. After that he was sent to the technical school at Karlsruhe for two years, and studied under the famous Professor Redtenbacher.

It was through a mutual friend that Lange's aspiration to work in the locomotive engineering field became known to Beyer, who offered him a place at Gorton Foundry. His earliest task after arrival, on 15 January 1861, was to acquire a general idea of the work in the shops, before moving in April to the Drawing Office, under Hermann Jaeger. He became involved with the plans for the expansion of the works, as well as with such important locomotives as those for the Tudela & Bilbao, South Eastern of Portugal, Metropolitan, Dutch State, and other railways. He speedily made his mark as a draughtsman of unusual ability, so that in 1865, when ill-health made it necessary to lighten Jaeger's work load, Lange was chosen to become Chief Draughtsman, at the early age of 28.

As Chief Draughtsman, Lange faithfully transformed Beyer's ideas and principles of locomotive design into working drawings, often incorporating various ideas of his own. In 1876, when Beyer died, Lange took his place as Chief Engineer and Joint Manager, holding these appointments up to the time of his own death, in 1892, while from 1888 onwards he was also a Director. In these sixteen years he worthily maintained the Company's reputation for progressive design, and was personally involved in the various new developments of the period.

A brief account of some of the patents with which Lange was involved will show how he contributed towards the high standing of the Company. His association with James Livesey resulted in the Lange and Livesey patents for mountain rack locomotives. James Livesey had been trained at Gorton Foundry before becoming Consulting Engineer to many of the South American railways. He founded the famous company known as Livesey & Henderson which played a leading part in constructing and equipping railways in South America. These two also developed an ingenious arrangement for working twin tank engines, placed back to back, with only one driver, but this attempt to form an articulated locomotive was never popular. Lange's development of the special starting valve, in association with Worsdell and Von Borries, led to the introduction of the compound locomotive in South America, where it was used with great success. However, a patent in the names of Lange and Peacock in 1890 for an ingenious form of drive for electric locomotives was never taken up.

Diagrams from Lange and Livesey's Patent Specification of 1886.

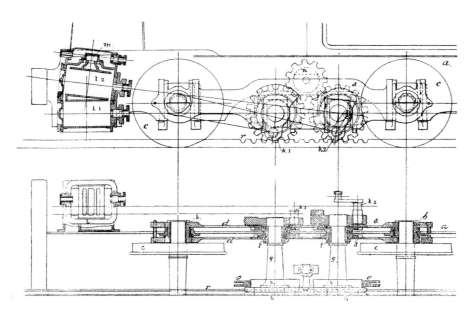

The designs of the locomotives he built show he was well abreast of the latest technical developments, such as the Belpaire firebox, or the use of steel castings, and he was not afraid to incorporate them into his designs if customers wished. Lange first used Walschaert's valve gear on the rack locomotives the Company built for the Puerto Cabello & Valencia Railway (Order 6909) in 1887, and was responsible for reintroducing it to Britain in 1890 (after its brief trial on the Swindon, Marlborough & Andover Junction Railway in 1881) when he used it on the Belfast & Northern Counties two-cylinder compounds of Order 7172.(8) In 1887 he pioneered the use for British railways of tank engines with the 2-6-2 wheel arrangement when he designed six for the Mersey Railway (Order 6925) and likewise the use of the 2-8-4 type in 1890, when he designed four narrow gauge engines for the Minas & Rio Railway in Brazil (Order 7182).(9) This was probably the first time a tank engine was designed with this wheel arrangement.

Lange was a man of great mental and physical energy, characterised by conscientious thoroughness in all he undertook. He had the capacity for both giving and inspiring friendship, and a kindliness that showed no distinction for any individual. His profound mechanical insight was combined with an unselfish devotion to duty that was to lead to his death, for despite a naturally strong constitution his health had been declining gradually for several years, as the result of over-application to work, and about three months before his death, he suffered a severe heart attack. He was advised to rest, but was determined to return to work, though still in feeble health. On regaining some strength, he insisted on resuming all his duties again, with the inevitable consequence that he had another stroke, from which he died on 14 January 1892.

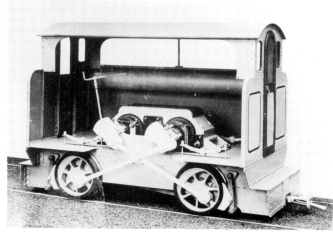

Lange & Col. Peacock's electric locomotive had the motors mounted on top of the main frames where they were easily accessible, while the wheels were driven through coupling rods.

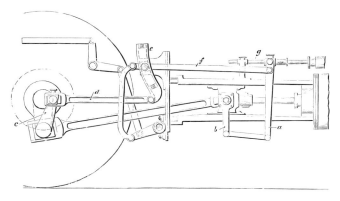

Walschaert's Valve Gear.

[Below] Puerto Cabello & Valencia Railway rack locomotive [6909] fitted with Lange & Livesey's patents.

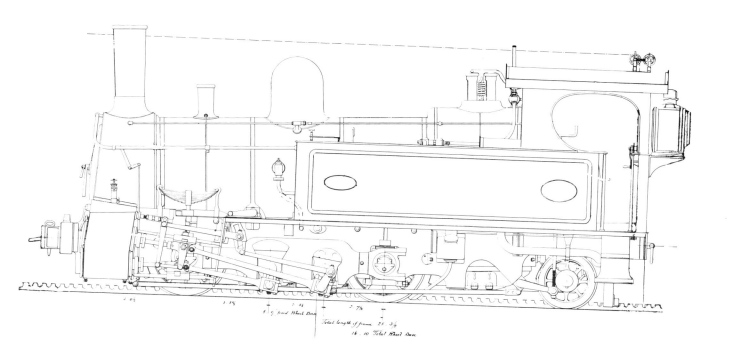

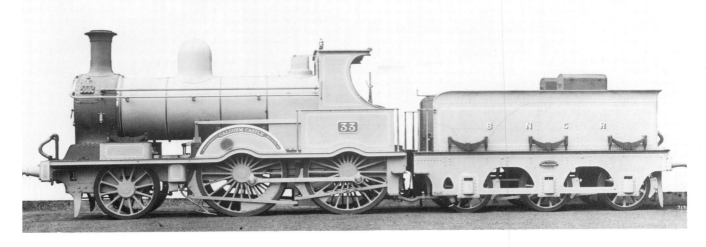

[Above] The two cylinder compound 2-4-0 for the Belfast & Northern Counties Railway [7172] built in 1890. Beyer, Peacock's name has been partially displaced from the wheel splasher by the name of the locomotive, "Galgorm Castle".

[Above] The 2-6-2 for the Mersey Railway [6925] in 1887 was another condensing tank engine design. It was fitted with a crosshead driven pump because the water in the tanks became too hot for injectors to force into the boiler.

Below] This 2-8-4 design for the metre gauge Minas & Rio Railway [7182] also appeared as a 6-coupled type for other railways.

Colonel Ralph Peacock, 1838-1928

Col. Ralph Peacock

After the death of Lange, Ralph Peacock, as Managing Director, alone carried the whole responsibility for running the Company, and continued to do so for the next ten years. Richard Peacock had married twice, and Ralph was the first child of the first marriage. He was born in 1838,(10) when his father was only eighteen. After his father moved to Manchester in 1841, he was sent to the Moravian School in Fairfield. At the age of sixteen, fear that Prussia might become involved in the Crimean War prevented him going to the Berlin Technical School, as had been intended. Instead he entered Gorton Foundry, and for the next six years set about learning the engineering business, passing through all the departments. Then, in order to gain further experience abroad, he was sent to Paris to work with the firm of Ernest Gouin et Cie., Gouin having worked under Beyer at Sharp Roberts. Here, during 1860 to 1862, he was employed in designing bridges, dredging machinery and lighthouses. In Paris, Ralph became engaged to a French girl, but her tragic death before they could be married was so great a blow to him that he never contemplated matrimony again.

Returning to Gorton Foundry, Ralph Peacock entered the Drawing Office, where he was employed in both the locomotive and machine tool sections until Beyer's death, when he became assistant to his father. He became a Director of the private limited company when it was formed, in 1883, and gradually assumed more of his father's duties, particularly after the latter's election to Parliament in 1885, and subsequent ill-health. On his father's death in 1889, he succeeded him as Managing Director, and for some time was more concerned with the commercial than the technical side of the firm. After Lange's death in 1892, his inventive abilities and managerial capacities were increasingly devoted to technical matters. He exercised close supervision over the purchase and testing of materials, and some of his notes have survived about testing steel blooms in 1885.(11)

Ralph Peacock took a special interest in machine tools and, while grinding machines are mentioned among the items sold in 1883 and 1884, his considerable technical ability is revealed by patents granted to him in 1887 and

1889 for precision grinding machines.(12) The one in 1887 was for a machine for grinding precision holes in case-hardened parts such as valve gear components. It incorporated a grinding spindle having a simultaneous planetary and vertical motion as it rotated, together with fine adjustment for the planetary motion. In 1889 he was granted a further patent, for a version of this machine with a sliding table for carrying the work, which could be guided and controlled in such a manner that it moved under the tool in a path corresponding to the shape of the job in hand. This was particularly useful for grinding the curved surfaces of reversing links. These machines were also used for grinding plane surfaces, such as the inside jaws for valve gear rods, and many other applications. The parts made were more accurate, with a better finish, and machined with a great saving in time. About three hundred machines, many of them double-headed, were manufactured for sale at Gorton, and they were to be found in railway and locomotive builders' workshops right up to the end of the steam age. The planetary spindle, the most prominent of the new features in Ralph Peacock's invention, was, on the expiry of his patent, included by other manufacturers, in many other varieties of machine tools, and has since been applied to the grinding of cylinders for internal combustion engines.

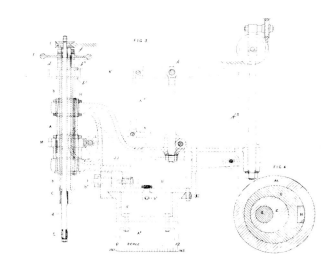

Col. Peacock's patent drawing of his planetary spindle grinding machine in his 1887 patent.

One of the later planetary spindle grinding machines with moving table and all the ancillary equipment such as grinding wheels of different diameters, etc.

Early planetary spindle grinding machine with two heads.

Gorton Foundry

With the death of Hermann Lange, the title of Chief Engineer lapsed, and the responsibility for locomotive design fell solely on the Chief Draughtsman, Robert Lister, since Col. Peacock never claimed any expertise in this field, and was in any case fully occupied in managing the commercial affairs of the Company. Charles Holt, who had been Works Manger from 1877, retired through ill-health in 1900 and died soon after. His successor was George Pilkington Dawson, who had been Assistant Works Manager from 1881 to 1882, and again from 1886 to 1889. He first came to Gorton Foundry as a pupil in 1876, was later married to Ralph Peacock's sister, and was a Director from 1897 onwards.

By the time Col. Ralph Peacock became head of the firm, the railway companies of Britain were building an ever-increasing proportion of their locomotive requirements in their own works, and some were thinking of encroaching on the business of the private locomotive industry by building for other railway companies. Thus the business of private locomotive builders became more and more to supply engines to foreign customers but, as the Industrial Revolution spread, more and more European nations acquired the plant and skills to cope with their own loco-motive needs, and started to sell abroad as well. The problems were not very marked in the seventies—possibly the disruption caused by the Franco-Prussian War delayed competition—but by the eighties, the rigour of the "Great Depression" of 1873 to 1896 began to affect the loco-motive industry. This was a time when buyers were getting very good value for money, and competition in locomotives, as in many other industries, became dangerous to the prospects of the trade.

Between 1871 and 1874, the London & North Western Railway supplied eighty-six 0-6-0 locomotives to the Lancashire & Yorkshire Railway, and in 1875 it was discovered that they were intending to make the supply of engines to other railways regular policy, thus entering into direct competition with private loccmotive manufac-turers. As a result of this, Charles R. Sacré, of the York-shire Engine Company, wrote to the following firms:

His interests outside the works did not embrace such a wide variety as those of his father, but to one cause Ralph Peacock devoted a great deal of his time; this was the Volunteer movement, the ancestor of the Territorial Army. He entered as a Captain in 1865 and eleven years later was promoted to Colonel. He took his responsibilities at Beyer, Peacock seriously, for in the 1890s the firm went through difficult times, and he remained at the helm more through a sense of duty to the family interests than from choice. The idea of converting the private company into a public one was never far from his mind, and this change occurred in 1902, when he retired as Chairman, though he remained a Director until 1906. He moved south to Avon Castle, at Ringwood in Hampshire, where he had a studio for indulging in his favourite hobby of painting. Then he bought a house between Ascot and Sunningdale, in Berkshire, where he died on 10 March 1928, aged 90.

R. R. Lister.

C. Holt.

G. P. Dawson.

Sharp Stewart & Co.   R.& W. Hawthorn
Neilson & Co.   Dübs & Co.
Avonside Wilson & Co.   Kitson & Co.
Beyer, Peacock & Co.   Black Hawthorn & Co.
J. Fowler & Co.   T. Brassey & Co.
Vulcan Foundry Co.   Manning Wardle & Co.

A meeting was called, which took place in London on 29 April 1875, with John Robinson (Sharp Stewart & Co.) in the chair.(13)

The first resolution was one moved by Richard Peacock in the following terms:

"RESOLVED   that it is the opinion of this Meeting that it is now necessary to take steps for the protection of Engineers and others against the competition of Railway Companies as manufacturers for sale".

A sub-committee was formed, composed of Peacock, Sacré and Kershaw, to instruct solicitors to draw up a case for the opinion of Counsel. An injunction was secured and not only did the London & North Western cease to build engines for the Lancashire & Yorkshire Railway, but the railway companies abandoned their plans to build locomotives for sale. Another result of this meeting was the formation of the Locomotive Manufacturers' Association, which held its first meeting in London on 4 June 1875. The first Committee of Management was composed of:

J. Robinson,   Sharp Stewart & Co.
R. Peacock,   Beyer, Peacock & Co.
C.R. Sacré,   Yorkshire Engine Co.
H. Dübs,   Dübs & Co.
J.L. Stothert,   Avonside Engine Co.

Peacock took the chair at the first few meetings, and in 1879 was referred to as President. In March 1876, it was decided to charge a levy on members at the rate of ninepence for each man employed. The amount thus raised was £360 6s. 0d. As this became a regular method of raising money for the Association, records were kept of the numbers of men employed by each firm. In the following table, it will be noticed that Beyer, Peacock was generally third in size, after Neilson and Dübs. The numbers also show the years of good and bad trade and should be compared with the figures of engines built and profits in Appendix I.

In these difficult years, the Locomotive Manufacturers' Association helped to share out orders in such a way as to ensure work to those firms that needed it most; to watch

Parliamentary legislation which seemed injurious to their interests, and organise opposition to it in Committee; to establish more equitable terms in contract agreements, and to safeguard the prosperity of the trade in general. While Beyer, Peacock warmly and unwaveringly supported the objects of the Association, they were not among the chief gainers by the agreement in its early years, often having so much work on hand that they were prepared to stand aside and allow others to take over orders.

The first two years of the new private company saw Gorton Foundry busier than at any other time in its history so far, with 144 locomotives built in 1883, a record which was broken the following year, when 149 were produced. Profit margins too were healthy, so that dividends of 10 per cent. were paid for the first three years. However, demand fell off in 1886, and at the Annual General Meeting that summer Col. Ralph Peacock stated:

"Orders are now very scarce. . . I do not see how prices can be any lower".(15)

Production that year was also affected by a strike at Gorton Foundry. In 1887, the firm built only sixty locomotives, and lost on one order, so that for the first half of that year, a dividend of only 5 per cent. was paid. A similar payment was made in the next half year, but, early in 1888, Col. Peacock was able to inform a correspondent that

"trade here is better and prices are rising".

In stating that they would pay 10 per cent. on the first half year's results, he thought,

"the future of our trade looks brighter and if no war breaks out on the Continent, I think we ought to do fairly well next year".

Locomotive orders were back to their normal level in 1888 and, while the dividend was only at 7½ per cent. in the last half of that year, by early 1889 there were two years' orders on the books, at improved prices. The dividend was maintained at 10 per cent. until 1892, and 1890 proved to be another record year, with 168 locomotives produced. There was a considerable demand for compound locomotives, and in February 1890 there were orders in hand for 131 locomotives of this type, for all classes of service, goods, passenger and tank. The boom gradually passed, and by the end of 1892 orders were scarce again; some were even taken at a loss to maintain employment of men and plant. By 1893, Col. Peacock declared the outlook to be

"as bad as it well can be. Very little work of any kind is in hand, and competitive prices below cost".

Table showing numbers of men and boys employed in the workshops of members of the Locomotive Manufacturers' Association, 1876-1899.

Manufacturer	1876	1883	1884	1885	1888	1889	1890	1891	1892	1893	1894	1895	1896	1897	1898	1899
Avonside Engine Co.	800															
Beyer, Peacock & Co.	1218	1690	1820	1708	1501	1735	2159	1971	1292	1359	1239	1196	1727	1756	1792	1866
Dübs & Co.	1267	1850	1988	1404	1400	1744	1960	1940	1697	1775	1465	1773	1868	2004	1931	2017
Fox Walker & Co.	200															
Hunslet Engine Co.	180			166	257	286	263	282	240	256	234	242	245	271	270	300
R. & W. Hawthorn	729															
Kitson & Co.	860	808	1165	1043	1150	1260	1255	1270	1268	1079	1143	915	1192	1192	1357	1440
Manning Wardle & Co.	400			278	437	589	493	447	267	293	236	314	370	483	355	590
Nasmyth Wilson & Co.	335	300	450	397	354	518	474	419	377	320	349	337	459	443	517	526
Neilson & Co.	1400	2150	2400	2456	1772	2166	2505	2584	2307	1896	1617	1510	2360	2600	2937	3275
Sharp Stewart & Co.	1290	1042	1008	1024	1014	1330	1336	1565	1507	1246	1145	1178	1333	1432	1435	1561
R. Stephenson & Co.	704	800	838	425	408	300	530	659	455	344	320	387	586	885	894	1047
Vulcan Foundry Co.	490	690	691	583	385	538	679	666	561	486	610	514	770	792	713	820
Yorkshire Engine Co.	439															

[14]

The numbers of locomotives built at this time reflect his pessimism with production at the lowest level for nearly twenty years. Dividends fell to 5 per cent. and continued at that level until 1896, when important orders started to flow in and soon two years' full work was on hand. The dividend dropped to 7½ per cent. for the year ending June 1900, when the Boer War caused prices of materials, particularly fuel, to rise, but otherwise the last six years of the private company were prosperous ones, with a 10 per cent. dividend maintained, despite a large capital expenditure in re-equipping the works. The value of the work sold in 1902 was more than double that of 1876, and a considerable increase over 1883, when the partnership was wound up.

The accounts show that in a five-year period towards the end of the life of the private company no less than £62,600

turning heavy work such as gun barrels, propellor shafts and the like, were marketed, powered by individual electric motors.(18) Soon afterwards plans were drawn up for electrifying Gorton Foundry on the three-phase system after exhaustive enquiries abroad into this new development. At that time, the only such installation at work in this country was the model one erected at Hartlepool by Richardson & Sons, in conjunction with the Swiss firm of Brown Boveri & Co. The work at Gorton was finished by 1904 and Col. Peacock's move was therefore accounted a very bold one at the time, but was abundantly justified, as this system came to be accepted universally.(19)

In 1890, Beyer, Peacock built the frames and other mechanical parts for fourteen 0-4-0 electric locomotives (Order 7314) for the City & South London Railway, while Mather & Platt, of Manchester, supplied the electrical

The first engines built at Gorton Foundry to have cast steel wheel centres were these 0-6-0 goods engines for the Lancashire & Yorkshire Railway [6906].

was spent on new plant. In 1887, a goods locomotive (Order 6906) was built for the Lancashire & Yorkshire Railway with wheel-centres of cast steel and, with the increasing call for this material, small scale manufacture of crucible steel started at Gorton Foundry in 1890, using a coke-fired furnace with three pot holes. Many engineers needed convincing before they would accept the new material, so it was not until 1900 that the last wrought iron forged wheel-centres ceased to be made,(16) but after that steel rapidly replaced cast iron in most parts of the locomotive.(17) In 1899, a steel foundry had been added to the works, and Beyer, Peacock was the first private locomotive builder in Britain to have such a facility.

Colonel Peacock's receptivity to new ideas was also displayed in his advocacy of electric power. In 1899 a large railway wheel turning lathe, and also a lathe for

gear. The line was formally opened by the Prince of Wales (afterwards King Edward VII) on 4 November 1890.(20) One of these locomotives can be seen in the Science Museum, South Kensington. As they had two 50 horsepower motors built round the axles, where they were inaccessible, Lange and Col. Peacock took out a patent for mounting the motors on the main frames and driving the wheels by coupling rods, but it was never applied in quite this form. The advent of the electric locomotive and the rapidity of its technical development abroad were watched by Col. Peacock with no small anxiety in view of its likely effect on the steam locomotive industry in general, and Gorton Foundry in particular.

Not only was there now competition from electrification, but the struggle for orders with other private locomotive builders, both at home and abroad, was increasing.

[Above] The 7ft. diameter wheel turning lathe built in 1899 with early ''Edison'' electric motors which drove the heads through a belt and worm-gear arrangement.

[Below] The first electric locomotives for the City & South London Railway [7314] were built by Beyer, Peacock and Mather & Platt in Manchester. One is preserved in the Science Museum, South Kensington.

For example, Neilson & Co. at Springburn employed 1,400 men in 1876, while in 1899 they had 3,275. Outside this country, the production figures at the Baldwin Works in America rose enormously.

Year	Engines produced
1894	313
1895	401
1896	547
1897	501
1898	752
1899	901
1900	1,217
1901	1,375
1902	1,533

(21)

As long as this colossal production was absorbed by a voraciously expanding home market there was no threat to British builders, but, by 1900, Baldwin's was looking overseas to the markets which were traditionally supplied from Britain. The threat to firms in this country came also from more competitive prices, through cheaper production methods. The American Consul in Glasgow, Bret Harte, reported in 1900 that Neilson, Reid was producing 200 locomotives a year with 2,500 men, at a time when Baldwin's was producing 300 locomotives with 1,400 men.

(22)

To sell its locomotives, Beyer, Peacock established a number of agents throughout the world to whom it sent photographs of its engines and other details. Correspondence with one agent, W.J. Adams in Sydney, New South Wales, gives a rare glimpse of Beyer, Peacock's commercial policy. The letter was sent in 1894, in the middle of the worst slump.

"We will thank you to cancel all the list prices we have given to Mr. Brewster, as many of the engines in his album will require modernising before we can offer them again. . . . If we decide to continue our Australian Agency, we shall probably compile a New Album altogether, and ask you to return the present one, many types being more or less obsolete."

Another letter to him suggests that Beyer, Peacock's pricing policy was based on what it thought the market would stand, and, in order to keep Gorton Foundry busy, was prepared to lower prices.

"Referring to the list of selling prices etc. which we sent you on the 27th September, as we could very well do with more work here it occurs to us to say that if you think there would be any greater prospect of doing business with Railway Contractors, or others, supposing our discounts were somewhat increased, thus reducing our prices, we should be prepared to consider the matter, and would then instruct you how to act, and in the meantime do not lose an opportunity of looking up orders from all sources."(23)

It is a pity there is so little other information to show how Beyer, Peacock weathered this storm and staged such a remarkable revival in the closing years of the nineteenth century.

Col. Peacock was a bachelor and had no direct dynastic interest in the future of Beyer, Peacock, although other members of the families of the original partners were still connected. In 1900, the Board of Directors consisted of Colonel Ralph Peacock, Captain Frederick William Peacock, G.A. Pilkington Dawson, Sir Henry Beyer Robertson, and Samuel Rider. By 1902, at the age of 64, Col. Peacock felt that he had fairly discharged his duty to his relations and friends in the business, and determined to sell his share. He forsaw that great new developments were ahead, particularly in the sphere of electrification, and preferred that younger men should face them. Therefore, with Gorton Foundry in good shape, he decided that the Private Limited Company must give way to a public one.

Two 0-6-2 tank engines were built in 1888 for the 3ft gauge La Guaira & Caracas Railway [7045], Veneuzuela, which rose on a gradient of 1 in 27 for nearly twenty miles with a succession of sharp curves. One engine was still in service in 1919 when it had run over a million kilometres.

[Above] One of ten 4-4-0s supplied to the Victorian Railways [6320] in 1884.

[Centre] These Midland 4-4-0s [8522] built in 1900 were identical to the ones sent to the Midland & Great Northern Joint Railway the previous year.

[Below] The curtains on these tram engines purchased by the Serajoedal Steam Tram Co. [7875] in 1895 were presumably for keeping out rain or sun.

The front of a La Guaira & Caracas Railway [7045] engine.

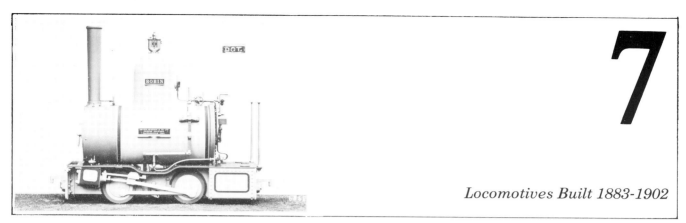

Ordinary Locomotives

During the lifetime of the private limited company, from 1883 to 1902, just over two thousand locomotives were constructed, of which roughly 68 per cent. were exported, though this bare statistic hides the fact that the annual proportion going abroad was on a rising trend throughout the period. In fact the new company relied on exports to a very great extent in the last ten years, because home orders would have been distinctly thin on the ground without the hundred and seventy-five engines built between 1893 and 1902 for the Manchester, Sheffield & Lincolnshire Railway, and its successor, the Great Central. In 1891 the former railway had experimented with an 0-6-2 side tank engine fitted with a Belpaire firebox, which was the first time it had been tried on any British railway, and was inspired by Lange's design for the Dutch State Railways. The experiment was successful, for in 1893 the Manchester, Sheffield & Lincolnshire Railway ordered thirty 0-6-2 tank engines with Belpaire boilers (Order 7722) from Beyer, Peacock. This type of firebox was adopted by many other railways because it had many technical advantages, with its greater space for water closest to the fire, but in later years, the need to accommodate

very large boilers, coupled with improvements in design and materials, led to a reversion to round-topped fireboxes.

The success of the "Metropolitan" tank engines, with their condensing apparatus, led to the design by Lange of locomotives for another underground line, the Mersey Railway. The section between Liverpool and Birkenhead had gradients of 1 in 27, to take the line under the River Mersey, and engines capable of starting a load of 150 tons on such an incline were needed. For this Lange designed the most powerful engine built in Britain up to that time (1885), an 0-6-4 inside-cylinder tank type, with the condensing apparatus fitted in the side tanks (Order 6532).

[Heading] ''Robin'', an 18inch gauge locomotive supplied to the Horwich Works of the Lancashire & Yorkshire Railway [6868] in 1887.

[Right] A Manchester, Sheffield & Lincolnshire Railway 0-6-2 built in 1893 seen at the end of its life in 1954.   [H. Ballantyne]

[Below] The 0-6-2 tank engine for the Manchester, Sheffield & Lincolnshire Railway [7722] with Belpaire firebox, boiler pressure 160 p.s.i. and Tractive Effort 17,500lbs.

These engines, of which nine were built, had outside frames to accommodate the large diameter of the cylinders and were also fitted with James Sterling's steam reversing gear.(1) In 1887 six outside-cylinder 2-6-2 tank engines, again with condensing apparatus, were built for the same company (Order 6925)—the first with this wheel arrangement to work in Britain.(2) The pioneering spirit must have been strong in the area, for in 1896 the Wirral Railway had the first 4-4-4 tank engine to be designed (Order 8033).(3)

Mention might at this point be made of the smallest engines built by Beyer, Peacock. The design originated in 1886 with an 0-4-0 (Order 6692) for a Mr. Parnell. It was for the 1ft. 6in. gauge, and must have been some sort of experimental engine, for the cylinders look as if they may have been built on the "Uniflow" principle, with the exhaust ports in the centre of the cylinder walls.(4) This idea was dropped when four were built in the following year, (Order 6868), one for the internal works system at Gorton Foundry, and three for the new Horwich Works of the Lancashire & Yorkshire Railway. Two are preserved: Beyer, Peacock's own in the Talyllyn Museum at Towyn, and "Wren", from Horwich, in the National Railway Museum, at York.

[Below] One of the 0-6-4 condensing tank engines for the Mersey Railway [6532] has been preserved for display in the Merseyside County Museums in Liverpool.

[Foot] The 4-4-4 tank locomotive built for the Wirral Railway [8033] in 1896.

[Above] "Dot" and her sisters were the smallest locomotives Beyer, Peacock ever built. "Dot" was the works locomotive at Gorton Foundry and hauled engine parts between the various shops. It is shown restored for display in the Narrow Gauge Railway Museum at Towyn in Wales. The boiler was circular with the grate inside it, more like a "Cornish" boiler than the "Stephenson" locomotive type.

Of course a large number of engines were built to existing designs, but these gradually became outmoded as trains became heavier and more power was needed. In 1891, for example, the Commissioners of New South Wales determined to introduce engines that would be sufficiently powerful to work their main line trains without double-heading. A 4-6-0 design was therefore produced (Order 7450) for passenger work. Fifty were built in the next couple of years, and a further twenty-five in 1901 (Order 8583). These were followed by a basically similar 2-8-0 type for goods trains. Five were constructed in 1895 (Order 7989), and sixty had been completed by the end of 1902.(5) There were similarities between these engines and a 2-6-0 design supplied in 1895 (Order 7948) to the Midland & South Western Junction Railway, for working goods traffic over the heavy gradients between Cheltenham and Southampton. Then in 1899, six 0-6-0 goods engines (Order 8468) were purchased by this Company to work a fast through goods service, run in conjunction with the Midland Railway between Southampton and Scotland. These engines were a great success.(6)

[Top] The engineering press of the time commented on the high quality of craftsmanship put into these passenger engines for the New South Wales Government Railways [7450] which of course was to be expected as they had been built by Beyer, Peacock.

[Centre] The earlier New South Wales 2-6-0 design [6063, see chap.5] has been enlarged into this 2-8-0 [7989] with some of the modernised features of the 4-6-0 added.

[Foot] The powerful 0-6-0 goods locomotive for the Midland & South Western Junction Railway [8468] built in 1899 to tackle the steep gradients of the Cotswolds.

In a similar way, traffic on the Dutch State Railways outgrew the capacity of Lange's last 2-4-0 design. It was perpetuated until 1895 (Order 7970), but was replaced in 1899 by a 4-4-0 with slightly larger dimensions (Order 8446). The same basic characteristics were retained, with the outside frames, but the fixed leading wheels were replaced by a bogie. One hundred and twenty-five of this type were built up to 1906, but something larger and heavier was needed to work the mail trains from Flushing to Boxtel, a distance of 139 kilometres, without a stop. To avoid an axle load of over 15 tons, a pair of trailing wheels was added, and the firebox enlarged to cope with larger cylinders. Five of these were built in 1900 (Order 8458), and together with two for the Great Central Railway in 1903 (Order 9034) were the only tender locomotives with the Atlantic wheel arrangement ever built by Beyer, Peacock. At this time, practically every new locomotive for the Dutch State Railways came from Beyer, Peacock, invariably presenting an immaculate appearance, with gleaming brass and copper embellishments. It was once commented that Beyer, Peacock's name cast in brass around the wheel splashers was one of the best advertisements the Company ever had.

[Below] Lange's outside framed 2-4-0 [3878] had been extended at the front with a bogie. These engines [8446] had 18in. diameter cylinders and 7ft. driving wheels and developed 12,020lbs Tractive Effort.

[Below centre] This time Lange's design has been extended to the rear to become an Atlantic for the Dutch State Railways [8458]. The size of the firebox has been increased considerably, and the cab modernised.
[Foot] One of the Dutch State Railways "Atlantics" still running about 1930.

Compound Locomotives

In 1876, Anatole Mallet produced the first true compound locomotive. It had two outside cylinders, the high pressure one on one side exhausting into the low pressure one on the other. The primary intention was to gain an increase in thermal efficiency, thus saving fuel as well as giving a more even tractive effort. The disadvantage of this system was that on bigger engines, the low pressure cylinder became so large that it did not clear the loading gauge. In 1881 von Borries therefore introduced on the Prussian State Railways a two-cylinder type, with both cylinders inside the frames. T.W. Worsdell followed this style in 1884, with an experimental 4-4-0 type for the Great Eastern Railway, and continued building compound locomotives when he moved to the North Eastern Railway in 1887. In 1898, W.M. Smith developed a three-cylinder compound which had the high pressure cylinder between the frames, exhausting into two outside low pressure cylinders. While this gave a well-balanced engine, it suffered from the same major defect as the two-cylinder compounds, a lack of power to start heavy trains with only one high-pressure cylinder. (see also Chap 12 p.165 for Irish locos.)

In 1882, with this problem in mind, F.W. Webb introduced the first three-cylinder compound on the London & North Western Railway. It had two outside high pressure cylinders, exhausting into a single low pressure cylinder between the frames. Webb split the drive so that the inside cylinder drove the front driving wheels, and the outside ones the rear wheels, but the wheels were not coupled. This has always been considered a great mistake, and the design had another fault because the low pressure cylinder was made very large and in consequence the reciprocating forces of its piston were very large also. The answer to this problem was the four-cylinder compound with two high and two low pressure cylinders.(7)

Beyer, Peacock did build four-cylinder compounds with their Garratt locomotives, and three-cylinder compounds on the Smith principle, all of which will be discussed later. They also built in 1885 one example of the Webb type of compound, which was the only locomotive they ever exported to the United States of America, a 2-2-2-0 ''Dreadnought'' class (Order 7017), which looked exactly the same as the Crewe product.(8) Presumably it was built by Beyer, Peacock as a result of the decision in 1875 which prevented railway companies building locomotives for other concerns. Those few people who tried the Webb compounds were not impressed with them.

With this one exception, all the compound locomotives which Beyer, Peacock built as a private limited company were the cross-compound type, usually with two cylinders. The first was supplied in 1887, to the Buenos Ayres & Rosario Railway, which ordered one out of six 4-4-0 tender engines (Order 6816) to be fitted with compounded cylinders. This one was sold for £2,525, compared with £2,400 for the others, and was the forerunner of many two-cylinder compounds built for South America. The

[Below] The only locomotive which Beyer, Peacock exported to the United States of America was this Webb compound for the Pennsylvania Railway [7017] in 1888, a pure Crewe design.

[Foot] The low pressure side of the 4-4-0 compound engine built for the Buenos Ayres & Rosario Railway in 1888. The main frames sweep up by the smokebox to accommodate the large low pressure steam passageways, valves, etc. while the exhaust steam pipe is outside the smokebox. The disc on the side of the smokebox covers the special starting valve.

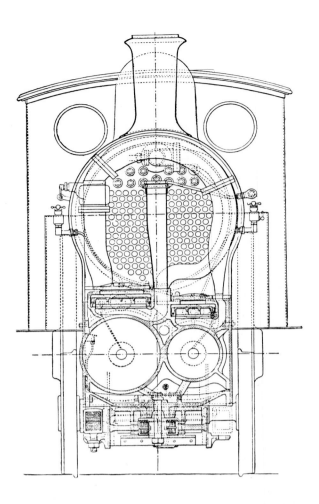

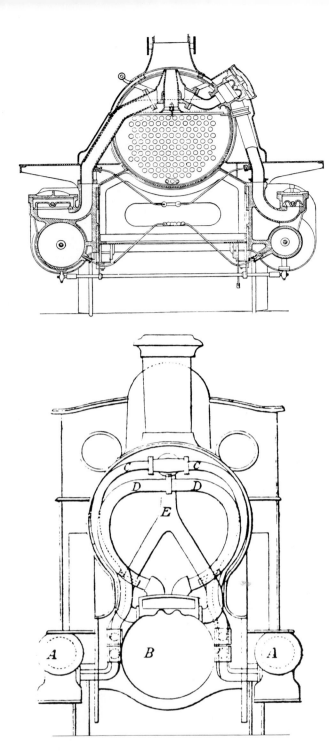

[Above] Cross section through the smokebox and cylinders of T.W. Worsdell's compound locomotive showing the high pressure cylinder on the right and the low pressure on the left, side by side between the frames.

[Above left] Cross section through the smoke box and cylinders of A. Mallet's locomotive showing the high pressure cylinder on the right and low on the left.

[Centre left and below] The F.W. Webb compound system with twin high pressure cylinders outside the frames exhausting into a single low pressure cylinder set well forward in the middle of the locomotive.

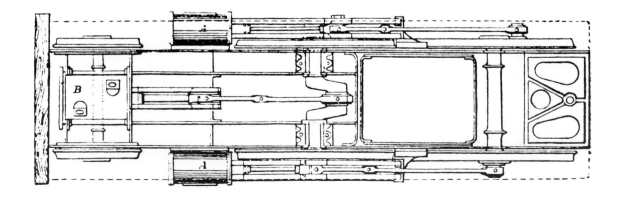

successful operation of these compounds was largely the result of the invention of a new form of intercepting valve which permitted both cylinders to receive live steam while starting and subsequently to change over automatically to compound working. Lange based his design on the work of Von Borries and Worsdell and produced a line of highly successful engines.

The Buenos Ayres & Rosario Railway must have been satisfied with its engine for it ordered another five in 1888 (Order 7011). In the same year orders were received from the Royal Portuguese Railway for four (Order 7087), and in South America, from the Central Uruguay for one (7108), and the Argentine Western for eight (Order 7151), all of which were to different designs. By the beginning of 1890, there were orders in hand for a hundred and thirty-one compound locomotives. In 1891, the Mogyana Railway of Brazil ordered an interesting 4-6-0 compound tender locomotive (Order 7469) as one of a batch of six

ordinary ones, which Lange had a hand in designing, just before his death. Another Brazilian railway, the Leopoldina, which was also metre gauge, purchased fifteen 260 ordinary tender engines in 1899 (Order 8477). Both these orders marked the start of long associations with the two lines, which were both later to order Garratt types. It is appropriate to mention here that in 1890 Beyer, Peacock sent to South America their first 4-6-0 tender design(9) (Order 7301), a batch of ten for the Buenos Ayres Great Southern, and in the same year and for the same company their last single drivers, a batch of five (Order 7236). With the exception of four 2-2-0 saddle tanks built by E.B. Wilson in 1856 for the Buenos Ayres Western Railway, which were the first locomotives in the Argentine, these five Beyer, Peacock 4-2-2 engines were the only examples ever employed on South American Railways, and are known still to have been at work in 1924.(10)

[Below] This 4-4-0 compound for the Royal Portuguese Railway [7087] has the same general features as the compound for the Buenos Ayres & Rosario Railway.

[Foot] This general arrangement drawing shows the layout of a typical 2-6-0 compound locomotive supplied to the railways in South America in the early 1890s. The arrangement of the steam pipes between the cylinders and the starting valve can be seen in the cross section through the smokebox.

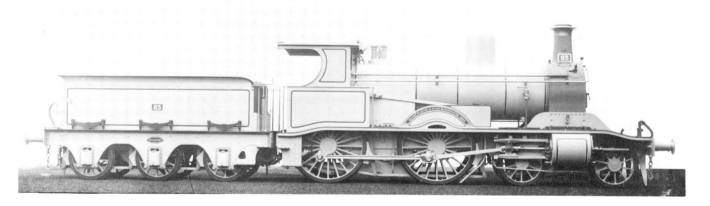

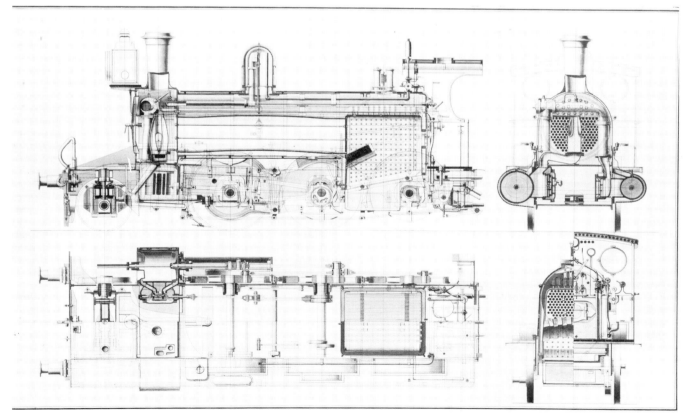

[Above] The low-pressure side of a 2-6-0 compound engine for the Argentine Western Railway [7151]. The cover over the slide bars and cross head was fitted to prevent dust gathering on the oily motion parts.

[Below] Beyer, Peacock's first order for the Mogyana Railway [7469], a 4-6-0 with the traditional inclined cylinders but using Walschaert's valve gear.

[Above] The 2-6-0 tender engine which was the first Beyer, Peacock sent to the Leopoldina Railway [8477] in 1899. The dome behind the chimney held sand which could be fed to the front two pairs of driving wheels. The fuel was wood, which could be stacked high in the tender.

[Below] The low pressure side of the compound 4-6-0 for the Buenos Ayres Great Southern Railway [7301] built in 1890.

[Above] The introduction of steam sanding gear prolonged the life of locomotives with single driving wheels for express passenger work because the sand could be blown under the wheels so they gripped better. These ones built in 1890 for the Buenos Ayres Great Southern Railway [7236] were the last produced at Gorton Foundry.

[Below] The plain exterior of this Belfast & Northern Counties Railway [7504] 0-6-0 tender engine conceals the compound cylinders and the Walschaert's valve gear.

[Above] Belfast & County Down Railway [7442] 2-4-2 compound tank engine built in 1891.

[Below] The Belfast & County Down Railway [7589/7793] compound 2-4-0 with 6ft. diameter driving wheels.

Returning to compound locomotives, and to Great Britain, in 1890, the Belfast & Northern Counties Railway ordered four 2-4-0 two-cylinder compounds (Order 7172), which were fitted with Walschaert's valve gear, and had the distinction of marking its proper introduction into the British Isles. Malcolm Bowman, their Chief Engineer, was so satisfied with these engines that in 1892 he ordered two 0-6-0 compound goods engines (Order 7504), and the first narrow gauge compound locomotives to work in Britain. These will be described in the next paragraph because in the meantime, in 1891, the Belfast & County Down Railway had purchased four 2-4-2 compound tank engines (Order 7442). They followed these with three 2-4-0 tender engines, with 6ft. diameter coupled wheels (Order 7589), and a couple of years later another one (Order 7793). In that same year, 1895, there were two with 7ft. diameter driving wheels for the Belfast & Northern Counties (Order 7853).(11) Both these railways continued purchasing compound locomotives well into the next century. Another faithful Irish customer was the Great Northern Railway which, besides goods and tank locomotives, started purchasing their 4-4-0 tender engines in 1885 (Order 6466), had the handsome **Rostrevor** (Order 8031) in 1896, and continued to develop this design until 1948.

The two Belfast & Northern Counties Railway narrow gauge tank engines (Order 7511) were destined for the Ballymena, Cushendall & Redbay, and the Ballymena & Larne 3ft. gauge lines. They were strikingly handsome 2-4-2 side tank engines with outside cylinders, the high pressure being on the left-hand side. Together they cost £2,060. The valve gear was Walschaert's, and arranged so that both cylinders were linked up simultaneously. In starting, high pressure steam was admitted to both cylinders, but after the first stroke of the piston, the high pressure steam was cut off from the low pressure cylinder and compound working began. Four more locomotives were built in Ireland to this design, the last one being completed in 1920. One of the first engines was rebuilt as a 2-4-4 tank, but was not so successful in this form. These lines were finally closed in 1950 when some of these compounds were still at work, showing the high quality of this pioneering design.(12)

[Below] The compound 2-4-0 with 7ft. diameter driving wheels for the Belfast & Northern Counties Railway [7853].

[Foot] The first [6466] of a long line of 4-4-0 tender engines which Beyer, Peacock started building for the Great Northern Railway of Ireland in 1885 and sent the last one, much altered, in 1948.

Beyer, Peacock did build a pair of engines experimentally as three-cylinder compounds for the New South Wales Government Railways (Order 7572). They were similar to the 4-6-0 passenger engines (Order 7450) built in 1891, except that the 21in. diameter high pressure cylinder was placed on the left side, which exhausted into two low pressure cylinders superimposed on top of each other on the other side. The two low pressure cylinders, each 22in. diameter, were parallel with their piston rods connected to the same crosshead. A single slide valve situated inside the frames admitted steam to both. This type was not repeated.(13)

[Below] ''Rostrevor'', built in 1896 as one of the long line of 4-4-0 engines Beyer, Peacock sent to the Great Northern Railway of Ireland [8031].

[Below centre] The handsome 2-4-2 compound side tank engines built for the narrow gauge sections of the Belfast & Northern Counties Railway [7511] in 1892.

[Foot] The common cross head, two piston rods and low pressure cylinders imposed one on top of the other of the three cylinder compound for the New South Wales Government Railway [7572].

Tram Engines

This period in the Company's history saw the rise and decline of the steam operated street tramway.(14) Although entering this field comparatively late, in 1882, during the next seven years Beyer, Peacock was quite successful in manufacturing ''tram'' engines, to replace horses on city streets. A new erecting shop was built especially for this work, and the name ''Tram Shop'' survived long after they had all disappeared from the streets. The first ones were built to the designs patented by John Wilkinson of Wigan,(15) and included many interesting technical features. A vertical boiler was placed in the middle of the frames of an 0-4-0 locomotive. There were two vertical cylinders, situated just in front of the boiler. Reduction gears transmitted the drive from the crankshaft to one axle and the axles were connected by coupling rods. Each engine had duplicate controls at either end, and was entered through a single door at one end, above the draw gear, with a passage round the boiler to the other driving position. The steam regulator could be moved from the fully open position, through a dead or shut position, to a point where steam was admitted to the steam brake on the engine. A separate brake was fitted to operate the brakes on the passenger car by means of a chain. The exhaust steam could be passed either to condensing apparatus on the roof, and a special air-pump was fitted to clear this, or could be passed up the chimney. So that the exhaust, when operating non-condensing, would pass up well clear of the houses, the steam went down inside the boiler to a box above the fire, where it was superheated before going up another pipe to the chimney. Exhaust steam from the cylinder blow-off valves, the steam brake cylinders, etc., was taken down to the ashpan and presumably drawn up through the fire.

Later another type of tram engine was developed, with a horizontal locomotive type boiler and horizontal outside cylinders. Some engines were non-condensing, but all had valances round them to prevent people falling under the wheels, or into the motion. A total of nearly two hundred was built. The boom in England was over by 1889, when eighty-nine had been sold to the North Staffordshire (Order 3986), South Staffordshire & Birmingham District (Order 6326), Manchester, Bury, Rochdale & Oldham (Order 6336), and other tramway companies. For this last company, Beyer, Peacock built their first compound locomotive design (Order 6754), which was finished four days before the one for the Buenos Ayres & Rosario on 27 January 1887. This design was never repeated. On Order 6741, for the Manchester, Bury, Rochdale & Oldham system, Beyer, Peacock charged £890 each, but these tram engines with locomotive type boilers actually cost the Company £1,207 to build. The estimators were not normally as far out as this.

The first type of 3ft. 6in. gauge tram engine supplied to the Manchester, Bury, Rochdale & Oldham Steam Tramways Ltd. in 1883 with vertical boiler and cylinders. It was fitted with a governor to control the speed and bells on the roof, presumably as warning devices although they seem hardly necessary.

The later type of steam tram for the Manchester, Bury, Rochdale & Oldham Steam Tramways Ltd., [6736] with condensing apparatus on the roof.

The final design of tram engine for the Manchester, Bury, Rochdale & Oldham Steam Tramways Ltd. [6754] with horizontal boiler and compound cylinders, but still with condensing apparatus on the roof.

Between 1882 and 1910, ninety-nine tram engines of various types were sent to Java to the Samarang—Joana, East Java, Serajoedal, and Samarang—Cheribon tramways. The prices of the first ones for the Samarang—Joana were:

Date	Order	Cost	Sold for	Profit
1882	6176	£861	£962	11.62%
1883	6373	£789	£962	21.92%
1884	6508	£854	£960	12.25%
1885	6614	£792	£950	19.87%

(16)

In England, three tram engines (Orders 7050 & 7563) with horizontal boilers were sent to the 2ft. 4½in. gauge Glyn Valley Tramway, on the borders of Wales, where they continued working for many years, long after their larger counterparts had disappeared from the urban streets.(17)

Two tram engines, both standard gauge, have survived because they were used as works shunters. One engine (Order 6413), without condensing apparatus, was sent to Sydney, New South Wales. It seems never to have moved beyond the harbour there, for it reappeared at Gorton two years later, in 1887, and was fitted with buffers and drawgear to serve as one of the yard shunters for over 60 years. It was known affectionately as the ''Coffee Pot'', and was eventually handed over to the Tramway Museum at Crich, near Derby, where it has worked occasionally under steam. The other engine (Order 6737) went from the Manchester, Bury, Rochdale & Oldham's line to Ince Forge near Wigan. It was much altered over the years, and lost the condensing apparatus and much else before it was taken into the British Transport Historical Collection. When that collection was restricted to railway items only, the tram was presented to the North Western Museum of Science and Industry, in Manchester, and is now being restored.

[Facing page right] 0-4-2 ''Sir Theodore'' of the 2ft. 4¾in. gauge Glyn Valley Tramway [7050].

[Facing page left] ''Sir Theodore'' and train on the Glyn Valley Tramway c.1930.   [J.S. Morgan Col.]

[Below] One of the first engines purchased by the Samarang—Joana Tramways [Java] 6176 in 1882.

[Foot] Probably the last city in the world to have a steam tram service was Surabaya in Java. Here is one of Beyer, Peacocks tram engines [8634] supplied in 1900 still at work in 1973. The tram ran until 1978.
                [E. Talbot]

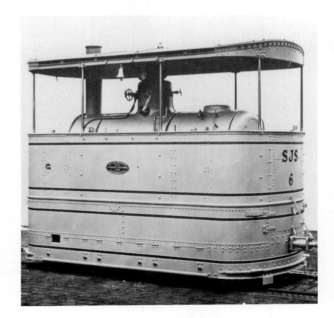

Rack Locomotives

In 1887, the first rack engine was built at Gorton Foundry, one of an order for two (Order 6909) for operation on a mountain rack section of the Puerto Cabello & Valencia Railway, in Venezuela, with an incline of 1 in 12½, and a length of 2¼ miles. This highly ingenious machine embodied patents held jointly by Lange and James Livesey. The trains were brought to the incline by ordinary adhesion engines and the rack engines took their place on it. They normally pushed four wagons, with a total weight of 70 tons, up the slope.

In some notes supplementing a paper about this line given by J. Carruthers before the Institution of Civil Engineers, Lange wrote:

> "It was determined from the first to obtain the propelling power of the engine by means of cogwheels and rack-rails only, instead of by both adhesion and rack, as the engines could then be of simpler and lighter construction and also because the country through which the line runs is subject to be suddenly overrun with locusts when the adhesive power would be of no avail."(18)

The engines had sloping boilers to compensate for the change of water level on the incline, and were the first engines built by Beyer, Peacock to have Walschaert's valve gear. Lange and Livesey's patent concerned the arrangement of the cogwheel frames and cylinders. There were two cylinders on each side, one above the other, with a single slide valve serving both, and two driving shafts, fitted with pinions to engage the rack in the centre of the track, the rear shaft being driven by the upper pair of cylinders, and the front by the lower pair. In Lange's words:

> "This arrangement ensures that each set of cogwheels will do exactly the same amount of work and at the same moment. As each cogwheel is enabled to accommodate itself freely to any irregularity in the rack-rails, the latter are much less strained and the friction between the wheel and rail is reduced to a minimum.
>
> "Further, the cogwheel discs are not fixed rigidly to the axles but, by means of a special spring device, can yield to a small extent and thus accommodate themselves to any irregularities in the teeth of the rack."

Lange and Livesey's patent rack locomotive for the Puerto Cabello & Valencia Railway [6909].

The driving shafts were mounted on a frame, supported on the axles of the adjacent running wheels; as a result the rack system always remained level with the track, and unaffected by the spring suspension of the locomotive. Six years later, it was reported that these engines were doing excellent work during tests to find out how they performed.(19) A third was supplied in 1895 (Order 7980).

In contrast to the easy gradients of many of the Argentine railways, the Argentine—Transandine, which makes the connection with the Chilean State Railways, climbs to an altitude of 10,500ft., with numerous rack sections on both the Argentine and Chilean sides. The gauge is one metre, and the maximum grade on the Argentine side is 1 in 16. For service there, Beyer, Peacock built four combined rack and adhesion locomotives in 1890 (Order 7257), designed by Lange, in conjunction with Livesey,

and incorporating their joint patents.(20) The design of the four-cylinder Puerto Cabello & Valencia engines was modified to allow for adhesion working. On the Transandine engines, the upper cylinders, 14 x 20in., were connected to the adhesion driving wheels, and were controlled by Walschaert's valve gear. The lower cylinders, 13 x 18in., drove the rack pinion, and had Stephenson's motion situated inside the frames. Although these engines performed satisfactorily, increasing traffic led to more powerful engines being ordered, but not from Beyer, Peacock. On the lower sections of this line, Beyer-Garratts were used at a later date. (see Chap. 14)

[Below] The combined rack and adhesion locomotive for the Argentine Transandine Railway [7257]. The upper cylinders with outside valve gear drove the adhesion wheels while the lower cylinders with inside valve gear drove the cog wheels.
[Foot] One of the first batch of 2-6-0 rack and adhesion engines for the Imperial Railways of Japan [7868] with special chimney to take the smoke clear of the cab. A second set of cylinders inside the frames drove the cog wheels.

Another successful rack engine design (Order 7868) was constructed for the Imperial Railways of Japan. Between 1892 and 1902, Japan emerged as a valuable customer for whom Beyer, Peacock built a hundred and forty locomotives of various designs. In 1895, two rack locomotives were built for the Usui Toge incline, with repeat orders for four in 1898 (Order 8256), two more in 1902 (Order 8731), and a further four (Order 9837) in 1908.(21) These were the last rack engines built by Beyer, Peacock, but six more identical ones were built in Japan. The first engines were fitted with condensing gear and had a special modification to the chimney, which enabled the smoke to be directed over the top of the cab to the rear of the engine when working chimney first. This was because there were so many tunnels on the line that conditions in the cab became almost unbearable.

This design had the 2-6-0 wheel arrangement, with outside frames, outside cylinders, and cranks for the adhesion driving wheels. The cogwheels were mounted on Lange and Livesey's patent frame, and were driven through separate spur wheels from another set of cylinders inside the frames. To fit all of this into a 3ft. 6in. gauge locomotive was quite an achievement. These engines developed about 320 horse power on the incline, and could cope with loads of 75 to 112 tons, at speeds ranging from 3.20 to 5.52 miles per hour, on the 1 in 15 gradient. There were minor modifications to the later engines, including the addition of a rear carrying axle on all orders after the first, making it a 2-6-2 type, to provide for more water and fuel space at the rear, and the fitting of Holden's system of oil firing on the last two orders.

In 1896, there appeared the last design by Beyer, Peacock for a rack locomotive. This was a 2-4-0 with both rack and adhesion drives (Order 8127) for the Nilgiri Railway, in South India.(22) This again was a pioneering design on which certain restrictions were placed. When these were later removed, the Beyer, Peacock engines of course were underpowered for the increasing traffic. The ruling gradient on the rack sections was 1 in 12½, up which the engines were expected to take a load of 60 tons at 5½ miles per hour. Outside cylinders drove the adhesion wheels, which were placed very close together towards the rear. The Lange and Livesey rack frames were suspended from the leading wheels and the front pair of coupled wheels. Inside cylinders drove the rack gearwheels. The Engineer-in-Chief wrote about the first of these engines as follows:

"You will be glad to hear of the trial of the first engine; it was most satisfactory in every way and the gearing with the rack was perfect. There was no more noise or shaking than on an ordinary engine—very different from some of the Riggenbach rattle-traps I have been on. She entered the tongue very sweetly; every time depressing the spring, and gearing about the third tooth, the only sign of the entry on the footplate being a slight click as the spring went up."

[Right] The last rack locomotives were built by Beyer, Peacock in 1908 as a 2-6-2 version [9837] of the type for the Imperial Railways of Japan. They were also oil-fired.

[Below] "Panther", one of the Nilgiri Railway [8127] rack and adhesion engines built in 1897. The outside cylinders drove the four-coupled adhesion driving wheels at the rear, while inside cylinders drove the rack wheels which were suspended on a frame between the front carrying wheels and the front driving wheels.

Articulated Locomotives

Beyer wrote some comments in one of his note books on the Fairlie locomotive **Progress**, probably in 1871, and was obviously interested in keeping abreast of developments in this field. Another of Lange and Livesey's patents was for a twin tank locomotive design, which was in effect two tank engines placed back to back and not a true articulated locomotive. Various designs of this type had appeared over the years but Lange and Livesey's contribution was to couple the driving controls so that one person, and of course the fireman, could operate both engines together. In 1889 two pairs, which were connected together by a drawbar extending from the centre of one engine to the centre of the other, were built for the 3ft. gauge Mexican Inter-Oceanic Railway (Order 7123). The fire-boxes were raised to clear the drawbar, while the buffing casting had to be curved to allow the engines to move laterally. The cabs and footplates were made to overlap with each other

so they became virtually one. The regulator handle was connected with an arm on an overhead shaft, mounted in balljoints in the roof of the cab. Each reversing gear was operated by a worm and sector, with the worm fixed to a vertical shaft having a handle on the top. The vertical shaft was connected by a cross-shaft under the footplate at an angle of about 45 degrees with universal joints and bevel gears at each end. The steam and Westinghouse brakes were provided with two sets of pipes, one for each engine. Inside the smoke box a spark arrester and variable blast pipe were fitted. Although there was a saving in the cost of wages, the complications of the operating linkage and the confined space for carrying fuel meant that this design was never repeated.(23)

[Below] The Inter-Oceanic Railway [7123] was the sole purchaser of twin locomotives built to Lange and Livesey's patents. Only one crew was needed to work both engines.

[Foot] An unusually interesting works view of this 2-6-0 of 1894 for the Buenos Ayres Western Railway [7823].

In the year of its Jubilee, 1904, Beyer, Peacock wrote an account of its works, and another was printed in the January, 1907, edition of **Engineering**, to mark the production of its five thousandth locomotive. Both these accounts have been drawn on to describe here all the different departments and show how they had grown in the fifty years since the Company was founded. The complexities of locomotive manufacture are well illustrated for Beyer, Peacock had always tried to remain in the forefront of engineering practice to retain its reputation for building the best railway engines.

Originally the Gorton site comprised 12 acres of land, of which 1 acre was soon under cover. In 1864, the roofed-in area had been increased to 6½ acres, while such was the progress that by 1904 the buildings covered 9 acres, and the total ground within the boundary walls amounted to 22 acres. At that time the works was laid out in what could be described as one internal, or central, and three external blocks of buildings. In the three latter blocks, the earlier stages of manufacture were carried out, and from these the various parts were transported, either direct, or by way of the general machine shops, to the central block for final erection.

The heart of the whole works was the office block. It was rebuilt in 1881-4 to the designs of T. Worthington as a handsome two-storey building, 245ft. in length by 45ft., with an 85ft. clock tower. The ground floor was devoted to the commercial side, and housed the Managing Director's office, the Board Room, and all the accountancy staff. The upper floor held the main Drawing Office, 90 by 40ft., one end of which was devoted to the designing of machine tools. By 1907, the collection of drawings numbered about seventy thousand. The older ones, about twenty thousand,

The new office block from the yard, which has been tidied up and shrubs planted.

fully indexed, were kept in a fire-proof store-room; the more recent ones were filed in drawers under the drawing boards. The drawings of each section of the locomotive were kept together and stored in one case, so that when a new design was in preparation earlier solutions could be reviewed readily and used again if they met the specification. By a well thought-out system of numbering and classification, any individual drawing could be found at a few moments' notice.

The classification system also extended to the patterns, so that their storage corresponded to that of the drawings. When it was decided to re-adopt a previous design, the pattern was at once recoverable and work could commence immediately, thus facilitating and cheapening manufacture. This practice originated with Beyer, and was still in advance of the methods of many engineering firms in 1904. In the Drawing Office, there was also a model for trying out and finally adjusting valve and link motion details, prior to putting them in hand in the workshops. (see Chap. 15.)

The top floor of the office block also held the tracing department, where tracings were prepared by girls. Here too were the photographic dark room and negative store. From this store, about a ton and a half of glass plate negatives were removed when the works closed, and are now preserved in the North Western Museum of Science and Industry. In the Works Manager's office was a system of diagrams, or graphs, whereby the state of progress of every locomotive being built was recorded, each separate operation being represented by a distinctively coloured cube on the sectional square representing a date. In this way, the Manager could see at a glance whether and when all the iron castings had been completed for any one engine, or whether there was any delay in one or other of the machine shops. Every week graphs were also prepared for each department to show the volume of work passing through, the number of men employed, and their total wages. Comparative standards could thus be set defining the relation between these three crucial items of expenditure.

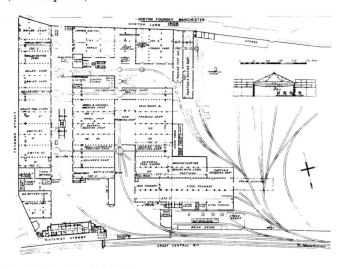

[Above] Plan of works in 1906.

[Below] The Drawing Office. The equipment is very basic, yet the drawings were superb.

By 1904, the whole works had been electrified with the first extensive use of the three-phase system in England. Initially the generating plant consisted of three 220 horse-power compound steam engine sets, for three-phase current, and three 110 horse-power triple expansion engine sets producing direct current for lighting and crane-driving purposes, one set in each case acting as a stand-by. The steam was supplied from locomotive boilers fired by gas. This original installation supplied current at 40 cycles and was so successful that it was later decided to electrify the whole works. An agreement was made with Manchester Corporation to provide the equivalent of 500 horse-power from their three-phase mains, but this was generated at 50 cycles, so the two systems were incompatible. By a new agreement completed before 1907, the Corporation supplied the whole of the electrical needs of Beyer, Peacock at 6,500 volts, enabling the Company to replace its steam engines and generators with six static transformers of 150 kilowatts each, giving a total output of 900 kilowatts of 50-cycle three-phase current at 210 volts. In addition, there were two motor converters of 200 kilowatts each, giving a total output of 400 kilowatts for crane services and lighting. The whole of the yard space was lit by arc lamps, while incandescent lamps were also used in the workshops and offices.

As regards the method of power transmission, group-driving was generally adopted throughout the works, although some of the larger machines had separate motors. The old line-shafting was retained and utilised in the shops and the wall engines formerly used to drive a double length of shafting were replaced by two or four electric motors, some of the line-shafting being divided in two. The longest length of shafting run from one motor was about 70ft., the motors ranging in size from 5 to 30 horse-power. As the cranes were formerly operated by rope belt and were quite efficient it was decided to make the minimum change, and a direct current motor was therefore installed on each crane which drove, through flat leather belting, the existing mechanism. After this had been done it was discovered that the rope drive to the crane in the long erecting shop absorbed 25 horse-power, which was indicative of the economy effected by the abolition of rope-driven cranes throughout the works.

Raw materials entered the works either by rail at the north-west corner, or by road at the south side, and were conveyed either to the central stores, or direct, by suitable sidings, to the foundries, forge, boiler shops, and other departments where the earlier operations commenced. The transport from these shops to the respective machines in the central block was facilitated by a network of 18in. gauge track laid throughout the works, and having a total length of nearly two miles. One locomotive sufficed to operate the whole system.

The first buildings approached from the general offices contained the pattern-making shop and pattern stores, the former occupying an area of 10,000 square feet, and the latter over 20,000. There was, in addition, a covered shed of 4,300 square feet for drying timber. The patterns were arranged by the type of material from which the castings were to be made, e.g. brass, iron or steel, and further sub-divided into locomotive and machine-tool areas, so that it was possible to have immediate delivery to the foundries of patterns of duplicates for engines constructed, in some instances, as long as twenty-five or thirty years previously.

In the pattern shop, there was a 24in. planing machine, a thicknessing and truing machine, a 9in. edge planing machine, and a general tool for tenoning, grooving, setting and mortising. One of the circular saws ran at an exceptionally high speed, and all of them were fitted for ripping and cross-cutting. There were three turning lathes, dealing with jobs up to 12ft. in diameter, and a core-box machine to groove holes up to 24in. diameter. All the machinery, with the exception of a 48in. saw for rough-sawing and the three lathes, was driven from underground shafting.

[Below] View of the yard in the middle 1890's with "Dot" and one of the Dutch State 4-4-0s carefully posed. The other locomotive is probably one of the New South Wales 4-6-0 passenger engines. Part of the yard beyond the boilerhouses has been roofed over since the 1870's.
[Foot] The pattern shop with various patterns for driving wheels, horn blocks, etc. in course of construction.

The iron and steel foundries were located in one building, 370ft. long by 94ft. 8in. broad, divided into two bays. The steel foundry occupied 230ft. of the length and also a side annexe which covered the furnace platforms, sandhouse, core-stoves, etc. There were two acid Siemens-Martin furnaces of 5 and 12 tons capacity respectively, which were of up-to-date construction, possessing long ports and large chequer chambers brought under the charging-platform, and having easily accessible dust-chambers, under the down-takes from the hearth. Runs of 300 to 400 charges were made without repairs being necessary. In front of the furnaces was an ingot pit in which ingots weighing about 23 cwt. were cast.

The annealing furnaces were a special pit type with removable sectional roofs. They were gas-fired, and reversing, but had heating chambers for the air only. The core-stoves were gas-fired by burners constructed on the Bunsen principle and gave very quick drying. Machine moulding was used for quantity production, and a large new wheel-moulding machine, by Scott & Hodgson of Guide Bridge, was installed for the machine-moulding of gear-wheels up to 30ft. diameter, for casting in steel or iron. About 5,000 tons of steel could be melted annually for either castings or ingots. Nothing but the purest brands of Swedish pig and British haematite, combined with the best scrap, were used. In addition to the castings for the firm's own requirements, other castings were made for outside firms, including the Admiralty and other Government departments.

Parallel with the annexe and close to the furnaces were the gas-producers. These were an improved Dawson type with steam-driven blowers supplied from two Cochrane tubular boilers. Alongside were the material and coal sidings, stock-banks, and brick stores. On the moulding side of the steel foundry the crane gantry was prolonged through an opening into the yard, giving ready access to the moulding box stores. Adjoining this end was the shop for the dressing of steel castings. This was served by hydraulic jib cranes, while compressed air mains supplied power for the pneumatic chipping tools.

Beyond the dressing shop was the machine shop for dealing with steel castings. For parting off the heads of the larger wheel-centre castings preparatory to their final annealing, were two 4ft. 6in. wheel lathes with gap-beds, and 7ft. 6in. face plates, of the firm's own make. These were separately driven by Siemens 6 horse-power direct current motors. The smaller wheel centres were dealt with on a Craven's double spindle headstock lathe, with 4ft. 8in. face-plates, which was also arranged for boring and finishing. The parting and rough machining of the wheel-centres were done with high-speed tool steel, using cutting speeds up to 50ft. per minute. A group of cold-cutting circular saws removed the heads and runners from the general work, and small castings were ground on emery wheel grinders. This machine area was served by a 3 ton electric walking crane built by P.R. Jackson, of Salford.

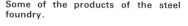
The 25 ton travelling crane in the steel foundry.

Some of the products of the steel foundry.

The iron foundry with castings for cylinders, chimneys, flanging plates, etc.

In the iron foundry were two large cupolas and a smaller air furnace capable of producing 3,000 tons per annum. These were supplied with air at a pressure varying from 20 to 30 inches water gauge from a fan placed to the rear of the cupolas and operated by an electric motor, while a pneumatic hoist served the cupola charging stage. The largest casting ever made there was the anvil block for an 8 ton hammer in the works forge, which weighed 34 tons. Castings of 15 tons for machine tools, etc., were not infrequent, although the greater part of the work was of a very light character, locomotive cylinders, weighing between two and three tons, predominating; the average number of cylinders cast was about 450 per annum. Compressed air was used for cleaning out the moulds, and small electric finger lamps were used for inspecting the cores and other less accessible portions of the mould. The core stoves were all coke fired as this gave the best results for iron. All the cylinders were tested hydraulically before leaving the foundry; the preliminary pressure which had to be met was from 1 1/8 to 1¼ times the working pressure, ranging in some cases up to 300lb per square inch. The metal used for these cylinders was subjected to a dead load deflection test to give not less than ½in. deflection with 40cwt., on a 3ft. bar of 2in. x 1in.

The main foundry building was equipped with the following cranes: on the melting side were three electric overhead travellers, one of 25 tons and two of 15 tons capacity, which could be used together for heavy casts. In the other bay, where the greater part of the moulding and annealing took place, there were three electric travellers, one of 15 tons and two of 10 tons capacity. For light work, a number of radial hydraulic cranes of 2 and 3 tons capacity were installed, and the area occupied by the cylinder moulding was, in addition, served by a hydraulic revolving cantilever crane of 5 tons capacity.

The brass foundry, which was joined to the main foundry building, had an output of about 300 tons per annum. The melting plant consisted of ten crucible potholes, each contained in an independent casing accessible from a common pit. Special attention was paid to the production of high quality brass, bronze and other alloys, and research had produced a metal for ''brass'' axle boxes giving mechanical tests comparable with those for mild steel. All the standardised small work for locomotives was plate-moulded. All copper scrap from the shops was remelted into ingots in a 1 ton air furnace placed outside the foundry, and all the moulding sand was passed through a washing process to recover any metal.

Before following the castings of iron, brass or steel into the machine shop, reference may be made to the forge. The original forge, designed by Beyer for making wrought iron wheels, had by this time been dismantled because all the wheels were made from steel castings, but a considerable amount of forge work was still undertaken. There were five hammers, of 7½ tons, 60cwt., 50cwt., and 30cwt., all of the "arch" type, and a 15cwt. of the Rigby type. The 7½ ton hammer was served by two furnaces — one coal fired for iron, and a large double-doored gas-fired reversing furnace for steel. In the latter, the ingots were heated prior to reduction, as also were the blooms for large forgings, such as coupling and connecting rods, axles, outside cranks, etc. At the 60cwt. and 50cwt. hammers, less heavy forgings were made, such as the smaller rods and shafts, foundation and fire-hole rings, cross-heads, slide-bars, dome-rings, roof-bars, reversing and brake-shafts, etc. The 60cwt. hammer was served by two coal-fired furnaces, the waste gases of which heated overhead Lancashire boilers, which supplied steam at 70lb. per square inch for the hammers. The 50cwt. hammer was served by one gas-fired reversing furnace, and one coal-fired furnace. At the 30cwt. hammer, still smaller forgings, such as reversing screws, axle-box wedges, axle-fork keeps, bogie swing-links, eccentric straps and sheaves were made. The 15cwt. Rigby hammer was used almost entirely for stamped work, such as boiler seatings, hand-rail pillars, bogie centre pins, various carrying brackets, etc. In view of the tendency to adopt standard units in successive designs, die stamping was resorted to very extensively in connection with all the motions, springs, links, connecting rods, brake rods, roof stays, etc. The motion parts generally were case-hardened after being machined, and this department was fitted with a furnace and quenching tanks specially for this purpose.

The smithy was 171ft. long by 120ft. wide, and had 56 fires. A large proportion of the forge work came here to be finished, the moulds, as they were termed, being shaped, or bent and welded, at the smith's hearth. In this way such work as reversing and brake-shafts, valve buckles, spring buckles, bogie spring beams, and fire-box rings were built up. For the most important welding work, Low Moor or other selected best Yorkshire iron was used. In another portion of the smithy were Horsfall's patent nut, bolt and rivet-making machines which were served by their own furnace. Other welding and light stamping work was done here too.

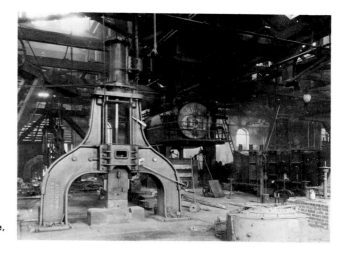

A 60 cwt. steam hammer in the forge, with furnaces to the right.

The smithy with hearths on either side and two small steam hammers in the centre. The electric arc lamps, hanging from the roof, can be seen in many of the other shops too.

Just before 1907, the whole layout of the shops where the boilers were made underwent considerable alterations. The former wheel-making forge was converted into the coppersmiths' department, with brazing hearths and blowpipes, pipe-bending machines, polishing lathes, shears and all accessories for the manufacture of dome casings, safety valve funnels and casings, all kinds of boiler clothing and pipe work of every description in wrought iron, steel or copper. The machine shop nearest this smithy was set aside for dealing with all the various boiler forgings. Machine tools here included two duplex slotting machines, a 6ft. planer, special milling and drilling machines for foundation rings, and special roof bar drilling and tapping machines, designed and made by Beyer, Peacock. In this shop were also the plate shears and the bending press for the copper fire-box wrapper plates.

Grouped together in the next bay, and served by a large 4 ton walking crane, were special machines of the Company's own make for dealing with most of the plate drilling. These included two duplex double-spindle drills, and one six-spindle drill for the tube-plates, a double-spindle wall-traversing drill for the wrapper plates, a duplex side-planing machine with two cutting tools to each head capable of dealing with the widest plates, a

number of radial arm drills, a band saw for the copper plates, a horizontal drill for corner holes, a double-spindle machine for either drilling or sawing, and other machinery. Within the same area were the lathes for turning and boring the dome seatings, boiler-throat plates, smoke-box doors, and other flanged and pressed plate work.

The adjoining shop had, by 1907, become the heavy boiler machine-shop, containing a large vertical-spindle milling, boring and sawing machine for dealing with fire-box front and back plates, and a large radial arm multiple spindle drilling machine for plates, etc., having an area up to 30ft. long and 10ft. wide. There was a large planing machine with a capacity of 30ft. by 10ft., and another edge planing machine for smaller plates. A high speed overhead travelling crane served these machines. The hydraulic flanging press, which had a capacity of 300 tons, was served by two furnaces. There were plate straightening rolls and plate bending rolls which could take plates up to 12ft. wide. In this shop were the punching and shearing machines and bending rolls for angle iron. Plate flanging and work for the dome smiths was done here too.

In each boiler erecting shop was a large hydraulic riveting machine, served by a powerful hydraulic crane, the press and crane levers being controlled by one man in each case. In the first shop, the boilers were put together, while they were completed in the second. Both shops were well equipped with movable drilling, reaming, tapping and hydraulic riveting machines. Pneumatic caulking, riveting and drilling tools were worked by compressed air at a pressure of 100 lb. per square inch. In the adjacent end shop were placed the machines for dealing with the rolling and drilling of boiler barrels, which were put together here before being taken to the large riveting machines. The complete boiler-making plant had a capacity of about 250 heavy boilers a year. Before leaving the boiler mounting shop, the boilers were tested under water and steam pressure, and were subsequently conveyed to the engine erecting shop, there to be dropped into the frames already prepared. The boilers were tested fully fitted out with their valves, cocks, etc., which saved time in the erecting shop.

The machinery for supplying the pneumatic and hydraulic power was housed in the stores building, which was placed centrally. Two duplex double-acting pumps supplied water to an accumulator with a 16in. diameter ram and a 20ft. stroke which was weighted to give water pressure of 1,700 lb. per square inch. The air was compressed by two large compound two-stage air compressors and distributed throughout the works at 100lb. per square inch.

The machine shops were laid out conveniently beside the erecting shops, and were grouped according to the class of work, so there was better supervision and greater economy. All marking out of work for machining was done centrally by men who became very experienced and accurate in their work. All tools were ground in a special department, and were served out from a central store in exchange for checks, issued by the foremen. The first machine shop was devoted to brass-turning, stud, nut and kindred machining. Here were made safety-valve pillars, connecting rod ends, big pipe flanges, pumps, water-pipe connections, whistles, lubricators, gauge and mud cocks as well as copper stays, studs and screws of all sorts. The work was done on a wide variety of lathes, and on other turning, facing and screwing machines, many classes of work being machined on the limit gauge system.

In the cylinder shop, a walking crane moved along the centre, serving machines on either side. The cylinder-boring machines were designed and made by Beyer, Peacock itself, and included both single- and double-spindle borers. On the machines, twin cylinders could be bored at the same time to ensure accuracy of alignment. There were two machines which could bore and plane cylinders at the same time, on which a side planer with the usual tool carriers worked in parallel with the boring bar, all controlled by one operative. A large multi-spindle vertical drill by Bausch and Harris, which could make sixteen holes at once, was used to drill the holes in the cylinder covers. In addition, there were other drills, and vertical and horizontal borers for piston-rings, steam-brake cylinders, pipe-flanges and the like. When the cylinders were finished they were fitted up and taken to the testing house adjoining the machine shop. Here they were tested with hot water to a pressure 50 per cent. in excess of the steam pressure at which they were to be worked. In a second test, they were tried with steam at full working pressure for an hour, a drain cock being fitted temporarily to carry off condensation. Only then were they taken to the erecting shop. Other work carried out in the cylinder shop included the manufacture of stays, handrail screws, bolts and boiler stays, most of which was done on automatic or semi-automatic machines.

[Top] The old plate shaping foundry where the sheets of metal were bent to the shapes required for making boilers.

[Centre] Boilers being erected in the old boiler shop.

[Foot] One of the machine shops with a "walking crane" in the centre aisle between the machines. The rails supporting the top of the crane are part of the structure carrying the lineshafting as well.

The general machine shops were situated between the small and larger erecting shops, and were divided into four bays, each 160ft. in length and 43ft. wide. Here the wheels, tyres and axles were machined. The roughly machined smaller wheels came from the steel foundry, and were bored on four vertical borers before being mounted on mandrels for the rims to be turned on 4ft. wheel lathes. This method was found to give greater accuracy. Larger wheels were rough turned, bored and bossed and then passed on to the remaining tools to be finished. There were about a dozen lathes for wheels ranging up to about 8ft. in diameter. The corresponding tyres were machined on similar tools. Most of these lathes were made by Beyer, Peacock itself. After the tyres had been shrunk onto the wheels, they could be turned in a special lathe made by Beyer, Peacock, which trued both tyres on an axle at the same time, and profiled them by former plates set to the correct tread. Crank pin holes were bored out in the large boring machines, and there was a variety of other machines for drilling and tapping holes in the rims, tyres and balance weights.

In this shop, all the axles were finished. Straight axles were turned and finished on a group of specially designed lathes, while crank shafts were roughed out on one heavy lathe, fitted with six cutting tools, and then finished on another. The crank-webs were slotted on one machine, and their sides planed square on another. Wheels were pressed onto their axles on a 120 ton hydraulic press. Here too were heavy milling machines for dealing with connecting rods and other motion parts, including the crank pins. One of these had an inclined head for milling the edges of rocking and reversing shafts so that the cutter and spindle could be set at any angle, and in addition it was fitted with a revolving table so that all the edges could be milled at one setting. When fitted with a cone-shaped cutter, bosses could be milled quite close to the spindle shaft.

Machines were adapted for carrying out work on particular parts, so that more and more specialised tools were evolved. Reversing, brake and rocking shafts were turned on special lathes, slotting machines were adapted for making expansion-links, cross-heads, valve-spindles and rods, regulator tops and valves, safety-valve levers and so on. For planing small work in quantities, such as brasses, expansion-link stud-plates, etc., there were high-speed planers with quick-return drive. There were boring machines fitted with either two or three vertical spindles for boring the ends of coupling rods for either four- or six-wheeled locomotives. There were also large vertical traversing drills of the same type for the connecting rod ends, and a number of horizontal traversing drills, both single- and double-headed, for long rods, cross-heads, keys, pins and a variety of general work. The boring of steam brake cylinders, reversing and brakeshaft carriers, drilling holes in eccentric sheaves and straps, was done at a group of single- and double-headed horizontal borers of the Company's own make, and fitted with special chucks for repetition work.

In this shop were a number of the special precision grinding machines for truing up the case-hardened parts of the motion work which were based on the designs of Colonel Peacock. The grinding headstocks were adjustable lengthwise or crosswise, and the tables were either fixed or traversing, so that a variety of work could be carried out, such as grinding the radius links or other parts of the motion which needed to be case-hardened and then accurately finished to give them long working lives. One machine here could grind up to 6ft. in length by 10in. in width. In this part of the shop, there were also ordinary grinding machines where all the tools for the rest of the works were reground. All cutting tools for lathes, planers, shapers and slotters were standardised and kept in quantities ready ground in the central tool-stores, where

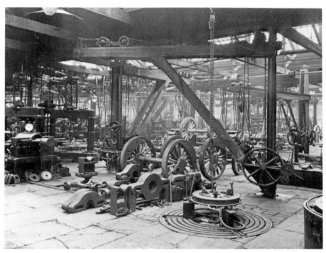

[Top] The Cylinder machining shop with a "walking crane" in the aisle.

[Centre] The turning shop where the wheels were finished, forced on their axles, tyred, etc. A gas "ring" for heating the tyres before they were shrunk on can be seen in the foreground.

[Foot] The jungle of belting in the small parts shop before the days of electric motors on each machine. The loss of energy must have been enormous, but then the heating bills were probably proportionately lower.

any worn tool could be immediately changed for a new one. Standard charts were exhibited, each tool being designated by a number, showing the correct shape and cutting angle which had been worked out scientifically for different classes of work. High-speed tool steel was used in short lengths contained in specially designed standard tool-holders. In the case of drills, the drilling machines were numbered, and each operator was given a full set of drills stamped with a corresponding number, thus affording complete supervision against misuse. All drills were periodically passed back to the tool-room and gauged for accuracy. In this shop, the two lathes which Beyer had purchased from Richard Roberts in 1854 were still, in 1907, earning their keep.

Along one side of this area, and also partly adjoining the new framing shop, were the benches for the fitters employed upon the rod-straps, wedges and brasses, steam regulators, steam brake cylinders, eccentrics, valves and valve-spindles, pistons and piston-rods, slide-bars, crossheads, reversing-screws, motion-work, etc. The parts of the motion work, when completed, were brought to a trying-over table, where they were gauged, set up, and tried over, the limit gauges ensuring accuracy up to 1/2,000 in. From here, the parts could be easily taken to the erecting shops and the locomotives.

The framing shop had been recently added to the works through roofing over an open yard, giving an area of 220 x 174ft. On two massive frame slotting machines, frames over 40ft. in length and 1in. thickness could be mounted so that eight pairs of frames could be slotted by six cross cutting heads at once. Half a dozen short-stroke machines slotted light plate work for cabs, side splashers and the like. A 4-spindle horizontal angle-iron drilling machine could be operated from the rear by one man who could manipulate the four heads simultaneously, together with the rising/falling table, so that holes, which were some-times too closely pitched to be drilled at one setting, could be easily drilled on this machine.

The machinery in this shop was principally related to manufacturing all the parts for the frames. Angle irons and brackets were ground to fitting gauges on a large side-grinding machine, and, on another grinding machine, the horn-blocks and wedges were finished after case-hardening. Both the block and the wedge were ground simultaneously to ensure that the faces would be absolutely parallel. There were three special horn-block planing machines fitted with eight rests, four horizontal and four vertical, for planing two blocks simultaneously, on both the top and the sides. The benches for fitting up the axle-boxes ready for the erecting-shop were placed in the section of the frame-shop nearest to the work, as was most of the other machinery relating to this stage of manufacture. Drilling, slotting, shaping and planing machines were installed for dealing with axle-box parts, wedges, liners, etc. In close proximity were the benches for fitting the springs, bogie-swing links, keeps, spring-links, hangers, etc.

The engine, tender and bogie frames, after slotting and drilling, were taken into the old framing shop, and there fitted with horn-blocks, keeps and angle-irons. The bogie bodies and frames were brought to a setting-out table, and the holes drilled through them from the frames by means of drills worked by compressed air. Most of the bogie riveting was done by hydraulic power, but for joining the frames to the bodies cold riveting was principally used. There were, of course, many more machine tools in these shops than have been mentioned.

A double-headed grinding machine with moving table, built in 1910 for the South African Railways.

[Above] The frame shop. One frame on the right is having the horn blocks fitted for the driving axles.

[Below] The main erecting shop. The engines were lifted across and wheeled on the mixed gauge track in the centre.

The small erecting shop, 160ft. long by 45ft. wide, with a 25 ton overhead travelling crane, was used for smaller locomotives, tram-engines and repair work, and also as an additional department for boiler mounting. The main erecting shop, 380ft. long by 45ft. wide, was served by three high-speed double-lift cranes, two of 10 and 40 tons and one of 8 and 25 tons lifting capacity respectively. A special feature of this shop was the provision of travelling wall cranes for carrying the hydraulic riveting machines. The locomotives were erected in two long rows parallel with the side walls. Alongside the walls were the fitters' benches, compressed air mains and light shafting, while down the centre ran a multiple gauge track. When the locomotives were so far ready, they were lifted bodily over to the track and onto their wheels. A large turntable half-way along the shop gave the necessary communication with the trial siding.

Up to this point, the work had progressed simultaneously in several departments, but by the diagram in the Manager's office it was possible to ensure that the progress of framing, cylinders, motion parts, wheels and boiler had a distinct relation to each other and arrived at the locomotive erecting shop in their correct order. This helped to speed up the production of locomotives. For instance, in the case of five locomotives built for the Great Central Railway, only six weeks elapsed from the receipt of the order to the completion of all castings; ten weeks to the delivery of all the parts in the erecting shop; while in thirteen weeks the first engine was under steam; in sixteen weeks all five were under steam; and in eighteen weeks all were delivered completely painted, although by specification a fortnight had to elapse for the paint on the engine to harden.

The tender department included two machine-shops and an erecting shop, covering altogether a space 143ft. long by 140ft. in width. In this department were also made the locomotive chimneys, ash-pans, tender brake work and draw-gear. The erecting-shop was amply supplied with hydraulic and steam riveting power, the latter being well suited to the thin plate work. Small portable emery wheels worked by compressed air were used for grinding off the tops of the countersunk rivets along the tender sides and chimney bases. The tender sides, back, coping plates, etc., were freed from scale by blasting. The blast-house, which was situated near the tender erecting-shop, used minute chilled cast-iron shot instead of sand. The air-blast had a pressure of 15 - 20lb. per square inch, while the floor was laid with perforated plates through which the shot fell into funnels so it could be taken away, cleaned and used again. A variety of other work was also shot-blasted; for example, buffer-plates, smoke-box plates, cylinder clothing, splasher and cab plates, etc., so that a completely smooth surface was obtained prior to painting.

The painting and packing shops were in two bays, one of 260ft. and the other of 200ft. in length, equipped with 25 and 20 ton travelling cranes respectively. These shops were steam-heated throughout and had direct communication with the railway siding. In addition to the manufacturing areas there were various stores, while in the yards were stocks of coal and other materials, and the swaging blocks, moulding boxes, etc. Ten acres of land were held in reserve for future extensions.

The tender erecting shop.

Just as in the Drawing Office there was a separate part for the design of machine tools, so in the period around 1900 there was a separate general machine-shop and a separate erecting-shop for their manufacture too. The development of locomotive building at Gorton Foundry was accompanied from the beginning with an equally thorough and progressive attitude towards machine tool development. Originally this work was undertaken by the Company primarily for its own needs, but demand for machines of its design quickly led to a considerable outside business. At this period, Beyer, Peacock was engaged in the manufacture of its patent grinding machinery, special equipment for railway workshops and also heavier machine tools, such as large lathes for the Sheffield armament trade and other important industries.

The general machine tool shop was a building 270ft. long and 81ft. 6in. wide, and the erecting-shop, 140ft. long by 48ft. wide, adjoined it. Here could be found similar machine tools to the rest of the works, but special mention must be made of two lathes, with 22 and 29ft. beds respectively, for turning and cutting long screws. By the simple process of welding fresh lengths of shafts onto a finished portion, guide screws of over 100ft. in length were made. The planers for large lathe-beds and other heavy work were arranged along the two sides of the tool erecting shop, which was served by an overhead travelling crane with lifts of 5 and 25 tons. One planing machine could take work up to 30ft. by 6ft. 6in., while the other had a stroke of 20ft. There was a testing department with a chemical laboratory as well as machines for testing the strength of materials, where valuable research work was carried out into the correct treatment and manufacture of iron, steel and other construction materials.

This account gives a brief survey of Gorton Foundry just after the turn of the century. Beyer, Peacock was always noted for the high quality of its locomotives, which was achieved by continually modernising the works with more advanced tools and processes. In January 1907, the 5,000th locomotive was being built, and it is fitting to conclude with the words of Ernest Lange, who wrote the article for **Engineering**:-

"It will have been sufficiently indicated, in the course of this survey of the workshops and plant, that no pains have been spared in keeping the concern abreast of the best-equipped locomotive works of the day, and that the energy and foresight which distinguished the management of the company in the past are fully maintained at the present time. Whilst the old reputation for the finest quality of workmanship is thus being zealously guarded, every advantage that modern experience can supply is also being employed in adding to the efficiency and productive power of the works, so as to enable the company to cope with a continuous increase of business, which, as far as one can read the signs of the time, bids fair to be maintained."

These words were to prove strangely prophetic, for the development of the Garratt locomotive in the next few years enabled Beyer, Peacock to remain in the forefront of steam locomotive engineering for another fifty years.

The packing shop with parts crated ready for dispatch.

Certificate of Incorporation.

No. 73505

I Hereby Certify that BEYER, PEACOCK & CO. (1902), LIMITED, is this day Incorporated under the Companies Acts, 1862 to 1900, and that the Company is LIMITED.

On 22 April 1902, a new company, Beyer, Peacock & Co. (1902) Limited, was officially registered; the 1902 was dropped the following year. Originally the capital of the Company was to be £500,000(1) but finally it paid £800,000 to take over Gorton Foundry as a going concern; which included a sum of £156,843 for "goodwill". Capital was raised by the issue of £300,000 4¼ per cent. debenture stock, 300,000 5½ per cent. cumulative preference shares and 200,000 ordinary shares, both of £1 each.(2) At the time of this reconstruction, 2,000 men were employed at Gorton Foundry, which was capable of producing 150 loco-motives per annum. The works occupied a site of 22 acres, of which buildings covered 41,800 square yards. The works, with plant and equipment, were valued at £422,737 and the other assets of the Company at £220,420.(3)

The new Company held its first Directors' meeting on 30 April 1902, when Sir Frederick Lacy Robinson, Sir Vincent Caillard and Colonel Peacock were formally elected Directors. Peacock was invited to join the Board to ensure continuity, and to guarantee customers the same high class of engineering to which they had been accus-tomed in the past. Sir Frederick was Deputy Chairman of the Board of Inland Revenue, and Sir Vincent a Director of Vickers Ltd., besides being a Director of the London, Chatham & Dover Railway, and later of the Southern Rail-way. He acted as Chairman at the second Board meeting, on 1 May, and was formally appointed to that office at the next one, at the end of the same month. At the second meeting, another Director appointed was Thomas Craven, a director of the Salford engineering firm of Gresham & Craven, and also of the Cambrian Railway.(4)

To ensure that continuity should be maintained, the new Company retained the services of all heads of departments at Gorton. In June 1902, G.A.P. Dawson, who had been Works Manager since 1900, was appointed Managing Director for a period of twelve months, and was also elected a Director; R.R. Lister replaced him as Works Manager, while S. Rendell was promoted to Chief Draughtsman. A.P. Jameson was appointed as repre-sentative of the Company in London.(5) As far as the personnel of the works were concerned, these changes made no important difference, for the Company continued to produce engines and machine tools of the same high quality as before.

The business the new Company had acquired was more concerned with quality of product than cheapness; without any sacrifice of quality it must be the study of the new owners to keep the firm in a condition to compete not only with other British firms but with the growing number of rivals abroad, who often had cheaper labour and material costs. An imponderable asset would be the morale of the workers, for they must feel that they continued to be members of a firm of prestige, and with a tradition of craftsmanship. As Sir Vincent Caillard put it:

"They are proud of the history of the establishment to which they belong, and they have reason to be. We confidently expect to be able, with their co-operation, to continue that history untarnished."(6)

Sir. Vincent Caillard.

At the first statutory meeting on 31 July 1902, Sir Vincent Caillard was able to assure the shareholders that trade was excellent, and that the business was flourishing. Though the accounts were not yet complete, it appeared that profits over the first half-year were running at an even higher rate than that during the last half-year of the old company, itself a record. Orders representing over half a million sterling were on hand, and the outlook was highly satisfactory.

Yet the new administration had problems to face owing to changing conditions in the locomotive industry. Com-petition was becoming intense through the continuing build-up of manufacturing capacity at home and in various countries abroad. Orders were still coming from some rail-ways in Britain, but the policy of building locomotives in their own railway workshops continued to operate. In Scotland, the three locomotive builders in Glasgow—Sharp Stewart, Neilson Reid, and Dübs—amalgamated in 1903 to form the North British Locomotive Co. Ltd., creating what was then the largest firm of locomotive builders in Europe.(7) Besides Beyer, Peacock, the Vulcan Foundry and Robert Stephenson also enlarged their capacities,(8) while there were many smaller companies in the industry also competing for orders. Similar expansion was taking place elsewhere in Europe (where Germany emerged as a serious competitor), in the United States, and also a little later in Japan, where a locomotive building industry was established in 1908.(9)

To meet this threat, the new Board investigated other lines which might be manufactured at Gorton Foundry, to lessen dependence on a single product. The introduction of electric tramcars, from 1885 onwards, had resulted in a great expansion of tramway routes, taking some passengers from the railways.(10) Some railways had responded by electrifying their lines and Colonel Peacock feared that electric traction would speedily replace steam. P.A. Creeke was therefore asked by the Beyer, Peacock Board to investigate what problems would have to be faced and what extra capital and manufacturing capacity would be needed if Gorton Foundry were to enter the electric traction field.

The first question to be decided was what Beyer, Peacock should endeavour to make. This was long before the days of the National Grid, so that any railway electrifying its lines had to purchase the generating equipment as well as the distribution system, e.g. substations, and third rail or overhead wires, as well as the electric trains themselves. Some companies, such as Brush Electrical Engineering Co., of Loughborough, made everything except, in their case, the steam boilers and cables. Others made only the motors and control gear, which were fitted into rail vehicles by different manufacturers. Then Beyer, Peacock had to decide what type of rail vehicle it was going to make; whether it should try to enter the locomotive, or multiple-unit field. Creeke took it:

"That at first, at all events, B.P. & Co. would not venture to take up the manufacture of generators but would confine themselves entirely to either the complete electric locomotive or else the motor trucks to be placed under coaches or cars made by the Railways themselves or other firms."(11)

The manufacture of generators would involve the use of very heavy tools, cranes and large shops, with consequent heavy capital expenditure. If a railway company wished to find one firm willing to undertake the entire electrification, Beyer, Peacock could tender for everything and sub-let what it could not build for itself. Creeke therefore recommended that:

"the rolling stock, whether in the shape of a complete loco., bogies, or motor trucks, would be designed here and that we should obtain the motors from outside firms (we might even supply them with the necessary steel castings) to our specified requirements; the controllers and switches would be bought from outside firms who make a speciality of this class of work. The wheels, axles, framing, cab and general erection would of course be done here in the usual way.

"A comparatively small sum would have to be spent in providing a motor generator to transform our works pressure up to 500 - 550 volts for trial runs and testing purposes and a length of road would have to be fitted with a third rail and possibly an overhead trolley wire.

"Eventually it would pay us to make the whole of the work ourselves, but even then we should still be able to utilize a large portion of our present plant, especially the framing and tender shops, wheel shop, etc."

Creeke went on to describe the types of motors then being used, and the equipment needed to manufacture them. Geared motors, instead of those built directly on the axles, were being introduced. Likewise, multiple-unit trains, with motors in different cars, controlled from one driving position, were beginning to appear. He thought that some of Beyer, Peacock's rivals, like Dübs, Neilson, or Sharp Stewart, would soon enter the electric traction field, and that great advantage would accrue to whoever took the plunge first. Beyer, Peacock would have an advantage with its own steel plant, the like of which other manufacturers did not possess.

Creeke proceeded:

"It may be said that, the business of B.P. & Co. being chiefly concerned with foreign railways, the effect of this change in the method of locomotion will not be felt for a considerable time, but granting even this, there is a wide field open in this country, which there is no reason why we should not take advantage of, and so allow the change, when it does come, to be more gradual, at the same time increasing our output and connection by means of the new work.

"In conclusion I strongly think that the question is a very pressing and urgent one and deserving of very earnest and careful consideration by the Coy. for the following among other reasons:

"(1) There is no doubt that within the next few years a great deal of electric traction work will be carried out for the various Railway Coys. who will be compelled to convert their existing steam lines, in order to compete with the tramways now being run or put in hand all over the Kingdom.

"The conversion of the main lines is probably not so close at hand, but even at the present day, for suburban service where a quick frequent series of trains are required, electricity is both cheaper and better in every way.

"(2) Most of the large engineering firms are now taking up electrical engineering as part of their usual work, and those who are first in the market and have the most experience will naturally have the pick of the orders.

"(3) B.P. & Co. having a good name and solid reputation, together with a long experience of the requirements of standard-gauge railway work, stand in a unique position for taking up electric traction and making a speciality of it for railway service, even if tramway equipments are not touched upon.

"(4) Having so large a plant and skilled workmen, the expense of starting will not be so great as in the case of a new firm or one not hitherto in the loco. or rolling-stock business.

"(5) The new method of locomotion will gradually replace the old during the future, but this need not affect the welfare of the firm so much if we are ready to meet the demand for the new work, otherwise its well-being will be seriously depreciated if we allow others to be before us in this matter.''

It will be remembered that this was the period when Beyer, Peacock was electrifying its own works, and had already used electric motors for driving machine tools. However, it was not to know that the prophecy of doom for the steam locomotive was half a century too early; but a few electric locomotives were built at Gorton Foundry during the ensuing years.

The invention of the internal combustion engine posed another threat to the dominant position of the railways, because it started the revival of road transport, not only with the private car, but also with public vehicles, for the first motor-bus service in London had commenced in 1899. In March 1903, Jameson suggested that Beyer, Peacock should erect an experimental motor-car which Harry Livesey had designed, and for which he would supply certain parts.(12) In May of the same year, Lister was sent to inspect the American Fischer motor vehicle, which had a petrol engine driving a generator and two electric motors, one for each rear wheel. A demonstration run was given through the most crowded streets in the centre of London, with a vehicle made into a thirty-seater omnibus. A little later, Lister went to investigate the Rochet Schneider motor-car which Captain H.H.P. Deasy hoped to build in this country, but it was realised that a completely different approach to production would be necessary to make a success of any of these projects. Locomotives were generally built in small batches, but motor-cars would need parts made in long production runs. This would not be possible with the machine tools then installed at Gorton Foundry, and the layout of the works did not lend itself easily for adaptation if the manufacture of railway locomotives were to continue as well.(13)

In October 1903 a visit of greater importance was made, to Serpollet's works in Paris, where a motor-car with a flash-steam boiler was demonstrated. Unfortunately, the rail cars fitted with similar boilers were not available for trials. Lister reported: "I am very favourably impressed and think the matter well worth going further into, in view of the fairly numerous inquiries now being made for railway Motor Cars''. Discussions were held with Serpollet, but no agreement was reached and the eight railcars that were built at Gorton all had conventional boilers, and single driving axles, with outside cylinders and valve gear. They were built for the North Staffordshire (Order 9281), United of Havanna (Order 9344) and London, Brighton & South Coast Railways (Order 9376) in 1905 but, even though they were well received, Beyer, Peacock never entered this field again, although many schemes were submitted.(14) Designs of road steam wagons were also investigated, and details of their performance appear in the draughtsmen's books. In the event, the only proposal acted upon was the construction of six road wagons, to Hoy's design with a special patent boiler, which were authorised in 1904 and finished in 1906, but that project did not proceed any further.(15)

The Beyer, Peacock design of railcar supplied to the North Staffordshire Railway [9281]. The boiler and wheels at the front are pivoted separately from the carriage. The vibrations from the driving wheels and coupling rods were transmitted to the passengers in the carriage, to their discomfort.

An experimental steam lurry.

Specification for the ''Gorton'' steam lurry.

Specification
OF
THE "GORTON" STEAM LURRY,
MANUFACTURED BY
BEYER, PEACOCK & COMPANY LIMITED,
GORTON, MANCHESTER.

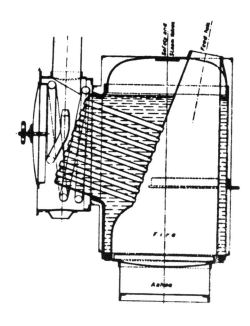

Hoy's design of boiler for the steam lurry.

Capacity.	Five (5) tons.
Deck.	13 ft. 3 in. × 6 ft. 6 in. = 86 sq. ft. Constructed of 1¼ in. red deal or elm, with hoop
Frame.	iron tongued joints, secured to strong oak cross stretchers. The whole firmly bolted to a Frame
Springs.	formed of 6 in. × 3 in. Channel Steel Girders mounted on Laminated Springs of the best make, and ample capacity.
Wheels.	The Wheels have Cast Steel elastic centres with wood cushioned rims, with Mild Steel or Wrought Iron Tyres 1 in. thick, unless otherwise ordered, the Loading Wheels being 2 ft. 9 in. diameter × 7 in. wide, and the Driving Wheel 3 ft. 3 in. diameter × 9 in. wide.
Footplate. Coke Bunker.	The Footplate is riveted to the Steel Channel Frames, and carries the Boiler through a well in the centre, with Coke Bunker right across behind the Boiler and men's seats, of a capacity of 5 cwts.
Tank.	The Tank of 200 gallons capacity is slung between the frames at the rear to give weight on the driving wheels when running light. It is fitted with an absolute tell-tale water level, and means of emptying tank and pipes in case of frost.
Boiler.	The Boiler is Hoy's Patent " Bottle-firebox " type with submerged tubes, built entirely of the best flanging quality steel plates.
	This Boiler is one of the chief specialities of our Steam Lurries. It has all the advantages of both the vertical and loco. type boiler, without their disadvantages and forms an unique combination of good points. It takes up the small room of the vertical type. It has the approximately horizontal submerged tubes of the loco. type, and a complete loco. type smoke-box, with door which can be opened at a moment's notice, admitting of no excuse by the attendant of difficulty in getting at, so that tubes and box can be cleaned in a few minutes, every morning, if dirty fuel is being used, or even on the journey with steam up. It has the further unique advantage of enabling one to see, at any moment, the whole of the fire-end of the tubes, so that a leaky one can be easily detected and plugged. The whole of the fire can also be seen through the firing hole, and got at with the trimmers, so that every spot is under complete command of the stoker.

Heating Surface.	Tubes	...	...	...	...	...	...	77	square feet.
	Firebox	...	...	...	..	...	...	18	,, ,,
			Total	...	...	...	...	95	,, ,,

Grate Surface.	3·47 ,, ,,
Blowing-off Pressure.	200 lbs. per square inch.
	Ample washout plugs and cleaning doors are provided.
Mountings.	These are of the very best description, compact and conveniently arranged :—"Klinger" type Unbreakable Water Gauge; Injector; Pump Clackbox, with bye-pass valve for regulating the feed; Pressure Gauge, with working pressure distinctly marked in red; two lock-up Safety Valves and Blower. The Tank is supplied with a steam water lifter and 30 feet of 1½ in. suction hose with rose.
Engine.	We will supply a Compound Engine if required; but since simplicity throughout, consistent with efficiency, has been our chief aim, we recommend an Engine of the enclosed " Simple " type. The slides are cylindrical and solid with the casing. The piston and valve rods are completely

The final form of the steam lurry which never went into serious production. It had a steam engine underneath with enclosed motion and chain drive to the rear wheels.

The concern for the future of steam locomotive manufacture shown by the Directors was doubtless accentuated by a considerable fall in production of locomotives which began in 1902, and continued through 1903. From then on, however, deliveries increased, with good years in 1906, 1907 and 1908, when over 140 engines were produced each year. It has to be remembered, of course, that locomotives of that period were becoming progressively larger, heavier and more sophisticated in their equipment, so that comparisons of annual output by numbers alone gives a distorted picture. Thereafter, steam locomotives were firmly re-established as the basic product of Gorton Foundry, despite the growing competition. In that field, increasing interest was being shown in articulated locomotives, to cope with heavier loads in conditions of steep gradients, light track, and severe curvature.

G.A.P. Dawson resigned as Managing Director in 1904. In his place the Board decided to appoint H.A. Hoy as General Manager, at a salary of £2,000 per annum, with a 2½ per cent. commission on the net profits. Hoy had been Chief Mechanical Engineer of the Lancashire & Yorkshire Railway, and with him from that Railway he brought A.E. Kyffin, who was appointed Chief Draughtsman, thereby demoting S. Rendell. Lister also resigned as Works Manager, and his successor was A.C. Rogerson, who had been Chief Out-door Machinery Assistant at Horwich, from whence Edgar Alcock also came, to be his deputy.(16) Towards the end of 1905, R.H. Burnett was appointed as a Consulting Engineer to the Company for the ensuing five years, and then was made London Representative, a post which he held until his death on 13 December 1916.(17) At the end of 1906, Colonel

H.A. Hoy.

Peacock, being then 68, resigned his directorship, thus severing the last direct link with the original partners. Sir Henry Beyer Robertson had given up his directorship when the Public Limited Company was formed in 1902, but years later his son was appointed to the Board. On the death of H.A. Hoy, in 1910, A.F. Halstead was appointed Manager and Secretary to the Company, and Rogerson had his salary increased as he took on greater responsibilities for production. Edgar Alcock was not promoted, so he left to become Works Manager of the Hunslet Engine Co. in Leeds.(18)

Continual improvements to the works were made during the period up to 1914. Apart from the electrification already mentioned, in 1902 the steel foundry was extended and in 1903 the old forge was turned into a coppersmith's shop, the Company thereby avoiding having to send certain work to firms outside. The most important alterations made before the First World War were the building of a new paint shop (equipped with heavy overhead cranes), a new three-storey pattern store, and the roofing-over of a large area for a new frame shop, all in 1913, at a cost of £15,500.(19)

In 1907, the Directors, having dreams of expansion abroad, purchased a site for a proposed locomotive works at Montreal in Canada, referred to in the records as the "Lachine Site". It is interesting to speculate how this bold proposition might have prospered, but all sorts of problems were encountered and eventually the site was sold in 1912, when the Company was no doubt glad that the money tied up in it ceased to be the subject of questions by some shareholders!(20)

* * * * *

The second crane engine was of a similar design (Order 7419), mounted on the rear of a 0-4-2 saddle-tank locomotive and was ordered in 1891 by the 5ft. 6in.-gauge Buenos Ayres & Rosario Railway. Provision was made for power slewing by fitting outside cranks to the crankshaft of the hoisting engines. Connecting rods transferred the motion from the crankshaft, at the top of the crane, to a jackshaft near the base and then, through gearing, to a wormshaft which engaged in the wormwheel mounted on the crane. A reversing clutch was provided to change the direction of rotation, and also to throw the slewing gear out of action. It was unusual for one set of engines to perform the double function of lifting and slewing. The capacity of this crane was 3 tons, at 11ft. 5ins. radius.

The next order, chronologically, was in 1902 for two 0-6-0 saddle tanks with cranes mounted at the rear, but they were of an entirely new design (Order 8742), for the 3ft. 6in.-gauge Queensland Government Railways. The crane was mounted immediately behind the firebox on a post, with the bottom bearing located between the engine

The works shunter of 1879 was extended with lengthened frames and a pair of trailing wheels to take a crane.

Crane Locomotives

This is the most appropriate place to include the history of the crane locomotives built by Beyer, Peacock, even though the first one was completed in 1885, when the frames at the rear of the works shunter were extended to convert it into a 0-4-2 tank (original Order 3701 of 1878; alteration Order 6677). The crane was mounted on a long cast-iron post and carried in top and bottom housings. It was the simplest possible construction, with a pair of non-reversing steam engines to provide the lifting power. The drive was through friction wheels, the second wheel shaft being mounted in an eccentric bearing. On rotating this eccentric by a hand lever, the wheel was brought into contact with the driving wheel on the crankshaft and, by releasing the lever, the crane became free and lowering was controlled by a hand brake.

frames. Lifting and slewing were operated hydraulically, the power being supplied by a duplex steam-driven pump. One hydraulic ram inside the crane post operated the lifting mechanism and could cope with 3 tons, at 10ft. radius. Two rams, placed vertically, one on either side of the crane post, provided the power for slewing through the medium of ropes and sheaves. As soon as the pumps were started, special hydraulic rams descended onto the axle boxes so that the weight of the load was transferred directly to the axles of the locomotives.

Another interesting design followed in 1908, again for the Buenos Ayres & Rosario Railway, which received two 0-6-0 side-tank locomotives (Order 9649) with the crane mounted over the middle of the boiler, on a special struc-

[Above] Another standard 0-4-0 shunting engine was lengthened to make it into a crane locomotive for the Buenos Ayres & Rosario Railway [7419] in 1891.

[Below] On the crane locomotives for the Queensland Government Railways [8742], to accommodate the post for the crane at the rear of the boiler, the firebox doors were placed at the side. The pulley at the top of one of the slewing rams can be seen beside the crane post.

ture of plates and steel castings, built up on the main frames. The locomotive itself was powerful, having cylinders 16 x 20in., and weighed 45 tons, while the crane could lift 5 tons, at a radius of 18ft. The lifting engines were arranged horizontally at the right-hand side of the locomotive, whilst those for slewing were placed vertically on the left, driving the wormshaft direct. Both were reversing, with Walschaert's valve gear. The crane post consisted of a cast-steel column, on which the jib revolved on ball and roller bearings. The jib was made from steel plate, suitably cross-stayed and extended at the opposite end to hold the counterbalance weight. The controls on the foot-plate were arranged so that the crane could be operated from either side of the engine, and to give a clear view, the cab had no side or front plates.

The last crane engines built at Gorton Foundry were a reversion to the 0-4-2 type (Order 9891), with the crane mounted at the rear of a side-tank engine, on a built-up box structure secured to the main frames. Two were delivered in 1909 to the standard-gauge New South Wales Government Railways. Both the hoisting and slewing engines were mounted vertically, the former inside and the latter outside the crane base. All the controls were duplicated on each side so that the crane could be manipulated by one man, with a clear view of the operations. The horn-block of the trailing coupled axle were arranged with less than the usual top clearance so that, when the crane was in operation, the frame settled down on the axle-boxes and formed a solid structure. These cranes could lift 5 tons, at 11ft. radius.(21)

Superheating

The most important development in locomotive detail design in this period was the superheater, introduced around the turn of the century, and gradually perfected.(22) There were problems to be solved in connection with its use: improvements in lubricating oil to withstand the great increase in steam temperature, new types of piston-rod gland packings for the same reason, introduction of efficient mechanical lubrication systems for the cylinders and valves, and the use of piston valves, instead of the old simple slide valves, to cope with the acute lubrication problems of the large sliding surfaces in the latter type. The greater economies given by superheating more than justified the expense of these developments.

The use of piston valves permitted two other important improvements. First, the steam passages between the valve ports and the cylinders could be shortened and straightened, which gave, among other things, a better flow for the steam. Then the valve travel could be increased to give better valve opening and the ''lap'' increased to give better valve events. These gave more efficient operation at high speed, with short ''cut-off'', as well as at full valve travel with late ''cut-off'' required when starting a train from rest. Locomotive accessories were also receiving increasing attention, notably injectors, feed water heaters and feed pumps, anti-vacuum valves and by-pass valves for cylinders, power-operated reverse gear for large locomotives, and braking equipment.

The first superheated engine produced at Gorton Foundry was the last of a batch of twenty-four 2-8-0 tender engines for the Buenos Ayres & Pacific Railway (Order 050) in 1910, followed by two 2-6-0 tender engines. for the Buenos Ayres Western Railway (Order 054). In 1911, the New south Wales Government Railways ordered one of its 4-6-0 passenger engines (Order 0193) and one of its 2-8-0 goods engines (Order 0191) to be fitted with 'Schmidt' superheaters; these were the first superheated locomotives in Australia.(23) The Great Northern Railway of Ireland received its first superheated 4-4-0 tender engines, fitted with Phoenix-type superheater, in the smokebox, in 1911 (Order 0229). The first Garratt locomotives sent to Western Australia, in 1911 (Order 0246), were not superheated, but the next batch (Order 0557), sent in 1913, were.

An early 4-8-2, Class 14 B for the South African Railways [0788]. Note the steam reversing gear on the running plate and the electric generator behind the headlamp.

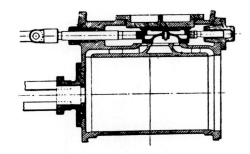

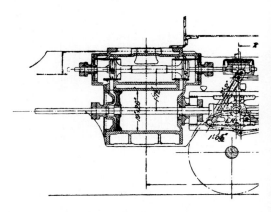

[Top] Typical layout of steam passages with slide valves.

[Lower] Piston valves enabled the steam passages to the cylinders to be straightened and shortened.

In 1914 an interesting case of locomotives deliberately not superheated was Order 0788 for fifteen 4-8-2 tender engines for the South African Railways. These locomotives were the first of this wheel type built at Gorton Foundry, and worked over the lower part of the Natal main line, particularly the Town Hill section near Pietermaritzburg, which included a 1 in 30 gradient, with frequent stops. Owing to these conditions, it was considered that superheaters would not be justified, but about six years after the engines had been placed in service there was a report in which it was claimed that the lower haulage power and increased coal and water consumption represented an annual loss to the administration of approximately £100,000. Soon afterwards, they were all fitted with superheaters.(24)

[Above] Beyer, Peacock's first superheated engine, a 2-8-0 goods type for the Buenos Ayres & Pacific Railway [050], was fitted with a "Schmidt" superheater in the smoke tubes. The motion work looks very complicated with outside Walschaert's valve gear and a feed water pump fitted to the crosshead.

In 1911, the Great Northern Railway of Ireland received their first superheated engines, these 4-4-0s [0229].

The smokebox of "Munster" showing the 'Phoenix' superheater elements.

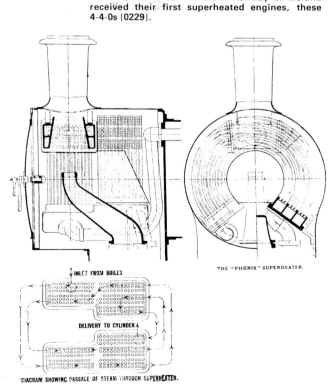

THE "PHŒNIX" SUPERHEATER.

INLET FROM BOILER

DELIVERY TO CYLINDER

DIAGRAM SHOWING PASSAGE OF STEAM THROUGH SUPERHEATER.

The Phoenix superheater.

"Slieve Gullion", a 4-4-0 delivered to the Great Northern Railway of Ireland in 1913 is now preserved and steam for enthusiasts trains. It was photographed at Cobh in 1976. [C.P. Friel]

Other Locomotives

In the period from 1903 to the time when locomotive building ceased for the duration of the First World War, over 1,500 locomotives were produced. An even higher proportion, 85 per cent., were for export, and once again the Great Central took the lion's share, with 78 out of the 220 or so built for England. There were some handsome and powerful 4-6-0 tender engines (Order 9032) with inside cylinders, and the Atlantic type as well (Order 9034) to the designs of its Chief Mechanical Engineer J.G. Robinson.(25) But the most interesting were four 0-8-4 tank engines (Order 9655), built in 1907, which were the first of this wheel-type in Britain. They had three 18 x 26in. cylinders, 4ft. 8in. coupled wheels, and 200 lb/sq. in. boiler pressure. They weighed 96.5 tons, and developed 38,350lb. Tractive Effort.(26) One of these engines was displayed at the Franco-British Exhibition of 1908, and beside it was shown the special arrangement drawing, coloured by Timothy Fox, already mentioned.

The three-cylinder 0-8-4 tank engine used for banking on the Wath incline near Sheffield by the Great Central Railway [9655].

At the other end of the size range, Beyer, Peacock constructed two 0-6-0 tank engines (Order 8868) for the Welshpool & Llanfair Railway, in mid-Wales. Notes by H. Guthrie in the draughtsman's book reveal that the design was based on the Glyn Valley tram engines, but was to be six-coupled, without condensing gear.(27) The engines were computed to weigh 19½ tons. There was no spark arrester and the motion was not be covered in. A bell was fitted, and there was to be steam sanding, with large boxes at both ends. Provision was to be made for the Le Chatelier counter-pressure brake to be fitted in the future, as there were four miles of 1 in 30 gradient to be faced.

The rough draft of a report on the trial run of the first of these engines has survived in the Beyer, Peacock archives and shows that new designs almost always had small snags which had to be sorted out. On the first trips in the yard at Welshpool, the hooks of the coupling gear rose when the engine was going over badly-packed sleepers, or where a change of grade occurred, and eventually disengaged, uncoupling the train. That ended trials for the first day and the hooks were modified, so that on the next day a run could be made up the line to Llanfair. Having just passed through Welshpool, the engine became derailed on a curve, and the front bogie of the following carriage dropped between the rails. When both had been re-railed, the journey was resumed and no further trouble was experienced. However, some modifications to the draw-gear apparatus were considered necessary, as well as a few other minor points.(28) If these problems were encountered in wild Wales, how much more difficult must the engine erectors have found their tasks in the remoter parts of the Empire, or other under-developed countries. These two engines remained the sole motive power on this railway throughout its working life. They were absorbed into

[Top] J.G. Robinson's 4-6-0 design for the Great Central Railway [9032].

[Lower] An "Atlantic" built by Beyer, Peacock for the Great Central [9034] at the same time.

[Below] "The Countess" as built in 1902 for the Welshpool & Llanfair Railway [8868] [photographed in 1923].

the Great Western Railway stock in the post-First World War grouping, and after the Second World War were nationalised, but they survived this and were taken over by the preservation society when this line was officially closed by British Railways and so have been saved for posterity.

In 1907 the British Mannesmann Tube Company ordered a 0-4-0 tank engine (Order 9636) with a special "Brotan" water-tube fire-box. The usual fire-box was replaced by a series of vertical tubes at each side, so that the fire could be placed in the middle, while the outsides of the tubes were covered with fire clay. This was believed to have been the first instance in this country of the use of a complete water-tube fire-box, and was intended to give better water circulation, with less maintenance, as the fire-box had no stays, etc.(29)

[Above] No. 822, originally "The Earl", with later Great Western Railway boiler, at Llanfair Caerinion in 1956. [H. Ballantyne]

[Below] The strange swelling over the boiler contains the top tube of the Brotan boiler used on this shunting engine for the British Mannesmann Tube Co. [9636].

In the export field during this period, the railways of Argentina, with 460 locomotives, provided by far the greatest volume of orders, followed by New South Wales with 230. In 1909 the Buenos Ayres & Rosario had an exceptionally heavy and powerful 4-6-2 compound tender engine built to the specifications of Livesey, Son & Henderson. There was a special semi-automatic intercepting valve so that, when the engine was in either full forward, or full reverse, it worked as a two-cylinder simple, with live steam being admitted at reduced pressure into the low pressure cylinder. In this way the engine could be driven as a simple when starting, or on heavy banks, and as a compound at other times. Twenty-six of them were ordered initially (Order 9923), followed in 1911 by ten similar, but simple, engines (Order 0200). These were typical of the bigger, heavier locomotives being ordered in large numbers at that time. (30)

[Above left] The firebox of the Brotan boiler partially completed.

[Above] The Brotan boiler without the firebox tubes in place.

[Below] The non-compound version of the 4-6-2 design for the Buenos Ayres & Rosario Railway [0200].

[Foot] The inside cylinder 4-6-0 passenger engine for the North Brabant Railway [9786], a typical British design of that period.

Ninety-two engines went to Holland, of which the North Brabant Railway had six inside-cylinder 4-6-0s (Order 9786), in 1908. These were the first six-coupled express locomotives to run in Holland. In 1910 the first 4-6-0s designed by Beyer, Peacock for the Dutch State Railways (Order 069) were built. These four-cylinder tender engines, weighing 113 tons, had fine sleek lines, and a tractive effort of 25,580lb. Repeat orders in 1911, 1912 and 1913 led to thirty engines of the class being built. These were the last express engines which Beyer, Peacock sent

to Holland and 1914 saw the end of the Company's connection with that country when it built twenty 4-6-4 tank engines for suburban work (Order 0787), again of handsome design. These weighed 93 tons, developed 20,620lb. Tractive Effort and had 6ft. 0 7/8in. coupled wheels. The twenty delivered were part of an order of 34 in hand at the outbreak of the First World War in 1914, and the last 14 were taken over by the War Department and sold instead to the Northern Railway of France, where they were operated by men of the Royal Ordnance Department.

While some markets were closing, others were opening up. In 1910, twelve 2-8-0 tender engines (Order 058) were supplied to the South Manchuria Railway, the first British-built locomotives sent to that railway. They had to be designed to withstand temperatures of 40 degrees below zero Fahrenheit, so that special care was taken with the arrangement of all the pipes.(31) In 1908, the Central Railway of Peru received three small 0-4-0 oil-burning well-tank engines (Order 9872), to be followed by many more in later years. Railways were still expanding in Africa, and in 1915 Rhodesia received six 4-8-0 tender locomotives (Order 0890), the forerunners in that country of the many Garratts which proved so outstandingly successful there.

(32)

[Facing, top] The 4-6-0 for the Dutch State Railways [069] had four cylinders, two inside and two out.

[Facing, centre] One of the Beyer, Peacock 4-6-0s for the Dutch State Railways in a typical Netherlands setting hauling the Roosendaal - Flushing express over a swing-bridge at Vlake, c. 1930.

[Facing, foot] These 4-6-4 passenger tank engines were the last of a long line of steam locomotives which Beyer, Peacock built for Holland [0787].

[Below] These powerful 2-8-0 tender engines for the South Manchuria Railway [058] were one of the few orders Beyer, Peacock obtained for Chinese railways.

[Below centre] This oil-fired well tank [9872] seems an unpromising introduction to the later trade that was to develop between Beyer, Peacock and the railways of Peru.

[Foot] These 4-8-0 tender engines were the first Beyer, Peacock sent to Rhodesia [0890].

The First World War

In the earlier months of the First World War, normal locomotive production continued at Gorton Foundry, but as such orders became scarce, munition work was accepted as well. On 18 August 1915, the works was put under complete Government control, and became almost wholly engaged in the manufacture of war material. The most detailed account of Beyer, Peacock's contribution to the war effort was given by the Chairman, Sir Vincent Caillard, in his Report to the Annual General Meeting in May 1920:

"I would now like to give you a brief account of our war-work activities, as no single firm among those not already engaged before the war in the production of war material has contributed more than we have towards the provision of necessary munitions of war, particularly in respect of heavy field artillery equipments.

"Already, before Mr. Lloyd George's appeal to the engineering industry in general and the formation of the Ministry of Munitions in June 1915, we, in co-operation with Messrs. Vickers, set about the manufacture of certain highly specialised war material, which our organisation and technical knowledge well qualified us to undertake.

"During 1915 locomotive work and munition work went on together. . . and for the three following years. . . we were almost wholly engaged upon the manufacture of munitions of war.

"The change-over to war work during a time of exceptional stress and strain reflected the greatest credit on our staff, and this was demonstrated not only by the excellence of the results obtained, but by the fact that a very large amount of completely new work was turned out without the purchase of special machinery for the same, much ingenuity being expended in devising special arrangements, and in adapting existing machines to novel machining operations. The possession of our own steel foundry proved a further valuable factor in speeding up production.

"Our record of war work i.e., equipments, etc., actually completed, comprises the following, in addition to a large number of items too varied and numerous to mention:

    1,773 howitzer equipments,
      164 bomb-throwers for ships,
      100 anti-aircraft gun carriages,
      100 gun-director towers for battleships,

and a number of railway trucks and ammunition wagons for 12-inch naval guns.

"A survey of the main items, in the chronological order, reflects the needs of those times; beginning with equipment for mobile 12-inch naval guns; then mountings for anti-aircraft guns, equipment for 18-pounders and 6-inch howitzers, 9.2-inch howitzer siege mountings, and field carriages; then gun-director towers for battleships, 6-inch and 8-inch howitzers, 35-calibre gun

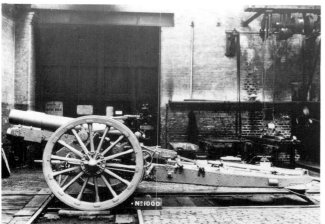

field carriages; mountings for 7.5-inch naval breech loading howitzers, and equipment for 18-pounders new type; ending with mountings for 10-inch naval bomb throwers and carriages of 5-inch 60-pounder field guns, both the latter marking very definite developments in the later stages of the war.

"Thus you will see our normal trade sacrificed to the exigencies of war, a fact which gives us more cause for pride than regret."(33)

[Top] First World War shell wagon made by Beyer, Peacock.

[Centre left] The one thousandth field howitzer made by Beyer, Peacock during the First World War.

[Centre right] 8 inch howitzer and carriage.

[Lower left] 10 inch bomb thrower.

[Lower right] A heavy howitzer with shell ready for loading.

Naval gun.

Background

The first year of the new public limited company was a record one, and saw the profit rise by more than £6,000 over the £98,758 of the previous year, which had itself been a record. A 10 per cent. dividend was paid, but orders fell in the next year, so only 5 per cent. was paid, then in 1904 and 1905 the dividend was passed on the ordinary shares. One trouble in this period was that the competition for such orders as were going was so intense that prices were forced down. Thus, in 1904, fourteen more locomotives were produced than in the previous year, but profits fell. The value of locomotives exported from Britain during the years 1902, 1903 and 1904 amounted, in round figures, to £2,300,000, £2,359,000 and £1,929,000 respectively. Beyer, Peacock decided it was better to accept orders at slight losses in order to retain the goodwill of its customers.

Trade improved, so a dividend of 10 per cent. was paid in 1906, and maintained at 7½ per cent. for the next three years, but dipped to 5 per cent. for 1910 and the next couple of years. The worst year since the new Company started was 1910, but at the Annual General Meeting it was announced that the manufacture of a new type of locomotive, the Garratt, had commenced, and that this seemed destined to have a great future. The outlook improved steadily from that time on; 1914 was another good year, with 1915 promising likewise, but unfortunately the war caused disruption. Profits fell from £109,782 in 1914 to £54,177 in the next year, but no further accounts were issued—or dividends paid—for the duration of the war. However, when all the adjustments for the costs of the war munitions had been made, a 40 per cent. dividend was paid in 1919 to cover the previous four years. During all these years, of course, dividends had to be paid on the debenture stocks, before anything could be set aside for the ordinary shareholders.

10

The Garratt Locomotive,
1907-1914

On 7 August 1907, Herbert William Garratt was appointed an inspecting engineer for the New South Wales Government Railways, which was having some engines built at Gorton Foundry. This proved to be his lucky break, because his ideas for a new type of articulated locomotive, for which he had taken out a provisional patent on 26 July that year, had been turned down by Kitson of Leeds. However, Beyer, Peacock must have seen greater possibilities in his proposals, because at the beginning of October, Garratt sent some blueprints and drawings to Manchester and S. Jackson, one of Beyer, Peacock's draughtsmen, prepared the first Garratt scheme on the ninth of that month. Early in November, Garratt moved with his family to Manchester, and the complete specification for his patent was deposited at the Patent Office on 24 January 1908.(1)

A letter written to the Great Indian Peninsular Railway in 1909, pointing out the merits of the new Garratt locomotive, said:

"You will observe that in detail there is no novelty, neither does the engine embrace any experimental and untried components. As a matter of fact, this design of locomotive embraces four leading features, the principles of which are old, and can be found in the 'Fairlie' engine introduced forty years ago, and other similar types now being presented by Locomotive Builders, but these features, as combined by Garratt, have resulted in the development of a locomotive of such striking originality and usefulness that it is a marvel to me how Fairlie—and others since who have been engaged in developing the articulated locomotive—could have missed such an obviously simple solution of reconciling a properly designed boiler of large capacity to the limits of the various loading gauges."(2)

* * * * *

H.W. Garratt was born in London on 8 June 1864. After being educated at various private schools in London, he served an apprenticeship from 1879 to 1882 in the locomotive works of the North London Railway, at Bow. Here his ability as a draughtsman was observed, and he was also an artist in his own right, for he enjoyed making sketches as well as painting in oils. A picture by him,

[Heading] The first locomotive built under H.W. Garratt's patent, order 9954, for the 2ft.-gauge Tasmanian Government Railways in 1909.

[Below] The drawing submitted in 1908 for the complete specification of H.W. Garratt's patent, drawn by S. Jackson.

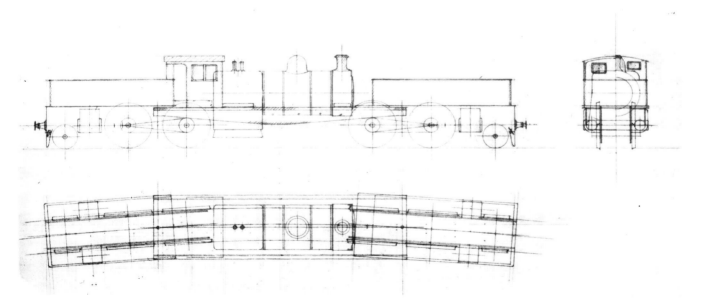

showing one of the last broad-gauge Great Western locomotives, was accepted by the Institution of Locomotive Engineers, and he himself illustrated the early brochures for his own locomotive. From Bow he went to Wm. Doxford at Sunderland, then served his time at sea as third engineer, finally making the voyage to New York, again as third engineer, in the United States Arctic relief ship **Alert**, before it left for the Arctic.

Garratt's connection with railway locomotives was renewed when Charles Douglas Fox offered him the post of inspector for some engines for the Central Argentine Railway, which were being built by Neilson in Glasgow during the first half of 1885. It was in this year that he took out his first patent—an idea for lengthening the slots in the radius links of reversing gears to allow, by an extra movement of the reversing lever, the slide valve to be moved by hand to open the port when an engine had stopped at dead centre.(3) Later he patented a method of keeping sand dry in sand boxes, by building the boxes partly inside the smokebox. When filling them in this position, sand would not be spilt all over the valve motion,(4) as so often happened. He also had ideas for a spark extinguisher, as well as an improved point lock and indicator, coupled to the distant signal. Then, until early 1889, he worked for A.M. Rendel, as inspector of railway material, before spending a few months on the London & South Western Railway, in conjunction with the Vacuum Brake Company. In this way he had gained a wide knowledge of locomotive design, as well as practical experience in their construction, and in the maintenance of steam engines generally.

The next part of his career was to give Garratt a great insight into operating railways in difficult country, for in April 1889 he was appointed temporary head draughtsman on the Central Argentine Railway. He was subsequently put in charge of the installation of the vacuum brake on the engines and stock and also of the Pintsch system of gas lighting for the carriages and workshops. During a fitters' strike at Rosario he looked after the works and three years later accepted the post of District Officer in charge of the running sheds at Pergamino, where in June 1896, he managed to keep his engines running during a strike of drivers, even though it meant wearing arms for protection. He ought to have been granted leave every three years, but such was the pressure of work that it was not until he had been in the Argentine for eight years that he returned to England in February 1897. He was asked to inspect some engines being built in England and had his leave extended. Garratt decided to seize the opportunity of returning in a boat on which his younger brother was engineer, but this unfortunately delayed him, and he arrived back late. The new General Manager dismissed him, even though he recognised that Garratt had done a good job.

Garratt's next appointment was in 1900, as Locomotive Superintendent with the Cuban Central Railways. He reorganised the workshops and was very popular with the men, but the management ordered him to place a young person straight from his apprenticeship in England as Second Foreman in the Concha shops, and demote the Spaniard already holding the post. Garratt protested and decided it was best to accept a financial settlement and resign. The man in question was a failure in Cuba, and returned to England. He was dismissed a second time after proving equally useless on the Algeciras Railway!

Garratt followed this in March 1902 with a one-year appointment on the Lagos Government Railway, which he

H.W. GARRATT, 1864 - 1913.
[This photograph was taken while he was in Lagos.]

[Below] The Lagos Government Railway 2-6-0 being assembled under the supervision of H.W. Garratt in the record time of 32 hours. [Garratt archives]

found in a chaotic state. Only three engines could move; no spare parts had been ordered from England, and it was feared that the railway might have to stop altogether. Yet, by dint of extraordinary exertions, Garratt was able to pull things together so that within seven weeks he was able to inform the Traffic Superintendent that the full train service could be resumed. Some new engines arrived from England and Garratt supervised their erection, and one was finished in the record time of 32 working hours. He also reorganised the locomotive department so that considerable savings were made in running expenses. Unfortunately the climate did not suit him, and the Crown Agents were not willing to renew his appointment, although he had worked on for an extra three months. He had not been well in the Argentine either, so seems to have had a history of indifferent health.

From Lagos he returned home sick, but was soon abroad again, this time in 1904 to the Lima Railways in Peru, as Resident Engineer and Locomotive Superintendent. Unfortunately, this railway was taken over and electrified, so his services were no longer needed and he was given a first-class passage home to England. However, it will be seen that Garratt had acquired considerable experience of operating railways of many different types, under many different conditions, and well knew the problems which locomotive superintendents had to face abroad with poorly-laid track, on sharp curves, and steep gradients. His book of press cuttings shows that he had been interested in the design of articulated locomotives since at least 1900 and had studied the various types. He also had first hand experience of the difficulties of raising steam in the boilers then fitted to most narrow-gauge engines, with fireboxes restricted in width by the driving wheels. He knew, too, how vital it was for the drivers to have a clear view of the road ahead, particularly on lines laid in remote areas, where animals or other obstructions might have blocked the running track. All these points were borne in mind when he was planning his own locomotive.(5)

The new type of locomotive which Garratt conceived had a pair of bogies which were really locomotives without boilers. The fuel bunkers and water tanks were superimposed on these bogies, while the boiler was mounted on a frame slung between them. Garratt's original drawings show an 0-4-0 + 0-4-0, with large-diameter driving wheels, powered by cylinders at the inner ends of the bogies. The wheels were set well clear of the boiler, which could thus be dropped low in the frames to give an unusually low centre of gravity. At each end of the boiler cradle were placed driving cabs, so that the engineman would have a clear view of the road ahead; his engine was thus a perfect "double-ender", and could travel equally well in either direction. How did his ideas differ from other existing articulated locomotives, and why were they so great an improvement?

The history of the articulated locomotive may be traced back almost to the start of rail transport, for in 1815 one of the Wylam locomotives was mounted on eight wheels, four of which were on a swivelling truck. The Semmering trials of 1851 marked the real beginning of the development of articulated engines, because the line through the pass of that name in Austria abounded in steep inclines, sharp curves, tunnels and lofty double-deck viaducts.(6) Various ingenious ideas were patented, and tried, to produce a locomotive with many coupled wheels on a flexible base, but by 1900 three main types had emerged, the Fairlie,

[Above] A tramway type of Fairlie locomotive built for the Saxon State Railways [Garratt archives]

[Below] An 0-6-0 + 0-6-0 Mallet compound locomotive built by the American Locomotive Co. for the Central Railway of Brazil. [Garratt archives]

[Below] These two drawings were prepared by H.W. Garratt to show how his engine would look. He envisaged a girder frame to support the boiler, and arranged a cab at both ends to give the driver a better view as the engine could travel equally well in either direction. The large driving wheels show that he realised his engine would be capable of high speeds.   [Garratt archives]

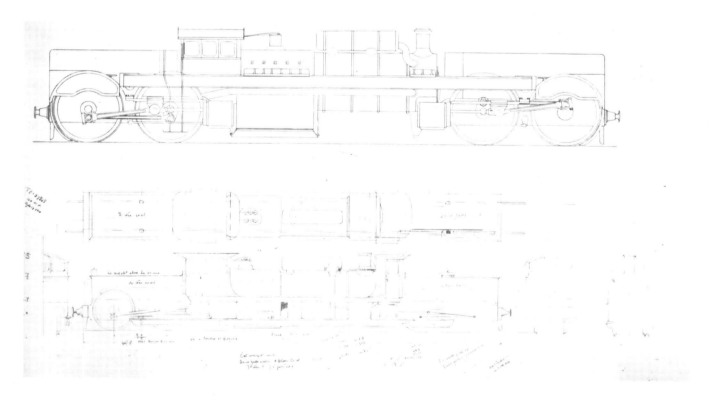

the Meyer, and a semi-articulated type, the Mallet, all named after their originators.

The Mallet(7) locomotive had one set of driving wheels mounted in the main frames, underneath the firebox, and further forward, underneath the boiler barrel, was a second frame, with its own cylinders and driving gear, pivoted at its rear end to the fixed frame, and having a sliding support for the boiler barrel. The type originated in France around 1889, and by 1900 was very popular, but at this time it was still only a slow-moving goods engine with, generally, only driving wheels and no carrying or guiding wheels. The diameter of the wheels was restricted by the need to place the firebox between or above them, and of course the converse was true, the boiler being restricted by the wheels. This also applied to the full articulated types, the Fairlie and the Meyer, where the power bogies were placed underneath the boilers.

By placing a bogie at each end of his boiler, Garratt realised that the diameter of the wheels could be increased, so that his locomotive would be capable of reaching much higher speeds, but this would not have been enough on its own because the bogies would have lacked stability, so Garratt planned a feature unique to his system. To quote from his patent:

> "The coal and water tanks are principally carried on and so form part of the self-driven bogie. . . thus tending to keep the bogies steady as against the disturbing forces of the steam acting on the pistons, which in previous double-bogie engines has caused the bogies to have a wriggling movement. especially at high speeds."

How effective this was may be seen in the case of the Garratts built for South Africa in the 1920s, which were reaching speeds of over 50 miles per hour, while the Mallets were unsafe at 30. The Fairlie type also lacked stability at high speed.(8)

By placing his fuel and water tanks on the bogies, Garratt not only lessened the strains and forces on the pivots, but completely altered the existing concept of boiler design. While still retaining the basic locomotive type, his design of engine enabled the boiler to be developed to almost the maximum permitted by the loading gauge. The fireboxes on Mallets had to be either narrow, or shallow, to fit them in between, or over, the driving wheels, and this also applied to the Meyer in its original form, the bogies being connected, with the boiler, tanks, bunker and cab mounted on a single frame over them. While the Fairlie(9) could have a deep firebox, the width was limited because the double-ended boiler had to be fired from the side. The water tanks and fuel bunkers also limited the diameter of the boilers on both Fairlie and Meyer. In 1894 Kitson of Leeds improved the original Meyer concept by separating the bogies and pivoting them individually under the boiler frame.(10) This gave the Meyer a new lease of life, because the firebox could be dropped almost to rail level, but the width was still restricted by the water tanks carried at the sides.

The Garratt single boiler and firebox was much cheaper to construct and maintain than the double one of the Fairlie, and was restricted in width only by the carrying frame and steam pipes passing along the sides. The firebox could be dropped almost to rail level and was easily accessible for washing out and removing ashes from the ashpan. The diameter of the boiler barrel could approach the limits of the loading gauge, and it could remain low, not only to keep the centre of gravity low, but also to provide a better view from the cab, and give adequate height to the steam dome and chimney. With the large diameter, a greater number of tubes could be fitted inside and, just as important, the barrel could be shorter. The boilers on some Mallet locomotives had become excessively long, with resulting loss in efficiency. The evaporative power of boiler tubes decreases rapidly with length, and a number of short tubes is more efficient than fewer tubes of greater length, giving the same area of heating surface. Also, with long tubes, an excessive draught is needed in the firebox, which can only be obtained by a corresponding increase of back pressure in the cylinders.

The reduced length of the Garratt boiler had an extra advantage over both the Mallet and Fairlie on lines with steep gradients, because the extreme variations in water level did not cause the top of the firebox or the ends of the tubes to become exposed. So Garratt realised that the boilers of his new design would be safer, as well as steaming more freely, which his experience on railways abroad had taught him was very necessary. He also realised that his design would give a more stable engine, because the boiler frame did not stretch beyond the pivot centres. On the Mallet, the front half of the boiler stretched beyond the fixed frames and so hung over the outside edge on curves. This also happened with the tanks and bunkers on the other articulated designs. Garratt's locomotive had

> "The very great advantage that the centre line of the whole length of the central portion, when so travelling round curves, forms a chord of the circle, which is the centre line of the rails forming the said curve".(11)

[Below] A combined rack and adhesion locomotive built by Kitson on the Kitson-Meyer principle of articulation for the Transandine Railway in 1907.

Typical boilers for Garratt locomotives in their frames.

The sharper the curve the more other articulated loco-motives hung over the outside, while Garratts moved inside. In this way the whole of his engine was inherently more stable than any other existing articulated type. To sum up, Garratt had evolved a design which was capable of having a boiler of ample dimensions, yet with free-steaming characteristics, which had the potential of travel-ling at high speed, not only through the possibility of having large-diameter wheels, but was more stable with the fuel and water tanks situated on the bogies, and which was inherently a better system of articulation through the way in which the various units were linked together.

The Design Office at Gorton Foundry had been aware for a long time of the demand for articulated locomotives, and had had one brief excursion into this field with the back-to-back engines for the Inter-Oceanic Railway. In the 1890s, schemes were produced for one simple and three compound Fairlies, two of these being prepared for the Mogyana Railway. A "modified Fairlie", with two separate boilers, was proposed for the Burma Railways, later a major customer for Garratts. Early in the 20th century, three designs for Mallets were prepared and, in April 1907, two slightly different schemes for a 2ft.-gauge Mallet locomotive were sent to the Tasmanian Govern-ment Railways; these were destined to play a vital role in the development of the Garratt (Schemes 70249, 70250).

While these Mallet schemes were being discussed in Tasmania, a 2ft.-gauge 0-4-0 + 0-4-0 Fairlie scheme (No. 71101) was prepared for the New South Wales Government Railways. This engine is shown with only one firehole, a fault corrected forty years earlier! The date for this drawing is July 1907, the same month as Garratt deposited his Provisional Specification. Either Garratt heard about these proposals through his New South Wales connections or he may have seen them in the Drawing Office when he had to go to Gorton, but he realised that here was his golden opportunity to introduce his new loco-motive and, three months later, the first Garratt scheme (No. 71411) was prepared. This obviously was a replace-ment for the Fairlie scheme, for it had the same wheel arrangement, and the same cylinder and wheel dimen-sions. A year later, a larger version for a New South Wales 2ft. 6in.-gauge system (Scheme 73453) was pre-pared, but no engines were ever built.

Meanwhile, there must have been further correspon-dence with the Tasmanian Government Railways, for in April 1908 a slightly heavier version of the New South Wales first Garratt scheme (No. 72537) was despatched to them. Both these designs followed Garratt's original concept, with the cylinders at the inner ends of the bogies. This latest scheme had the same wheel diameter as the Mallet proposal, and the same stroke, 16in, but the Garratt was to be a simple, with all four cylinders 10in. bore. This was not accepted by the people in Tasmania, who wanted a compound engine. Accordingly, a modified design was sent in January 1909 (Scheme 73850); on this the rear bogie had the 11in. high-pressure cylinders, and the front bogie the 17in. diameter low-pressure cylinders. Both these dimensions were the same as those in the larger Mallet proposal. Using larger cylinders on the front bogie meant that the boiler frame had to be cranked to clear them. Boiler pressures ranged from 180lb. for the Mallet, 160lb. for the simple, and 195lb. for the compound Garratt. The designs show the great advantage of the Garratt principle. The firebox on the Mallet was long, narrow and shallow, for it had to be perched above the driving wheels. The Garratt firebox was short, broad and deep, with 10 sq. ft. greater heating surface, and nearly 3 sq. ft. larger grate area. The Garratt boiler was shorter, but the surface area of the tubes remained almost the same, because their number was increased from 152 to 170, of larger diameter.

A new locomotive was needed, because there was a motive-power crisis on the 2ft.-gauge North East Dundas Tramway, which carried lead ore from the Hercules Mine to the smelters at Zeehan. Their two Sharp Stewart locomotives were very small and could not handle the traffic adequately, for they could haul only twenty tons. They also had a Hagans 2-6-4-0 tank, a large German-built engine which had two cylinders driving the main set of wheels, and a system of links to power the rear wheels from the

same cylinders.(12) This engine weighed 40 tons and, under favourable weather conditions, could haul 90 tons up the worst gradients, but it knocked the line to pieces. The General Manager decided to compromise and order something midway between a locomotive having the hauling power of the Hagans, which the Mechanical Engineer wanted, and a light locomotive which the Permanent Way Engineer wanted because it would not damage the track. Therefore, on 29 January 1909, the Tasmanian Government Railways ordered one Garratt locomotive and followed that in March with a second (Order 9954).

While these discussions were in progress with Tasmania, other schemes were in hand, and the second one, drawn up in February 1908, shows an 0-6-0 + 0-6-0 standard-gauge engine, with cylinders at the outer ends of the bogies, and steam reversing gear (Schemes 72372 and 72538), for the Commonwealth Oil Corporation, in New South Wales. The total length would have been 61ft. and the weight, empty, 72 tons. In July of that year, a slightly larger 0-6-0 + 0-6-0 scheme (No. 73117) was prepared for the 5ft. 3in.-gauge Central Railway of Brazil, and

[Below] S. Jackson's scheme 70250 for a Mallet compound locomotive for the 2ft.-gauge Tasmanian Government Railways in 1907.

[Foot] The first Garratt scheme, [71411] prepared for the New South Wales Government Railway in 1908.

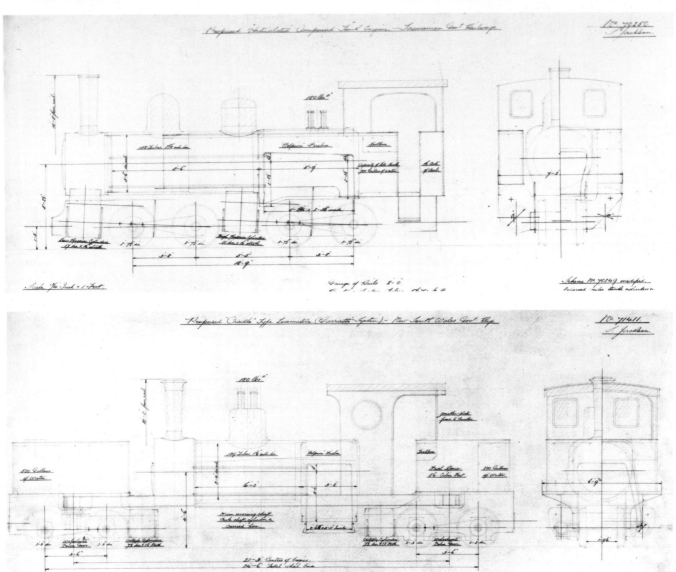

a compound Mallet (Scheme 73105) was submitted at the same time. Designs for a Meyer (Scheme 73412) and a Garratt (Scheme 73416) were sent to the Anglo-Chilean Nitrate Railway, while the Burma Railways had plans for Fairlies (Scheme 73592) and Mallets (Scheme 74653) to compare with Garratts (Schemes 73577 and 74654).

In June, Garratt was granted his patent, so that a formal agreement could be drawn up between him and Beyer, Peacock to settle the terms of royalties, licences, etc. This agreement, which was signed on 18 September 1908, has not survived, but, from later documents, it is clear that Garratt retained the English patent himself, because he, and on his death his executors, paid all the patent fees. On the foreign patents, which included Australia, Belgium, Canada, France, Germany, Italy, India, Japan, and Russia, the costs were divided equally between Beyer, Peacock and himself. He, and his executors, received a fee of £2 per ton on all engines built by Beyer, Peacock, and probably also on those built under licence.(13) Beyer, Peacock was granted sole rights of manufacture in this country.

Having such a close relationship with Beyer, Peacock, Garratt's post as Inspector for the New South Wales Government (checking on work done at Gorton Foundry) would sooner or later have put him in an impossible position. A problem arose with the Consulting Engineer, Mr. Davis, over some drawings, and, on 31 August 1908,

Garratt resigned his position to devote all his time to developing his new locomotive. A four-page brochure was printed to explain the features of this new design, and various railway companies were approached. Garratt set up an office in Albert Road, Levenshulme, near Gorton, and had paper printed with his own letter heading. In 1908 a scheme was prepared for converting Beyer, Peacock's own 1ft. 6in.-gauge works shunter into an 0-4-0 + 0-4-0 Garratt, with cylinders at the inner ends of the bogies (Scheme 73120). Then, in April 1909, the Drawing Office was ordered to get out complete drawings and estimates for a standard-gauge Garratt which could be used as a demonstration engine to help convince engineers of the practicability of the design.(14)

TELEGRAMS: "LOCOMOTIVE, LEVENSHULME."

GARRATT'S PATENT LOCOMOTIVES.

HERBERT W. GARRATT, M.I.MECH.E.

LOCOMOTIVE ENGINEER.

LEVENSHULME, MANCHESTER.

Agents:
GT. BRITAIN, BEYER PEACOCK & CO., LTD. MANCHESTER.
U.S. AND CANADA, THE BALDWIN LOCOMOTIVE WORKS, PHILADELPHIA, PA.
GERMANY, HENSCHEL & SOHN, CASSEL.
BELGIUM, SOC. ST. LEONARD, LIEGE.

H.W. Garratt's Visiting Card. [Garratt archives]

The boiler unit of the first Garratt locomotive being assembled at Gorton. [Garratt archives]

By the end of 1909, over 45 different schemes for Garratts had been prepared, ranging from four- to eight-coupled engines, and 1ft. 6in. to 5ft. 6in.-gauges, including an 0-6-0 + 0-6-0 for English railways (Scheme 74334). In order to help introduce this type of locomotive more quickly, it was proposed that two or three 0-8-0 + 0-8-0s (Scheme 74174) be built for the South Manchuria Railway. One was to be sent there free on trial for two or three months

> "on the understanding that if that one fulfils the conditions we claim for it, they place an order with us for two more engines at the same price as the one delivered".(15)

These engines would have had 4ft. 2in. diameter wheels, 20 x 26in. cylinders, 143.5 tons weight and 63,650lb Tractive Effort. A year later a 3ft. 6in.-gauge design was prepared for what was then the Central South African Railway for another 0-8-0 + 0-8-0 Garratt of even more ambitious design (Scheme 76546), with 4ft. wheels, 22 x 26in. cylinders, 159 tons weight and 80,220lb. Tractive Effort. Years of design and development were to pass before any were built of that size and power, and, looking back on the experience subsequently gained, it was fortunate that orders were not placed in 1909/10 for these two designs.

The first of the Tasmanian Garratts was assembled on 6 August 1909, and tried in steam on 17 August, followed soon after by the second. They were tested on a short length of track laid out in the yard at Gorton before being shipped early in October. The compound design had led to certain complications, such as a special starting valve and pipes to admit high-pressure steam to the front cylinders and other more complicated pipe work. Some teething troubles were found when they were first tried in Tasmania, but these were very minor considering this was a brand new design. Industrial troubles at the Hercules Mine had cut down the amount of traffic on the Zeehan and Williamsford Tramway, so that the engines had not been fully tested when a report was sent to Beyer, Peacock in March 1910.

The engine units of the first Garratt locomotive being assembled at Gorton. The difference in size of the high-pressure cylinder [closest] and the low-pressure cylinder can be appreciated. [Garratt archives]

"Mr. Deeble advised me that on the one set of tests he was able to make, the 'Garratt' slipped very badly with 50 tons, and that 40 to 45 tons appears to be the maximum load for regular use. Mr. Deeble told me that this was due to no fault of yours, but that the engines were hauling as big a load as he could expect from the adhesion. . . Mr. Deeble is now looking into the question of putting some additional weight on the Garratt Locos. so as to increase the adhesion and bring the available load up to 50 tons. You must bear in mind considering this question, that Zeehan is one of the wettest and mistiest districts in Tasmania, and the rails are, therefore, very greasy. The only criticism Mr. Deeble had to offer concerned the regulator valve. . . which is very liable to stick at awkward moments. . .

"The best testimonial you could have I think, however, is the fact that Mr. Deeble is now in communication with you for a 3ft. 6in.-gauge 'Garratt' Loco. as this shows the two he has are giving every satisfaction.

The first Garratt locomotive being tested in the yard of Gorton Foundry. [Garratt archives]

Another serious defect mentioned in the report of 1911 was that of slipping. Although the boiler was not steaming at full pressure, the rails were dry, and sand was applied liberally, the rear bogies were seen to slip once and the front wheels slipped frequently. When the engine was on a 1 in 23 grade, the front tank could be empty, while the tank under the boiler was full and there was 12in. of water in the rear tank. Nearly two tons weight would be lost when the front tank was completely empty and it seemed that the front bogie was not heavy enough to maintain adhesion. It has been suggested recently that one problem was the excessive flange friction of the wheels on the trucks, caused by the steep gradients, sharp curves and longer trains which the Garratt ought to have been able to haul.(22) This could have been so severe on this railway that doubling the tractive effort would have given only a 50 per cent. increase in train load, which is what in fact seems to have happened.

In spite of this inauspicious start, the Darjeeling-Himalayan Garratt, having been modified slightly, was made to work satisfactorily. A letter written in November 1922 by W. Wakefield, who had erected the South African Garratts and had then been sent to India, said:

"In visiting the North Western Railway of India headquarters at Lahore, I found a good number of Officers and men who did not seem to know much about the Garratt Locomotive. I discussed with the officers re the Garratts in South Africa and the good work these engines were doing, and also showed them in print test results. Afterwards they seemed to favour the Garratt Locomotive, but some of them asked me why the Darjeeling Himalayan Garratt was a failure, and in consequence the whole of the Indian Railways were against adopting the Garratt Locomotive. I made it a point of duty on hearing this to proceed direct to the Darjeeling Himalayan Railway and find out about this from the Chief Mechanical Engineer, Mr. Kirby. Mr. Kirby told me that ever since he took over the post of Chief Mechanical Engineer it was his first duty to put this Garratt Locomotive into proper working order, which he has done and has had the engine in service continually He has had many Railway Engineers calling on him to see the Garratt at work. He has told them that the Garratt is a perfect engine and doing very well."(23)

Once it was in proper order, the engine seems to have worked quite well, although it retained its reputation for slipping. It had a long life and was not withdrawn until 1954. Considering the very difficult conditions for which it was designed, and also the fact that it was only the second type to use the Garratt principle, it is remarkable that there were so few difficulties and that it lasted so long.

At the Annual General Meeting in March 1911, the Chairman said he believed that the Garratt design was:

"destined to have a good future, and, as we hope, to replace all other existing types of articulated locomotives whenever it may meet them in open competition. It requires not test of time and experience owing to a new principle being involved, but rather constitutes a new application of sound proved and well-tried mechanical principles and it is this fact which is at the base of our confidence in its success. . . Probably few innovations in locomotive practice have met with so speedy recognition and appreciation."(24)

A new brochure explaining the features of the Garratt was produced that year, and it included pictures painted by Garratt to show what a larger version would look like. Garratt himself returned to London and took out his patent for mounting guns on locomotives but continued to take an active part in the development of his locomotive. He went back to Gorton to take photographs of later types when they were being tested. He also went to Belgium and photographed the trials of the Garratt for the Congo Railway, which had a special type of oil-fired boiler. Surviving papers show that he was involved with the order for the 0-6-0 + 0-6-0 engines (Order 0588) which were built in 1913 for the Arakan Flotilla Co., Burma, which set them to work on the Buthidaung-Maungdaw Tramway.(25)

[Above] H.W. Garratt's letter heading incorporating his painting of how he envisaged a larger version of his engine would look.
[Garratt archives]

[Below] The only tramway type of Garratt built by Beyer, Peacock was supplied to the Arakan Flotilla Company for the Buthidaung-Maungdaw Tramway [0588].

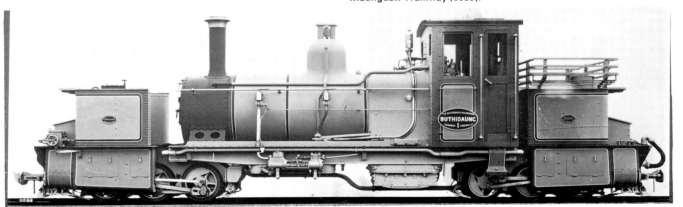

They were the only tramway type Garratts built by Beyer, Peacock, and were the smallest Garratts it ever built, though the Société Saint Léonard of Liége had built smaller ones under licence for the 60cm. Chemins de Fer Vicinaux du Mayumbe (Congo Belge), in 1911. In 1913 Garratt was certain that an order would be received from the Great Indian Peninsular Railway and he was hoping for one from the Bengal Nagpur Railway too. His early death, on 25 September 1913, at the age of 49, prevented him seeing the full development of his locomotive, but by that time important orders had been constructed already.

In 1911, the Western Australian Government Railways, whose Mr. Hume presumably had seen the Tasmanian Garratts at work, ordered six 2-6-0 + 0-6-2 engines (Order 0246) for their 3ft. 6in.-gauge lines, to work over a part with gradients of 1 in 22 and curves of 328ft. radius. Six different types of exhaust-pipe nozzle were tried, to see which gave the best results. The findings were communicated to Beyer, Peacock in September 1912,(26) with the request that the best type be fitted to the follow-up order for seven more (Order 0557), which were under construction at Gorton. The first six were unsuperheated, but the next seven, which were made in 1913, had superheaters and slightly increased coal capacity. On these later engines, in accordance with the practice prevailing at the time, the boiler pressure was reduced from 175 to 160lb. per sq.in. and so, to keep the tractive effort unchanged, the cylinders were increased from 12½ to 13¼in. bore x 20in. stroke. These alterations, plus an extra ton of coal, raised the maximum axle load to 9.35 tons, and the total weight to 69.8 tons. The railway authorities were well satisfied, since seventeen years later they built in their own workshops ten more locomotives of this type, with the boiler pressure restored to 175lb. per sq.in., and a slightly larger grate area, giving 26,775lb. Tractive Effort. All the first six Garratts survived until 1947, and the last of them was not withdrawn until 1955, so they had remarkably long lives.

The next two types of Garratts also had long lives, although they too had steaming troubles at first. So satisfied with his 2ft.-gauge Garratts was W.R. Deeble in Tasmania, that in 1912 he ordered two more designs, this time for his 3ft. 6in.-gauge lines.(27) Both classes had identical boilers, but the ''L'' class (Order 0304) consisted of two engines with 2-6-2 + 2-6-2 wheel arrangement and 3ft. 6in. coupled wheels, designed for goods traffic. These engines, with their tractive effort of 32,050lb., were 60 per cent. more powerful than the largest ordinary type of goods locomotive. But it was the ''M'' class Garratts (Order 0303) which were more interesting, for they were the first Garratts specially designed for main-line passenger service. The adoption of corridor carriages for the express trains had the effect of doubling the weight to be hauled, while the restrictions of the maximum axle load and fixed wheel-base precluded an ordinary type of locomotive.

The ''M'' class Garratts were designed with a 4-4-2 + 2-4-4 wheel arrangement and 5ft.-diameter driving wheels. Each engine unit had four cylinders, two outside and two inside the frames. The Walschaert's valve gear on the outside cylinders also operated the valves of the adjacent inside cylinders by means of simple transverse levers. They were the only eight-cylinder Garratts ever built. At first none of these engines steamed well and alterations had to be carried out to the exhaust pipe, chimney and superheater. The last engine was undergoing these modifications when R.S. York of the Schmidt Superheating Company Ltd. wrote in December 1912:

[Below] One of the first Garratts for the Western Australian Government Railways [0246] undergoing tests at Gorton. The bowler-hatted person leaning on the locomotive is probably H.W. Garratt.

[Foot] The Tasmanian Government Railwlays 3ft. 6in.-gauge Garratt [0304] for goods traffic.

[Above] The "Atlantic" Garratt for the Tasmanian Government Railways [0303].

[Below] H.W. Garratt photographed one of the "Atlantic" Garratts for the Tasmanian Government Railways while it was being assembled at Gorton Foundry.　　　　　　　　　[Garrat archives]

"The three engines that have been altered steam remarkably freely—superheat well up to 650°F, run very freely, draw very little ash into the smokebox, and, although no spark-arresters have been fitted since the alterations, throw practically nothing from the chimney. With smokebox arrangements as supplied by Beyer, Peacock & Co. the steam pressure could not be maintained even with the injector shut off, and, when put on, the pressure rapidly fell, necessitating stopping every few miles when working up heavy grades in order to get steam and water into the boiler. The highest superheat temperature that could be obtained was about 500°F."(28)

Perhaps it was lucky that the first Garratt was a compound so that the system of articulation could be proved without complication of the different strengths of the exhaust beats from four, or more, high-pressure cylinders set so far apart. An extract from the Launceston **Examiner** of 30 November 1912 shows that one of the altered express engines performed very well and put up a new speed record for their 3ft. 6in.-gauge.

"Behind her was a train which was more in length than the platform could accommodate. It was at the least double the load of the average express. 'Baby Bliss' had pulled it at something like double the average of express speed, and with a consumption of only about 25 per cent. more coal. . . Mr. Cameron (a member of Parliament) went on to express the most unqualified admiration of the engine and its performance. He said he had found the stoking easy, while in the matter of haulage, capacity, speed and steadiness, the engine had shown that, with the alterations made, it could do great work. On curves it behaved splendidly.

"There is no question, said Mr. Whitsitt, about the success of the engine. In some parts of the journey we did 50 or 55 miles an hour, and so steady was she that I would have been quite prepared to take the curves at the same speed if we had been allowed to. We had to keep a quarter of an hour behind the ordinary express, and consequently had to dawdle and stop!"(29)

Deeble was equally satisfied with his new engines, and their performance did much to establish the Garratt as a highly versatile type of locomotive, suitable for a wide range of duties. These engines were finally withdrawn in 1951.

The steaming troubles seem to have been overcome on the next Garratt engines, which were two 4-6-0 + 0-6-4 engines (Order 0322) built in 1912 for the Mogyana Railway. They were the first Garratts sent to South America, the first for the metre-gauge, and were the only ones built by Beyer, Peacock with this wheel arrangement. They were greeted with immediate acclaim on their arrival:

"Both the engines in question were erected with great rapidity, and in the words of one of the Railway Officials 'They went together like clocks'. Both were put under steam, and they ran about the yard for a day or two. In under a week the first engine was out on the road hauling a freight train of 185 tons. In this run she took a bank of 19 kilometres of 3% (1 in 33) without a let-up, in magnificent shape. She was brought in after this run, washed out, and then put on their rapid sleeping train. The load was only 60 tons but the coaches are brand new and ride stiff. However, in the whole trip she made 410 kilometres at an average speed of between 41 and 42 kilometres per hour. In this run she had the bad 19 kilometres to negotiate. The Locomotive Superintendent told the writer that she made well over 60 kilometres per hour in patches and rode very easily, though the curves on this part of the road are the worst on the line. . . The Loco. Super. said that she was heavy on coal and water, but this was due to the driver and fireman not knowing her yet. He said that she was blowing off most of the time, however hard they worked her. . .

"The second engine, after running around the yard for about a week, was put on a freight train and hauled 214 tons with ease."(30)

This letter is completely different in tone from the earlier ones about the other Garratts. These engines worked well on their mixed traffic duties and reached speeds of 40 m.p.h. on very light track. Three more were supplied in 1914 which were superheated, with reduced boiler pressure and increased cylinder diameter. Both classes had 3ft. 9in.-diameter driving wheels. All these engines were still running in 1947, and probably for some time after that, until they were replaced by diesels.

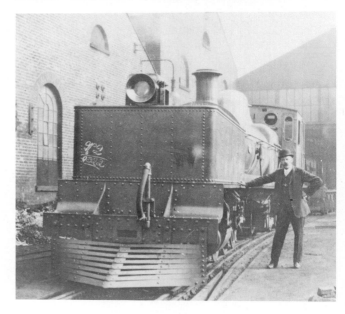

[Above] One of the Mogyana Garratts photographed by H.W. Garratt at Gorton Foundry while it was being tested. [Garratt archives]

[Below] The only 4-6-0 + 0-6-4 Garratt built by Beyer, Peacock was supplied to the Mogyana Railway [0322] in 1912.

[Foot] The metre gauge 2-6-0 + 0-6-2 Garratt for the San Paulo Railway [0537].

148

In 1913, another Brazilian railway, the San Paulo, ordered a Garratt (Order 0537) for its metre-gauge line. The maximum gradient of the Bragantina branch was 1 in 30, with the sharpest curve having a radius of 5½ chains. This line was 126km. long, with a further branch of 31km. off it. The Garratt was wanted for mixed traffic work. Tests on a 1 in 35 gradient showed that the 2-6-0 + 0-6-2 Garratt was more economical than an earlier Beyer, Peacock 4-6-0. The Garratt hauled 270 tons consuming 40lb. of fuel per mile, while the other locomotive hauled 120 tons using 36lb. The Locomotive Superintendent, C.R.Hillman, was very pleased with this engine and, in 1915, Beyer, Peacock received a letter saying:

> "The narrow-gauge Garratt is doing excellent service and is pulling her full load regularly. There is a boom in traffic on this section at present and if it were not for this engine the Railway would be hard put to it for power. If as they think possible this branch continues to do such good business, we think it is possible that a further order for a Garratt may be looked for in the future as Mr. Hillman is still of the same opinion — only strengthened — that this is the only type of locomotive for him for heavy traffic."(31)

The second order did not materialise until 1936, when an identical engine was built for this particular branch line.(32) Both engines continued to give good service until after the Second World War.

Before the entire works was switched to producing armaments for the First World War, three Garratts were built (Order 0810) for the 5ft. 3in. lines of the San Paulo Railway. This railway played an important part in the development of the State of that name, because it provided the vital link between the important city of Sao Paulo and the port of Santos. This line presented a formidable engineering problem in the early days of construction, as it was necessary to carry the railway over the range of mountains known as the Serra do Mar, involving a rise of some 2,625ft. in a distance of 7 miles. The escarpment was climbed by two cable railways, with gradients of 1 in 10 and 1 in 12½, on which small 0-4-0 tram engines provided additional braking and power. The section of the railway from the harbour at Santos to the foot of the inclines at Piassagueira had particularly light bridges, thus imposing a low axle-load. Yet traffic had developed so that it had become necessary to haul trains of 1,000 tons over this section.

To avoid overloading the bridges, a 2-4-0 + 0-4-2 Garratt design was produced, with 5ft.-diameter driving wheels. The wheelbase was spread over 47ft. 10in., which proved the salvation of these engines. The line from Santos to Piassagueira was only 19km. long, and perfectly level so Garratts would not normally have been necessary, but they were chosen because their weight was distributed over a large area. The engines, when finally built, worked out at 2 tons per bogie heavier than the specification.

> "When this became known to the Resident Engineer, he immediately insisted on this surplus weight being taken off, saying that the two weak bridges on this section would not stand it. Mr. Hillman was therefore compelled to divide off his tanks up into compartments in order to decrease their capacity, and he also carried less coal. The consequence is that these engines, even with 50 cars instead of their full load of 70 cars, have to take water at an intermediate station which means delays in traffic. It is a pity that this has occurred, as it has made a perfect engine imperfect."(33)

These 2-4-0 + 0-4-2 Garratts for the San Paulo Railway (0810) proved to be very successful engines after an inauspicious start.

However, Hillman ordered further deflection tests, because someone had remarked that more deflection was noticed when a fully-loaded 40-ton wagon was in the middle of the bridge than when a fully loaded Garratt was in a similar position. By April 1916 this was confirmed, and the Garratts were soon running with their full load of fuel and water, and also hauling their full trains.

> "The Sectional Locomotive Supt. asked us to make a point of telling you that during the 25 years he has worked with this Railway he has never had to deal with such fine engines as these 3 Garratts. He is most enthusiastic about them, and if given any encouragement whatsoever insists on showing off their points to all and sundry."[34]

These engines continually shuttled back and forth on their line, working shifts and often making seven or eight round trips a day, until they were replaced by diesels in 1950.

In the period 1908-1914, nine different designs of Garratts had been delivered by Beyer, Peacock covering seven wheel arrangements, and for five track gauges—a total of thirty-one locomotives.

The rear of one of the Buthidaung-Maungdaw Tramway Garratts.

11

The South African Garratts,
1915-1927

The First World War caused the designing and building of three different types of Garratts for the South African Railways to come to a halt. In 1915, preparation had started on the working drawings for a heavy 3ft. 6in. gauge 2-6-0 + 0-6-2 (Order 0941), and it was hoped to finish three 2ft. gauge 2-6-0 + 0-6-2s (Order 01060) by May 1916.(1) In the event, these three engines were not completed until November 1919, by which time a start had been made on the working drawings of the third design (Order 0942) for a 2-6-2 + 2-6-2 that was to be lighter and less powerful than the other 3ft. 6in. gauge one. The two larger engines were finished in November 1920, and March 1921, respectively. These orders proved to be among the most crucial ever received by Beyer, Peacock, for the eventual success of the largest type drew the attention of locomotive engineers to the great potential of the design, and also brought Cyril Williams from South Africa to England to become the chief salesman and advocate for the Garratt.

Beyer, Peacock sent W. Wakefield to South Africa to supervise the erection and trials of all these Garratts and his reports reveal how they triumphed over their critics. The three narrow gauge engines were the first to arrive and therefore the first which Wakefield had to erect.

[Heading] The "GA" Garratt [0941] for the South African Railways and "Dot" [6868], the largest and smallest locomotives built at Gorton Foundry up to 1920.

[Below] The first Garratt to work on the South African Railways was the 2ft. gauge 2-6-0 + 0-6-2 type [01060].

"The first trial of these engines was carried out in the presence of five senior officers of the South African Railways. The test was to try the engine around the triangle, as the officers remarked that if the engine went around the triangle there would be no fear of her negotiating curves on the main line. The engine was steamed and one officer and myself rode on the footplate to watch the action, while the other four watched movements on the ground. The engine in going round the triangle got its front unit bogie derailed. I knew exactly what was the cause of the derailment. The officers at once criticised this and said that the engine would not do for the main line. . . I asked (the maintenance engineer) if he would measure up the curve with me. This we did and found the curvature **well under** 2½ chains. I pointed this out to the officers and said that we had designed the engine to the South African Railways specification, which stated that the engine should be able to negotiate 2½ chain curves and grades of 1 in 40. On this statement of mine they admitted that the fault was theirs. I gave them the assurance that I would carry out a few adjustments. . . and succeeded in showing them the engine go round the triangle with great ease. The next trial was on the main line. One officer, who did not like the engine, passed a whole lot of absurd remarks re slipping, load, etc., but he was shown by me that his remarks were wrong. After the main line trial I had the

whole three engines working. The drivers and firemen at the commencement did not like the engines, but I showed them how much superior the Garratt was over the Baldwin engines they were driving, and after a month or two they were greatly taken up with the Garratts. One of the officers whom I mentioned not liking the Garratt Engine and who had them under his charge, kept finding fault with trivial things, and when Mr. Hendrie (S.A.R. Chief Mechanical Engineer) came down to inspect the Garratts with several other officials, this officer put before him a whole lot of complaints. . . I got Mr. Hendrie after this to ride on the Engine. The officer in question would not come along with Mr. Hendrie and myself. After Mr. Hendrie had run on the engine he was well satisfied.

''After five months of these engines continually in service, I approached this officer again. . . but he still would not admit they were good engines, and one day he had a wire stating that one Garratt engine had to be sent to Natal. He would not part with the engine as I heard that he had liked the Garratts, but Sir William Hoy insisted that one Garratt must go to Natal. When this engine was sent to Natal I went with it as I knew exactly what would take place. The senior officer of the Natal Section who had the engine under his charge, conducted the tests with me, and he was well pleased and liked the Garratt, but the driver and fireman at first did not like the Garratt. I waited for a little while in Natal and showed the enginemen and shed fitters exactly how this engine should be handled etc., and before I returned to Port Elizabeth, where the other two engines were, the enginemen admitted that the Garratt was a 'tip-top' engine and that they had no desire to go back to their old engines.''(2)

The first 2ft. gauge Garratts were not superheated, and had slide valves, but even so they were so successful that never again did the South African Railways purchase rigid-framed non-articulated locomotives for their narrow-gauge feeder lines. These engines performed the work of two ordinary ones and halved the number of man-hours required.(3) In 1927, Hanomag produced a heavier version with a 2-6-2 + 2-6-2 wheelbase that had piston valves and superheating, while in the same year a lighter type was developed by the Société Franco-Belge to work on lines laid with only 20lb. rails. More continued to be built over the years, and an order (No. 11188) in 1958 for seven of the heavy type was the last received by Beyer, Peacock for steam locomotives. The design was so good that the South African Railways ordered a further eight in 1965 from the Hunslet Engine Company as Beyer, Peacock was closing Gorton Foundry. These engines were preferred to a new untried diesel locomotive design.

Even though these narrow-gauge Garratts were so successful, it was the larger 3ft. 6in. gauge one which was to prove vital for the future of Beyer, Peacock. The South African Railways already had seventy-nine Mallets, the earliest dating from 1909, and the largest, the ''MH'' Class, which had been supplied in 1915 by the North British Locomotive Company, rated at 48,370lb. Tractive Effort.(4) The ''GA'' type was the most powerful Garratt up to that time and 46 tons heavier than any previous model; it was designed to rival the class ''MH'' Mallet. Its leading statistics were: maximum axle load 17.8 tons, weight 133.8 tons in working order, Tractive Effort 53,700lb., superheated with a Belpaire firebox. The boiler was 6ft. 10½in. diameter and the grate area 51.8 sq. ft. It was designed to be capable of operation on 1 in 30 un-compensated gradients with 4 chain radius curves.

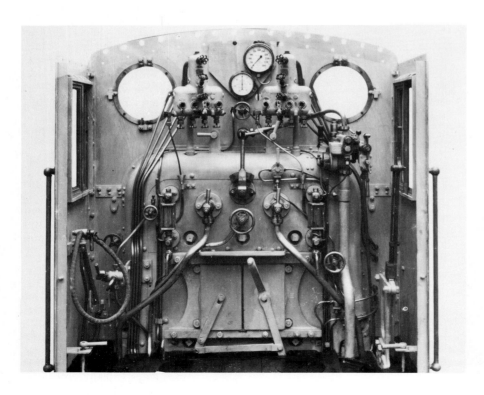

The footplate of one of the 2ft. gauge Garratts built in 1923.

[Above] This large "GA" Garratt [0941] was the only one of its type built, partly because it needed inner carrying wheels to help guide it round curves.

[Below] The class "MH" Mallet built for the South African Railways by the North British Locomotive Company in 1915.

When Wakefield had finished erecting the "GA" Garratt, he had to prepare it for a series of exhaustive tests.

"This was done by two senior officers (Mr. McNay and Mr. Gemmel) and myself; no junior officer was allowed until I had asked for someone in conducting tests of coal, water, load, speed, etc. I was given by the senior officer, Mr. Gemmel, a junior engineer, Mr. Williams, whom for a long while I taught how to conduct the speed, load trials, etc. When he knew exactly what was required several comparative tests against Mr. Hendrie's engines were carried out by him. I considered it was not wise for me to take part in these tests, as it meant that I would have been up against Mr. Hendrie, and further this junior officer upset Mr. Hendrie and Sir William Hoy in certain remarks he passed in his report. . . Mr. Hendrie. . . told me he would be conducting some tests with the large Garratt. Mr. Hendrie conducted his tests but did not give me an invitation, I saw him after the tests and he seemed well pleased with the large Garratt but admitted that he was not an advocate of Articulated Engines. There were only two faults that Mr. Hendrie, though a great critic, could find with the large Garratt. One was the quick wear of the driving flanges, and the other, the driver's outlook. . .

"I must mention that I have done a lot of propaganda work, firstly with the officers, secondly with the enginemen and running shed fitters, showing them how this large Garratt engine should be fired, driven, and handled to get the best results out of her."(5)

The junior officer, Mr. Williams, who was taught by Wakefield how to conduct the various tests was, of course, Cyril Williams. Possibly his enthusiasm got the better of his discretion, and he made some unfavourable comments about Hendrie's Mallets. To begin with, the Garratt was tested against the MC1 Class Mallet, 46,414lb. Tractive Effort, and Hendrie's 14th Class ordinary engines, Tractive Effort 36,370lb. The Garratt proved to be far superior to both these, having the same coal consumption as the 14th class when hauling 100 tons more. The Mallet was chiefly used for banking purposes.(6)

A final load test was carried out on 22 June 1921, on a 4½ mile section with a ruling gradient of 1 in 30 on 275 and 300ft. curves, and rising 683ft.

"A trial of 401 tons short for 48 axles was hauled up grades of 1 - 30 uncompensated and 300ft.

curves. The engine hauled this load with no difficulty, on one bank of 1 - 30 with a reverse curve the engines showed slight signs of slipping. Sand was applied and the train brought to a standstill for a few seconds. On starting the engine picked up her load and showed no signs of slipping. The Official in charge of the test was greatly surprised at the way in which the engine moved off on a bank of 1 - 30. I was informed by the Official that one section of the track by Fields Hill contained a grade of 1 - 25 uncompensated, he further stated that he was well pleased at what the engine could do.''(7)

Then the engine was transferred to the Waschbank - Wessels Nek section, and tested against the big ''MH'' class Mallets. On a gradient of 1 in 75, the results were as follows:

Engine	Weight	Load Hauled	Time
Garratt	133 tons	1,451 tons	26½ min.
Mallet	179 tons	1,303 tons	32½ min.

On tests between Ladysmith and Glencoe, the Garratt's coal consumption was 14.18lb. per 100 ton-miles, compared with 16.57 for the Mallett. It was estimated that the Garratt brought in £25 more revenue per trip, due to the extra load she could haul.(8)

Part of the success of the Garratt must be ascribed to the boiler design. Dimensions of the ''GA'' Garratt and the ''MH'' Mallet boilers were:

Type	Garratt	Mallet
Boiler Pressure (p.s.i.)	180	200
Grate Area (sq. ft.)	51.83	53.17
Max. diam.	6ft. 9in.	6ft. 4¼in.
Length between tubeplates	11ft. 8¼in.	22ft. 0on.
Firebox Volume (cu. ft.)	311	327
Firebox heating surface (sq. ft.)	211.3	250
Tube heating surface (sq. ft.)	2343.3	2961
Super heating surface (sq. ft.)	526.5	616
Empty weight (tons)	24.8	35.5

(9)

A study of the proportions of some of the largest Mallet boilers shows that they were approaching the limit for satisfactory steaming and a boiler with very long tubes is not ideal where heavy continuous steaming is required.(10) On the other hand, the Garratt boiler had a deeper, wider firebox, no combustion chamber, shorter barrel and weighed 11 tons less. With a relatively short distance between the tube plates, and its large diameter barrel, it was ideal for sustained hard work. In addition, it did not have to be driven so close to its capacity, and the maintenance costs were expected to be lower than on the Mallet. The Garratt had a further advantage with its short boiler because, on lines with very steep gradients, the extreme variations in water level did not cause either the crown of the firebox, or the ends of the tubes, to become uncovered. For this reason the large Mallets were banned from certain sections of the railways in Natal, but the Garratts could travel anywhere. (11)

The ''GA'' Garratt was the only one of its class built, for it was found that there was heavy wear of the inner driving wheel flanges through the lack of inner carrying wheels and, except for one repeat order (No. 02406) in 1925 for

The boiler off the ''GA'' Garratt.

its narrow-gauge Garratts, all the subsequent ones for the South African Railways had inner carrying wheels. The "GA" Garratt spent most of its life in Natal, finally on passenger trains from Ladysmith to Harrismith, including the climb of 1 in 30 up the Van Reenen's pass. It was scrapped in 1938, but had, however, served its purpose and shown what a Garratt could do.

Meanwhile the other Garratt, Order 0942, had been finished by Wakefield in May 1921 and was put through its trials. This "GB" type was a 2-6-2 + 2-6-2 design with a 7.5 tons maximum axle load, and a total weight of only 70.56 tons, for use on branch lines laid with very light track.

> "A load of 7 coaches with passengers and a van with luggage weighing 138 tons short was tried on 10/6/21 between Durban and Illovo River, a distance of 22 miles. In this section the ruling grades are 1 - 30 compensated for curves of 300ft. radius. The engine on this occasion did very well, taking the grades with no difficulty and keeping time. The boiler made steam easily with the 3¾in. plain cap, on the 1 - 30 grades she worked with a cut-off of 40%, on the flat a speed of 35 miles was obtained.
>
> "On the return journey Illovo River to Durban, the train left 15 minutes late due to the line not being clear. On arrival at Durban after 9 stops were made at stations the engine made up 14½ minutes, ½ minute behind schedule time.
>
> "On this trial the Mechanical Engineer and the Chief Transportation Officer were present. They were well pleased with the engine."(12)

Wakefield was able to report that this last Garratt gave no trouble whatsoever, and it was on this one that he had a cradle slung under the boiler barrel so that he could watch the action of the wheels. From this, he was able to point out the importance of the inner carrying wheels in helping to guide the bogies round curves. He finished his report by saying:

> "There is a very big field for Garratt locomotives in South Africa and it is only a matter of time, as the South African Railways financial position at present is a bad one. Sir William Hoy gave me the assurance before I left South Africa for India that he intends having more Garratts."(13)

The Garratts continued to give outstanding performances over the next three years and were highly praised in his Annual Reports by Sir William Hoy, the General Manager of the South African Railways:

> "1921. In certain tests made with the main line 'Garratt', it not only took a much greater load than the heavy main line engines, including a Mallet engine against which it was tested, but its running times were better and its water and coal consumption less. The performances of all these 'Garratt' engines have exceeded anticipations, but it would be unwise to regard their success as conclusive until they have had a more extended trial. A narrow-gauge 'Garratt' engine, placed in service on the Stuartstown branch, Natal, has effected a saving of one engine and train crew.
>
> "1922. The branch line 'Garratt' engine has been employed on the North and South Coast line in Natal and has proved an **unqualified success**. **Excellent results** have been obtained from the tests conducted with the main line 'Garratt' engine in the Ladysmith and Germiston-Witbank districts. The narrow-gauge 'Garratt' engines are **most economical** and have **reduced train mileage** and **trainsmen's hours** on the narrow-gauge lines on which they are employed.
>
> "1923. In my last report I stated that both the standard- and narrow-gauge types of 'Garratt' locomotives were giving satisfaction on the sections on which they were employed. I am pleased to **reaffirm** that both types of engine **have continued to perform equally good and economical service** during the year under review."(14)

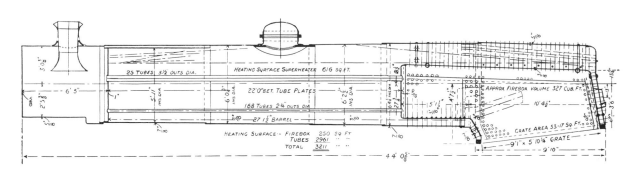

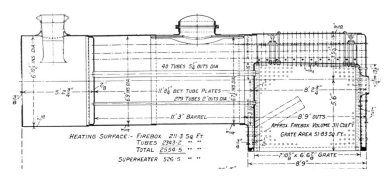

Above: Sectional view of boiler of M.H. Mallet locomotive, South African Railways. (Weight of boiler, 35 tons 10¾ cwt., steel firebox).

Below: Sectional view of G.A. Garratt locomotive, South African Railways. (Weight of boiler 24 tons 10 cwt., copper firebox).

Both drawn to same scale.

The "GB" class [0942] proved to be a very successful type and one is now preserved.

[Above and Below] The cab was modified on the repeat order for the "GB" class [02393] in 1923. Note the steam reversing gear underneath the running plate of the boiler frame.

As a result of these three years' experience with their Garratt locomotives, during which period they went to the shops for their first general overhaul, the South African Railways placed an order in November 1923 with Beyer, Peacock for twenty more of four different designs. Two more 2ft. gauge ones, but with superheaters and piston valves (Order 02406), were delivered in 1925. There was also a repeat order (No. 02393) for six of the "GB" type, with a few minor modifications such as side windows to the cabs. These engines were used for many years on the Aliwal North-Barkly east line, which included compensated gradients of 1 in 30. They had long useful lives and the last were not withdrawn until 1966. One has been scheduled for preservation.

The "GC" class (Order 02400) was developed from a prototype 2-6-2 + 2-6-2 (Order 02304) sent in 1923 to the New Cape Central Railway. This was intermediate in power between the "GA" and the "GB", having a maximum axle-load of 10.5 tons and total weight 94.9 tons. Similar engines were built for the Natal Navigation Colliery (Order 111) and two wood burners for the Trans-Zambesia Railway (Order 02386). The "GC" class were used for working one of the sharpest-timed suburban services in South Africa, at speeds up to and over 40 m.p.h., on the South Coast line out of Durban. They were designed for operation on 45 and 50lb. rail, and their introduction postponed considerable capital expenditure on relaying and bridge strengthening, for the Garratt system enabled locomotives of greatly increased power to be operated on existing lines. These locomotives operated without turning and, with their superior acceleration, resulted in a quicker service and at the same time enabled extra coaches to be hauled. Thirty-nine more locomotives, to a slightly modified design, were obtained from German manufacturers in 1927 and 1928, and show what a successful type this was.

[Above] The New Cape Central Railway [02304] ordered a 2-6-2 + 2-6-2 Garratt which became, in effect, the prototype of the South African Railways "GC" class.

[Below] The New Cape Central Railway design was modified as a wood-burner for the Trans-Zambesia Railway [02386].
[Foot] The South African Railways "GC" class [02400].

The six remaining engines from this large order were to a 2-8-2 + 2-8-2 type called "GE", built 1924-25 (Order 02405). They were the first Garratts to have this wheel arrangement. With 52,290lb Tractive Effort, on a maximum axle-load of 12.75 tons, and carrying 29½ tons of fuel and water, they were a tremendous advance in motive power for light 3ft. 6in. gauge tracks, and their introduction revolutionised operating on the 60lb. rail, virtually doubling the line capacity. At this time, they were the most powerful locomotives in Africa, and possibly in the world, operating on this weight of track. An order for another ten followed in 1927 (Order 1116), on which the original style of square tanks was modified to one with rounded corners fore and aft along the tops. A self-trimming bunker, reduced in width to improve the cab outlook rearwards, and a new design of self-emptying ashpan were also introduced. Another couple were built in 1930 (Order 1169).

These locomotives were employed principally on the Johannesburg - Zeerust and North Coast lines. The former line, a distance of 149 miles, has a ruling gradient of 1 in 40, with curves as sharp as 477ft. radius. One bank, twenty miles long, is practically continuous 1 in 40, and the engines were worked for 70 minutes with full regulator and 60 per cent. cut-off—a test for any boiler. The goods train load on this section was 500 tons, and this class, despite driving wheels of only 3ft. 9½in. diameter, regularly hauled the Rhodesian Mail train, reaching speeds of 45 m.p.h. Loads on other less severe sections of the lines were often over 1,000 tons.(15)

Shortly after their initial large order, the South African Railways placed an order (No. 113) for an express passenger Garratt, capable of speeds up to 60 m.p.h., for trials on their most important passenger service between Johannesburg and Cape Town. This was the experimental 2-6-2 + 2-6-2 "GG" class, with a steam-operated coal-pusher built into the bunker to assist the fireman by bringing coal forward to the shovelling plate. The engine

The footplate of the South African Railways "GE" class.

worked the mail trains out of Cape Town, over the Hex River Pass, which included 15 miles of 1 in 40. Although in one test run the 9 5/8 miles from Belleville Junction to Salt River were covered start to stop at an average speed of 46.3 m.p.h., and the engine reached 57 m.p.h., the design was not repeated. To gain extra speed, the driving wheels had been increased in diameter, but the cylinders had not been enlarged proportionately, so the engine lacked tractive effort and also probably needed a four-wheeled leading bogie to give greater steadiness at speed. This engine, being non-standard, was scrapped in 1938.(16)

Missing from this sequence so far is the "GD" class. Fourteen 2-6-2 + 2-6-2 Garratts were ordered (No. 116) in 1925 to work on the 60lb. rail. They were a further development of the "GB" class, having 36,300lb. Tractive Effort, maximum axle-load of 12.5 tons, and were built to the same dimensions as four "Modified Fairlies", so that the Garratt could be compared with this new type of arti-

[Above] The original design of the "GE" Garratt [02405] with square tanks built in 1924 compared with [lower] the modified version [1116] with rounded tank tops and self-trimming bunker built in 1927.

[Above] The experimental "GG" [113] which was capable of 57 mph, but which was never repeated.

culated engine developed by the North British Locomotive Company. These Fairlies, which gave more trouble than the Garratts, and were not repeated as a type, were withdrawn in 1957, while the Garratts worked on another ten years at least.

The "GD" Garratts were first employed on the Cape Town - Caledon branch, which contains the famous Sir Lowry's Pass bank, 10 miles in length, on a gradient of 1 in 40, combined with numerous reverse curves of 330ft. radius. The engines operated both goods and passenger trains, the loads for the former being 380 tons on 60 axles. Some engines of this class were employed for many years on passenger trains on the North Coast line in Natal, over a distance of 118 miles, with gradients of 1 in 30 and 300ft. curves. Perhaps the severest tests to which these engines were subjected were on the Pietermaritzburg - Franklin section and the Mossel Bay - Outshoorn line, where loads of 400 tons were hauled on 1 in 40. On this last section,

passenger trains were sometimes double-headed by two class "GDs" hauling fourteen bogie coaches, equal to 560 tons. In 1929, further locomotives of this class were ordered from German manufacturers.(17)

The difficult operating conditions under which these Garratts worked has been emphasised intentionally to show how the design could cope with some of the most arduous locomotive demands in the world. It must not be forgotten that they were often put to work on narrow-gauge track, indifferently laid, with ballast of sand or cinders, or sometimes non-existent. In addition, the grades were often severe and continuous, with many sharp curves. The Garratts had to be able to stand up to merciless pounding on such onerous duties. It was a great credit to Beyer, Peacock that it had been able to develop this new design, which showed that it was keeping abreast of the latest technical developments.

The "GD" Garratt [116], above, which proved to be better than the "Modified Fairlies", below, built by the North British Locomotive Co.

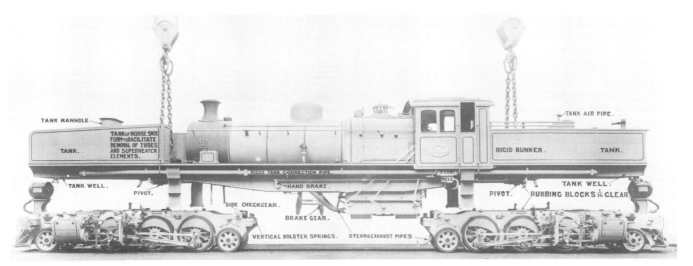

In the early summer of 1921, Lange and Rogerson made a tour of various Continental locomotive works and railway companies to see what competition they were facing from factories reconstructed after the War. The importance of keeping abreast of technical developments was brought home to them many times:

"My account of our Dutch interview would not be complete without a special reference to one matter that impressed itself upon Mr. Rogerson and myself several times, and that was the great interest taken by the Dutch railway people in all the most recent technical improvements in locomotive design and construction. This has increased the influence of the German engineers in Holland, as the Dutch look rather to the German for technical thoroughness than to ourselves. . . Formerly under the regime of Mr. Stas Sloot and well into that of Mr. Haagsma, the predecessors of Professor Franco, the Dutch State Railway people looked to Beyer, Peacock & Co. as the embodiment of the best technical knowledge of locomotive construction, and we must seek, said the Professor, to recover this prestige in Holland, a prestige which however he did not doubt was maintained as before in other quarters.

"There is no doubt at all that we must maintain not only our old reputation as the best locomotive builders, but our old position as the best designers and cleverest exponents of all the technical science involved in the building of locomotives and the means relative thereto. It may be said (Mr. Hoy often said it) that orders were merely a question of price. This is doubtless true in the main, but it is not wholly true, railway men are notoriously enthusiasts, we certainly found them so in Holland, and, other things being equal, they cannot but be influenced by their regard for those Firms whom they can look up to as leaders in the subject that interests them most.

"The exploitation of the 'Garratt' patent has a value for us beyond its commercial success, and everything should be done to extend its duration. The Dutch Colonial Railway engineers were much interested by our account of what this new type of locomotive had accomplished and in more than one quarter we were advised to push its adoption on the Java State Railways, where the conditions in many parts lend themselves to its peculiar advantages."(18)

The development of the Garratt certainly helped to keep Beyer, Peacock in the forefront of locomotive design, but these engines still had to be sold to the railway companies. Here again the South African Garratts played an important role, for, in 1923, W. Cyril Williams, who had helped to test the main line Garratt Order 0941, was appointed Beyer, Peacock's Technical Sales Engineer, later becoming London Representative.(19) This marked the beginning of a long and successful career as the spearhead of the Company's sales force, and the success of the Garratt must be partly ascribed to his sales ability. He, and the General Manager, toured all the continents of the world to sell these engines. Unfortunately there is not enough space in this book to recount many of his adventures, but in the days before air travel, and when the network of railway lines was still far from complete in the remoter districts of South America or Africa, he had to face many hazards.

Cyril Williams descending 100 miles on the Central Railway of Peru without a push.

During a 45,000 mile tour in 1926, Cyril Williams went by train across South America from Buenos Aires to Mollendo. The trains through the three countries of Argentina, Bolivia and Peru did not link up and the overnight accommodation was best forgotten. He suffered from mountain sickness at Crucero Alto, where the Southern Railway of Peru reached a height of 14,688ft. above sea level, and then at Mollendo had to be transferred from a small boat in a 9ft. swell to reach his ship, which had to lie a mile out in the Pacific. On a later trip to the Central Railway of Peru, it was suggested that he should return by push-trolley from Rio Blanco, 11,500ft. above sea level, to Lima, 11,000ft. lower. While he had an impressive view of the country on the three- or four-hour trip, he arrived at Lima to discover he was stone deaf. Luckily he recovered in a few days.

On one trip across Africa to reach the railhead of the Benguela Railway, which was in course of construction, he had to leave the Rhodesia Railways at N'tenke, an unattended crossing loop, and be driven by car on a journey that took a week for 300 miles, and was possible only in the dry season. Three cars were used and special precautions had to be taken against sun, fever and insects, as well as breakdowns. After the Benguela Railway had been reached, the rail motor trolley taking him to Lobito Bay had to be stopped to allow a leopard to get off the track. Such were the hazards of selling Garratts!(20)

W. Cyril Williams.

12

Gorton Foundry Between
The Two World Wars

The Top Personnel

[Heading] The works transport.

In the years immediately after the First World War there were many changes in the personnel responsible for running Gorton Foundry. In 1923, Sir Vincent Caillard, who had been Chairman since the Company went public in 1902, retired and was succeeded by Sir Sam Fay. Fay was famous for his career as General Manager of the Great Central Railway, an appointment which ended when that railway disappeared in the 1922 grouping. He was also a director of several railway companies in South America. One year later, J. G. Robinson, the Great Central's renowned Chief Mechanical Engineer, became a Director of Beyer, Peacock.(1) Many people, including H.N. Gresley of the Great Northern Railway, had expected him to become the first Chief Mechanical Engineer of the new London & North Eastern Railway, but he was already in his sixties, and the younger, highly talented Gresley was preferred.

The Manager and Secretary, A.F. Halstead, resigned at the beginning of 1919, when A. C. Rogerson was appointed General Manager. On his death in 1921, he was succeeded by C. A. Watson, but unfortunately he had to retire through ill health just over a year later.(2) He was replaced by the well-known figure, R.H. Whitelegg,(3) of the Glasgow & South Western Railway, whose appointment as Chief Mechanical Engineer had ended when his railway became part of the new London, Midland & Scottish Railway. Before that he had been Chief Mechanical Engineer of the London, Tilbury & Southend Railway. This massive influx of top management from railway service into private industry had undoubted advantages, yet proved rather a mixed blessing in a company such as Beyer, Peacock which had such an extensive export business, and had to deal with railways operating under vastly different conditions from those in the United Kingdom.

The person responsible for reorganising Gorton Foundry in 1919, and getting locomotive production back into full swing, was Samuel Jackson, an outstanding locomotive engineer of his time, who had been an apprentice at Crewe Works, before coming to Beyer, Peacock as a pupil in 1900. It was he who had prepared the first "Garratt" scheme in 1908, for he worked in the Design Department before becoming Assistant Works Manager in 1913. From 1918 to 1924 he was Works Manager and then was appointed Advisory and Development Engineer. When A. E. Kyffin, who had been Chief Draughtsman since 1904, left in 1925, Jackson became Chief Designer, and Works Manager in overall charge of all technical and

Sir Sam Fay, 1856 - 1953.

R.H. Whitelegg, 1871 - 1957.

manufacturing activity. C. H. Schobelt then became Chief Draughtsman; he died at the end of 1927, just before he was due to retire, and was replaced by James Pimm.(4)

From 1926 onwards Samuel Jackson maintained tight personal control over all activity in the Design Department and Drawing Office. Such was the pressure of work that in about 1922 a drive began to augment the Drawing Office staff, and among the many draughtsmen recruited from all over the country was James Hadfield from the old Great Central Drawing Office, opposite Gorton Foundry. He came in 1924 and was to play a very important part in the later years of the Company's history. In the same year Harold Wilmot joined as Cost Accountant, and eventually became Chairman and Managing Director.

While all these changes in management and staff were taking place, buildings and plant were being improved and extended. In particular, the new boiler shop block, planned in 1919,(5) and comprising three long spacious bays, with up-to-date plant for the complete manufacture of boilers, tenders and tanks, was finally completed and brought into use in 1925. When one looked at the old boiler shop, and compared the size which boilers for Garratts and tender engines were by then attaining, it was obvious that better facilities were an urgent necessity. The boiler shop alone cost over £100,000 and was only part of an extensive modernisation programme. In his Annual Report for 1926, Sir Sam Fay wrote:

> "In the past three years we have spent, in accordance with the policy of modernizing our shops which I have previously outlined for you, approximately £130,000, and I am glad to say that the sum spent last year is considerably lower than the figures for the preceding years—an indication that we are reaching the end of putting our hourse in order. We are already feeling the benefit, in lower costs and more balanced production, of the many improvements in new machinery and plant introduced. During the year, amongst other things we have extended our locomotive erecting shop, improved our stores and sidings facilities, extended the use of electrically driven power plant, etc. The capacity of our steel foundry has been increased by the addition of a new furnace."(6)

C.H. Schobelt, 1863 - 1927

In 1930, an electric steel melting furnace was brought into use and, of course, new machine tools and other improvements were being added continually.

* * * * *

Ordinary Locomotives

The success of the pre-war Garratts, followed by the excellent reports of those sent to South Africa, encouraged Beyer, Peacock to launch a vigorous sales campaign because it felt that in this "Development of our business ... by reason of its technical achievements and the practical experience we have accumulated therein, we may reasonably hope to defy competition for a long time to come".(7) In the early part of this period, however, Beyer, Peacock still depended upon the manufacture of ordinary locomotives to sustain Gorton Foundry, but the demand was gradually diminishing and, soon after the war, German builders were joining in the keen com-

The new boiler shop under construction in October 1920.

[Above] The new boiler shop completed.

[Below] The ''new'' boiler shop around 1945 filled to capacity.

petition for export orders. Unlike the Germans, the British builders had to depend almost entirely on orders from abroad and, with rising costs, profitability was low. The penetration of markets traditionally held by British manufacturers is well illustrated by what happened in Holland. In the period 1886-1895, 95 per cent. of the new locomotives for the Dutch State Railways were of British, 2 per cent. German and 3 per cent. Dutch manufacture. In the period 1896-1905, the proportions were 77 per cent. British to 23 per cent. Dutch and from 1906-1915, 45 per cent. British, 32 per cent. German and 23 per cent. Dutch. After the war, Beyer, Peacock sold no more locomotives to Holland, partly through electrification, but mainly because Continental builders were selling locomotives more cheaply. The four-cylinder 4-6-0 express engines (Order 069) designed by Beyer, Peacock in 1910 were, in a repeat order of 1913, shared between Manchester and Werkspoor of Amsterdam, each building thirty-six. Another order in 1919 for a further twenty-five went to two German firms, ten to the Hannoversche Machin Fabrik and fifteen to Henschel of Cassel, at a price 37 per cent. less than Beyer, Peacock could quote.(8)

The total number of locomotives built at Gorton Foundry during these twenty-one troubled years was 997, comprising 573 tender and tank engines, 415 Garratts and 9 sets of mechanical parts for electric locomotives. The business was more than ever concentrated on export orders, which reached over 90 per cent. of output. The Garratts represented about 42 per cent. of the total, and the great majority of these were exported; they also attained growing importance through their increasing size, weight and power—the average weight in working order being about 130 tons, compared with some 92 tons for conventional types.

The development of the Garratts has inevitably overshadowed the excellent ordinary locomotives built by Beyer, Peacock in the latter part of its history. For example, in 1919, production began with fifty heavy 4-8-2s for the South African Railways (Orders 01700, 01702, 01830). These Class "15A" locomotives, completed

[Below] The 4-8-2 for the South African Railways [01830] fitted with steam reverse gear above the crosshead.

[Foot] No. 1839 one of the South African Railways 1920 batch of 4-8-2s still at work in 1979.   [C. P. Friel]

in 1920-21, had a tractive effort of 41,670lb. compared with 53.700lb. for the Garratt Class "GA", but they were very successful, and some were giving good results on passenger and goods trains over fifty years later.

With increasing attention to standardisation, many orders were repeats or modifications of existing designs, with, wherever possible, the latest improvements incorporated. Those locomotives built for service in the British Isles kept their clean lines and most of the pipe work and other parts concealed beneath the boiler cladding. In 1920, four 4-6-4 tank engines (Order 01160) were purchased by the Belfast & County Down Railway. These were used on its suburban passenger services, and had rather pleasing lines and good accessibility, due to outside cylinders and Walschaert's valve gear. The Great Northern Railway of Ireland maintained the policy of purchasing its locomotives from Beyer, Peacock by acquiring, for example, five more 4-4-0 passenger engines (Order 1524) in 1932. These good-looking engines, with 6ft. 7in. driving wheels, were designed with the help of Derby Works, for they were three-cylinder compounds using the same W. M. Smith principle as the Midland 4-4-0s. The 17¼in. diameter inside high-pressure cylinder exhausted into two outside 19in. diameter low-pressure cylinders, but for starting, or heavy work, the "Derby" regulator admitted high pressure steam to all the cylinders for the first part of its movement, while for the remainder of its opening it admitted steam to the high pressure cylinder only. The cylinders were cast in one block, and the balancing was so good that the total weight on the coupled wheels at 84 m.p.h. including static and hammer blow forces was 7 tons less than the older two cylinder design.(9) The valve gear was Stephenson's link motion, one set for each cylinder, all between the frames. Not only were they the last compounds for Northern Ireland, but they were also the last built by Beyer, Peacock.

The Irish connection was maintained by engines for Cork, Bandon & South Coast (Orders 01034 and 01870) in 1919 and 1920, the Dublin & South Eastern (Order 02160) in 1922 as well as others to both the Belfast & County Down and Great Northern (Ireland) Railways. In 1926 the last steam locomotive for the Isle of Man (Order 144) was shipped; this was also the last steam locomotive built for hauling passengers on a narrow gauge railway running a regular service in the British Isles. It also marked the final evolution of the 2-4-0 tank designed in 1863 for the Norwegian 3ft. 6in. railways. Although it was the largest and heaviest of this type, it produced only 8,810 lb. Tractive Effort, and must have

[Above] The suburban tank engine for the Belfast & County Down Railway [01160].

[Below] Eight of these 4-6-0 tank engines were built for the Cork, Bandon & South Coast Railway between 1906 and 1920.

been the smallest engine built at Gorton Foundry since well before the First World War and, except for some diesel shunters, until the works closed.

Many orders were received from South America where most of the railways had been built with British capital and still retained British engineers. In 1920, twenty 0-6-0 tank engines (Orders 01835 and 01836) were sent to the Central Argentine Railway, to be followed in 1926 by twenty 2-8-2 tender engines (Orders 153 and 154).

These were the last of the long line of two-cylinder compounds sent to that country. They were fitted with "Dabeg" feed water heater and pumps, and weighed 145½ tons. The cylinders had 21in. and 31½in. bores x 26in. stroke giving a tractive effort of 25,160lb. In 1928, the Buenos Ayres Great Southern received twenty oil-burning 4-8-0s (Order 159) intended for general purpose work. These had wheels of 4ft. 7½in. diameter and developed 36,580 lb. Tractive Effort. In the following

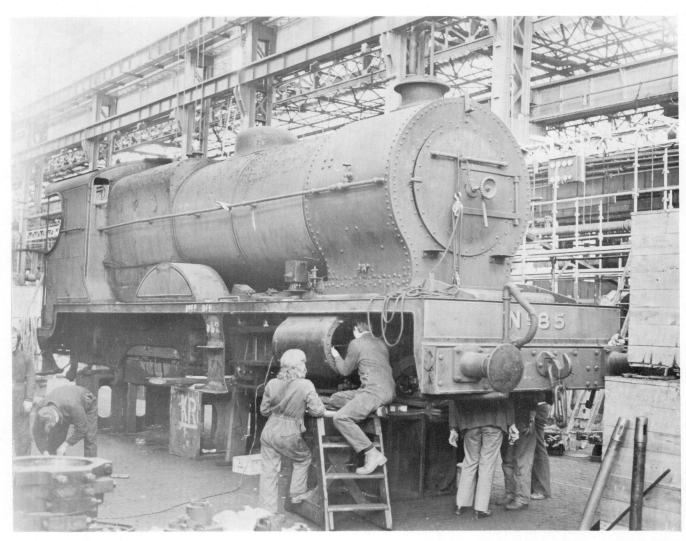

[Above] The preserved Great Northern Railway of Ireland [1524] three-cylinder compound 4-4-0 being refurbished at Harland & Wolff's shipyard in 1977. [C.P. Friel]

[Below] A further development of the 4-4-0 for the Great Northern Railway of Ireland [1524], this time as a three-cylinder compound.

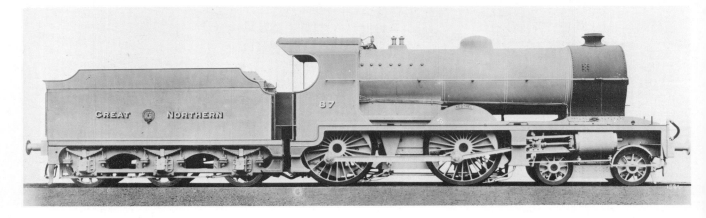

year the Buenos Ayres & Pacific was supplied with a new design, this time a 2-8-2 (Order 1518) weighing 205 tons, complete with its tender. With cylinders 24½in. x 30in., it had a tractive effort of 45,700lb., at 75 per cent. boiler pressure, this figure being quoted because the valve gear was arranged to have a maximum cut-off of 65 per cent. in full gear.(10)

After this no more orders for ordinary engines were received from the Argentine, but many continued to be sent to the Leopoldina Railway in Brazil, and in 1925, building a new type of 4-6-2 tender engine began (Order 151). Twenty-eight were completed by the end of 1928, and the design was modernised in 1939 when a further six were built (Order 1541), followed by five more after the Second World War (Order 1552). A neat 4-6-2 tank was tried in 1937, when two were supplied (Order 1422). These were specifically designed for suburban passenger traffic, which required rapid acceleration from station stops.(11) They were so successful that six more were ordered (No. 1423) in 1939.

[Above] This rather squat 2-6-0 for the Dublin & South Eastern Railway [01260] was fitted with coil springs on the driving wheels.

[Right] The Dublin & South Eastern Railway 2-6-0 No. 15 now preserved, photographed in 1968.   [C. P. Friel]

[Below] ''Mannin'' was the last of her type, not only for the Isle of Man Railway [144] but elsewhere in the world too. She is now preserved in the museum at Port Erin.

[Above] The 0-6-0 tank engine sent to the Central Argentine Railway [01835] in 1920.

[Below] The massive 2-8-2 for the Buenos Ayres & Pacific Railway was fitted with "Dabeg" boiler feed-water heater and pumps made by Weir of Glasgow.

[Above] The 4-8-0 for the Buenos Ayres Great Southern Railway [159] was built to drawings supplied by Armstrong Whitworth. Feed-water heating apparatus and Weir pump were fitted on the running plate.

[Below] The massive 2-8-2 for the Buenos Ayres & Pacific Railway [1518].

[Top] The original type of "Pacific" tender engine supplied to the Leopoldina Railway [151] in 1925.

[Above] The neat 4-6-2 tank engine designed for suburban passenger work on the Leopoldina Railway [1422].

[Below] The bodies of the tenders of the Buenos Ayres & Pacific Railway locomotives being transported to the docks.

[Above] Peruvian Railways No. 200, built by Beyer, Peacock shunting in Onoya yard in 1956.   [D. Ibbotson]

Another successful design originating in this period was a 2-8-0 tender type for the Peruvian Corporation. Both the Central and Southern Railways of Peru reached such an altitude that it was not until after the Second World War that aeroplanes could safely carry passengers across the Andes to compete with them. Also diesel engines could not develop enough power at such heights unless they were supercharged,(12) and so for many years the steam locomotive reigned supreme. Three of these engines were built in 1935 (Order 1527), with sturdy bar frames. In "Railways of the Andes"(13) Brian Fawcett describes the lines which operated up to about 16,000ft. with 328ft. radius curves, long stretches of 1 in 25 grade, steepening in places to 1 in 22, and of course ice and other appalling conditions. It is a tribute to the design and quality of manufacture that engines of this type withstood the constant pounding and continued to be ordered until 1957. The railways' regulations required a third braking system, in addition to the normal power and hand brake, consisting in this case of the "Le Chatelier" counter-pressure system in which the engine is put into reverse gear and jets of hot water under boiler pressure are injected into the cylinder to absorb the heat of compression thus generated.

Other locomotives of special interest, but not originally of Beyer, Peacock design, included five outside-cylindered 4-6-0 express engines (Order 02105), built in 1922, for the Great Central Railway. They were the last locomotives ordered before the amalgamation, but in 1928 the London & North Eastern Railway ordered ten 4-6-0s (Order 1513), based on Holden's inside-cylindered design, which originated on the Great Eastern. They were the first passenger engines in this country to be fitted with Lentz poppet valves.(14) In 1931, five 3-cylindered 4-6-2 tender engines, also fitted with Lentz rotary cam poppet valves and its associated gear (Order 1523), were supplied to the metre gauge Federated Malay States Railway. They were imposing locomotives, with their smoke deflectors and large cabs, and had a tractive effort of 29,480lb., a very reasonable figure for an engine of this wheel arrangement on such a gauge.

[Below] The Great Central [02105] 4-6-0 express engine built just before the railway amalgamation of 1923.

[Above] The first passenger engines in Great Britain to be fitted with Lentz valves were these 4-6-0 tender engines for the London & North Eastern Railway [1513]. The valve operating rod can be seen below the side of the smoke box.

[Right] A cylinder fitted with Lentz valves and oscillating mechanism.

[Below] Lentz valves worked by the oscillating system.

[Above] The 4-6-2 three-cylinder engines for the Federated Malay States Railway [1523] were fitted with Lentz valves driven by a rotary camshaft.

[Right] The driving mechanism for Lentz rotary cam valves on the Bengal Nagpur Garratt. [1166]

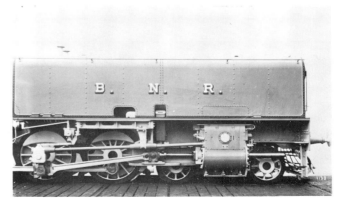

Electric and Steam Turbine Locomotives

In addition to selling the Garratt locomotive to railways all round the world, Beyer, Peacock was closely studying developments of other types of traction. C. A. Watson was authorised to investigate the manufacture of electric locomotives again,(15) and in 1924 parts for four 90-ton Bo-Bos for the Montreal Harbour Board (Order 02438) were built under contract from the English Electric Company.(16) Five more were constructed (Order 131) soon afterwards, and all these engines worked for over forty years, giving very reliable service.

The North British Locomotive Company and Sir W. G. Armstrong Whitworth & Co. had both built locomotives powered by steam turbines in this country, and more were in hand overseas. Beyer, Peacock studied developments closely and decided that the Swedish Company, Nydqvist & Holm appeared to have the most satisfactory design. After seeing a practical demonstration of one of its engines with a Ljungström turbine, a manufacturing licence was obtained in 1924.(17) Samuel Jackson was put in charge of this project and, in collaboration with the Swedish engineers, produced a design suitable for use on British railways. To give increased efficiency and as a greater attraction for overseas sales in desert areas, it was decided to build a condensing turbine locomotive, developing 2,000 horsepower. It was divided into two units. The front contained the boiler, water tanks and coal bunker, while the rear had the driving wheels, gear box, main turbine and condenser. It was 73ft. 11in. long over the buffers and, when carrying its full load of fuel (6 tons)

[Above] These Bo-Bo engines for the Montreal Habour Board [02438] were the second design of electric locomotive built at Gorton.
[Below] The Montreal Harbour Board electric locomotives under construction at Gorton.
[Foot] The body of a Montreal Harbour Board electric locomotive ready for shipping.

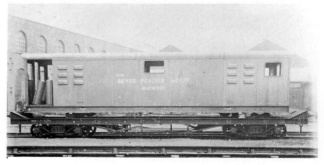

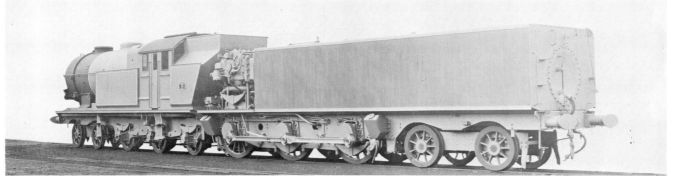

and 1,950 gallons of water, had a total weight of 143 tons 14 cwt., of which over 54 tons was available for adhesion. (18)

The boiler and cab were carried on five axles. At the front was a four wheeled bogie while the remaining three axles were mounted on the boiler frames, rather like a 4-6-0, but all the wheels were the same size, and were not coupled. The boiler pressure was 300lb. per sq. in., and the steam was superheated to 700°F. Because the engine was condensing, there was no steam passing up the chimney to create a draught for the fire. Therefore a turbine driven fan was placed in the smokebox. This fan drew the exhaust gases through the top half of an air preheater in part of the smokebox. Blades in a slowly revolving drum were thus heated and gave up their heat in the lower half of the casing to the incoming air which then was led by ducts to the ashpan.

The rear unit was also mounted on five axles, but this time the front three pairs of wheels were 5ft. 3in. diameter and were coupled with outside coupling rods. The remaining two axles were mounted in a rear bogie, which had 3ft. 3in. wheels, like those on the boiler unit. The steam passed through two regulators, an emergency one in the boiler, and the other on the turbine. Flexible pipes had to be used between the two units, which presented no difficulty to Beyer, Peacock after its experience with the Garratts. All the turbines were the Ljungström type. The main one had a rotor with a single row impulse wheel at its high pressure end followed by 18 rows of reaction blading. The designed maximum speed of the rotor was 10,500 r.p.m. which corresponded to an engine speed of 75 m.p.h.

The drive to the wheels was taken through triple reduction gearing with another gear mounted on an eccentric for reversing. Special interlocking arrangements had to be

[Upper pictures] The Ljungström condensing turbine locomotive built by Beyer, Peacock in 1926.

[Above] The main turbine of the Ljungström locomotive opened up to show the blading.

fitted to prevent reversing while the engine or rotor was moving or while there was any steam pressure. The leading set of coupled wheels was driven through a special

173

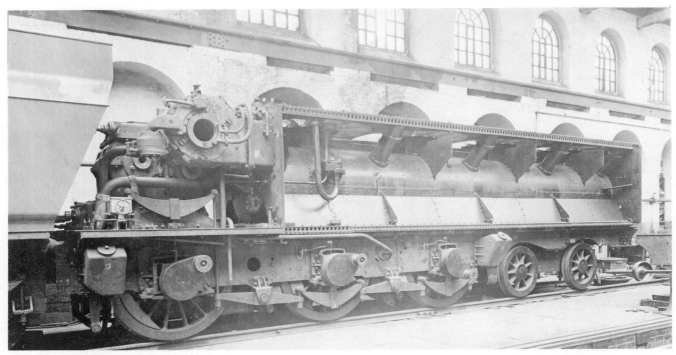

The turbine and condenser units under construction at Gorton.

quill drive to allow for the springing and movement of the wheels through the suspension. All this was enclosed for lubrication in a casing which had to be oil-tight.

The turbine was bolted onto the end of the condenser so the steam passed through directly and was condensed partly by water spray and partly by banks of surface condensers. The condenser tank was 27ft. 9in. long by 4ft. 6in. diameter, and contained 1,400 gallons, or about half the water supply. Pipes connected the top of it to the surface condensers on either side. Four 6ft. 9in. diameter fans mounted on top of the unit drew fresh air through the surface condensers. The fans were driven by bevel gears from their own 300 horsepower turbine, which could be controlled separately from the main one by the enginemen. There were circulating pumps and ejectors inside the condenser, while the feedwater was passed back to the boiler by two turbine-driven pumps through a heater which was heated by steam from the fan and auxiliary turbines.

The locomotive was completed in the summer of 1926 and, after preliminary steaming and control trials in the works yard, made its first trip on Sunday 4 July. This was from Gorton to Woodhead and back, and was repeated later in the day. A maximum speed of 45 m.p.h. was achieved, but minor faults were discovered, and it was over two months before the engine was again pronounced ready. On Monday 20 September, with Beyer, Peacock officials in the cab but in charge of a London, Midland & Scottish Railway driver, it left Gorton for Derby, at which shed it was to be based while running the trials for which that Railway's Directors had offered facilities.

After footplate familiarisation tests, the locomotive went into regular service on slow and semi-fast passenger trains between Derby and Manchester, always being driven by Derby crews. It ran on these duties for several months, but by December Beyer, Peacock decided that the time had come for it to be recalled for examination. Back at Gorton, the entire turbine and gearbox were stripped down and found to be in perfect order. Several alterations were made, in particular to the control and reversing gear, before it was returned to service.

It arrived back at Derby on 29 March 1927 and then began working both slow and express trains on the run to and from Birmingham. On these faster duties, one serious weakness soon became apparent, that of developing hot axle boxes. This occurred in both the axle boxes under the boiler unit and also on the driving axles. Various other problems appeared, such as difficulty with reversing through steam leaking past the regulator valve, but this was overcome by fitting a vacuum breaker on the condenser. Then it was decided to try the locomotive on express trains on the more exacting route between Manchester and Derby, beginning on 10 May. Trouble was experienced with the condenser when the vacuum dropped to 14 inches in Dove Holes Tunnel. For the next few days, the engine continued to work the same out and home trip to Manchester and it was quickly apparent that the loss of vacuum on 10 May was no isolated occurrence. Earlier accounts suggest that this was caused by soot from the roof of the tunnels being dislodged and blocking the condenser tubes but W. Bramley, the London, Midland & Scottish Railway official observer on all these runs, denied this and said that the condenser never needed cleaning. The most likely reason is that the proximity of the tunnel wall seriously impeded the air flow to the condenser which was further reduced by the aero-dynamic effect as the train pushed the air through the tunnel in front of it, leaving an area of low pressure along its sides and behind it. The reduced air-flow from these causes seriously reduced the efficiency of the condenser and caused the engine to run sluggishly.

After a mere ten days running to Manchester, it was decided to try her out on a much longer run and for this the obvious choice was the London road. The first trip was made on 20 May, and she performed well, steaming freely and easily maintaining vacuum. Despite her small driving wheels, the smoothness of the running was exemplary, and it was quite common on this and later trips to reach 85 m.p.h. approaching Napsbury. In fact the engine was so smooth running that the enginemen probably did not realise the speeds they were achieving, because no speedometer was fitted, and this may well have contributed to the problems with the bearings which soon appeared again. On Sunday 29 May, a train of over thirteen bogie coaches and the dynamometer car—a total weight of over 400 tons—was taken from Derby to Bedford and back as a special test run to see what the engine could do when extended. The train was worked to normal express schedules and had no difficulty in keeping time.

In the meantime, Beyer, Peacock had started negotiations with the Commonwealth Government Railways of Australia about the sale of this engine to them for use on some of their desert lines where water was difficult to obtain. Unfortunately, during the weeks the Ljungström worked on the London road, she was plagued by bearing trouble. It became a regular occurrence on returning to Derby shed to have to jack up the wheels, and remove the steps. Quite often they were found to be blistered, and occasionally they had actually run. When the latter had occurred, it meant not only stopping the locomotive for a whole day while they were remetalled and refitted, but also finding a substitute locomotive at short notice.

One afternoon in the first week of July when they reached Derby, having just worked the 2.25 p.m. from St. Pancras, Sir Henry Fowler, Chief Mechanical Engineer of the London, Midland & Scottish Railway, came over and asked if everything was allright. Bramley reported that one bearing was rather warm, but he doubted if the metal had actually run. Sir Henry said, "I want you to go back to London tonight, because Mr. Bruce, the Prime Minister of Australia, is visiting London and says he wants to see her. She is just what they want in Australia, because of the shortage of water". The bearing had run and the fitters worked all night to repair it. First thing next morning, Bramley reported to Chambers, the Chief Draughtsman, that they were already to go, but he was told the trip had been cancelled. Higher authority had decided that, in view of the engine's marked propensity for running hot, it could not be recommended to the Australian Premier.

This proved to be a fatal blow to Beyer, Peacock's hopes, and not long afterwards, the locomotive was returned to Gorton for overhaul and alterations. More trials were carried out in March and April 1928 when the Ljungström's performance was compared with tests the previous autumn of the recently introduced Horwich 2-6-0. The Ljungström was beset with minor troubles throughout the trials—faulty combustion, leaking firebox stays and foundation ring, leakage from all sorts of other places and a jammed damper in the air duct to the ashpan on the first trial on March 28. Although she generally kept scheduled section times and of course the consumption of water was far less, the consumption of coal, on a drawbar horsepower per hour basis, was four per cent. more than her smaller, much simpler and far cheaper rival.(19)

This sounded the death-knell of the Ljungström and in addition there seem to have been problems over the licensing arrangements with the Ljungström Turbine Company in Sweden.(20) The turbine locomotive was a most expensive machine to build costing around £37,000 compared with £6,000 for an ordinary engine and this, allied to the likely problems of maintaining a boiler with such high pressure, the complicated auxiliaries as well as

the condenser itself, outweighed the advantages there ought to have been from increased thermal efficiency. It remained stored out of use at Gorton Foundry until 1940. Then the stationary boiler feeding steam to the boilershop required replacement and, through the difficulty in obtaining materials for the construction of a new boiler, the one off the Ljungström was used instead.(21)

* * * * *

Financial Problems

Not only did Beyer, Peacock face the problems of starting locomotive production again in 1919, but wages and the price of raw materials had escalated during the war so that the costs of those contracts held over had increased enormously.(22) Most customers were willing to pay the difference but there was a further dislocation at the end of 1919 caused by a 5 months strike of moulders in the foundry. This led to a deficit of £17,000 in 1920, when the dividend on the ordinary shares was passed. Conditions improved and a 5 per cent. dividend was paid in both the next two years, but then came the slump after the boom at the end of the First World War. Recovery started again in 1925, with large numbers of both Garratts and ordinary locomotives being built, but Sir Sam Fay expressed dissatisfaction with the financial results because Gorton Foundry had been fully occupied, yet was producing ordinary engines at costs greater than those of their competitors.(23) A 2½ per cent. dividend was paid in 1927, while 1928 was a record year when a total of 5 per cent. was paid on the ordinary shares.

In his Annual Report of 1928, Sir Sam Fay wrote;

"The works have been fully employed; indeed at no period in the Company's history has a greater output been recorded. The fact that some of this work has been executed at unsatisfactory prices, in order to ensure a balanced flow of orders through the shops, is due to the acute competition for locomotive contracts both from home and abroad... "We have a very satisfactory amount of work in hand, in fact at no period in the history of the Company has there been a greater tonnage of orders on our books, representing today upwards of a million and a quarter pounds sterling."(24)

In 1927 the number of Garratts exceeded that of ordinary locomotives for the first time in any one year and this was to happen again in 1929 and 1930. Generally trading was satisfactory in spite of the fact that a great many orders had been placed for only a few locomotives of each type.

Following a very good year in 1930, when over ninety Beyer-Garratts were produced, the dividend was raised to 8 per cent. The Chairman's Report was full of optimism, but by contrast that for 1931 was a sorry tale, with a massive trading loss of over £67,000. The world-wide depression of the nineteen-thirties was biting hard, causing a sharp decline in orders for locomotives, and the reserves provided in the 1930 accounts were quite inadequate to meet such severe slump conditions. No dividend was paid on the ordinary shares from then until 1946, and payments were temporarily suspended on the preference shares. Workmen too had to be laid off. The total weight of locomotives exported from Great Britain fell from 50,566 tons in 1930 to 19,852 tons in 1931,(25) and other countries where locomotives were built suffered similarly. At Gorton, only forty-one locomotives were delivered in

1931, compared with ninety-six the year before, while in 1932 the number fell to only twelve. In 1933 it rose to thirty-two, but then fell drastically again to six in 1934 and nine in 1935.

In 1932, Beyer, Peacock purchased for £27,250 the Richard Garrett engineering works at Leiston, Suffolk, which was in the hands of the receiver following the failure of the Agricultural & General Engineers Ltd. Garretts had been famous for its steam traction engines, steam road lorries as well as agricultural equipment but, with the demise of the steam engine for road haulage and the rise of the internal combustion engined tractor on the land, could not make similar products in sufficient quantities to compete with other rival mass-producers. It is difficult to see why Beyer, Peacock should have been interested in this firm except for the rumour that Sir Sam Fay had a lady-friend at Aldeburgh and he thought that by having a subsidiary company near-by he could combine business with pleasure. At first Garretts did not help Beyer, Peacock's financial position, but, by securing orders to build Elliott shaping machines and then war munitions, Garretts began to produce a small dividend.(26)

In this period, there were many changes in the top personnel of the Company. R.H. Whitelegg's appointment as General Manager terminated in 1929, and he was replaced by Samuel Jackson, who became "Manager, Gorton Foundry" from 1 January 1930. At the same time, Harold Wilmot, who by then had become Chief Accountant, acquired the unusual designation of "Comptroller". In 1933, Sir Sam Fay resigned as Chairman and also as a Director, being succeeded for a time by Mr. Burchell, followed in 1937 by Captain Hugh Vivian of Vivian & Sons Copper Works, in Swansea. By the end of 1933, the entire factory was reduced to a mere "caretaker" basis with practically all employees suspended and the outlook grim. In fact, precautionary notices of termination of employment were given to all officials of the Company except Jackson, Williams, Wilmot and Welsh.(27)

In 1934, Harold Wilmot became General Manager, and in 1938 Managing Director. It was he who steered the Company's affairs through their worst period between 1932 and 1935, when they were in real danger of complete collapse, and thus began the "Wilmot Era" which was to endure for over thirty years. He was a powerful driving force and a mighty leader, ably supported by Samuel Jackson, who was responsible for all the technical side. James Hadfield, who had already been in the Drawing Office, and on the works management staff, returned to the Drawing Office as Acting Chief Draughtsman when it reopened in 1934. He moved to the works team in 1937 on the promotion of Fred Williams to Chief Draughtsman, a person highly respected and with long experience there.

This was the new team which was faced with the task of building up production as orders began to trickle in again. Some of the difficulties they experienced may be judged from the fact that in 1934, the total tonnage of work passing through Gorton Foundry, including the six locomotives built that year and spares, was only 615 tons compared with 6,000 to 7,000 in an average year. In January 1935, 179 men were employed on £24,475 worth of "Work in Hand", but by May the figures had shrunk to 81 and £16,948. Then the outlook began to improve, and in January 1936, 584 men were employed.(28) The amount of "Work Completed" in 1934 was £51,975, in 1935 it was £101,358 and in 1936, £282,237. The storm had been weathered. Orders for locomotives started to come in in reasonable numbers, with a preponderance for Beyer-Garratts. The gamble was at last paying off, in contrast with some other private builders. Hawthorn Leslie merged with Robert Stephenson in 1937 and Armstrong Whitworth was forced to stop locomotive production in 1937. Kitson followed suit in 1938, and Nasmyth Wilson closed down in 1939.

Throughout this period there was a severe shortage of capital, even to cover the reduced scale of locomotive building, and of course overheads were high. Special arrangements were made to finance the locomotives built for Russia, and then the Midland Bank and loans from the Prudential Assurance Company helped to keep Beyer, Peacock afloat. While the overdraft increased from £27,000 in 1931 to £126,000 in 1936, it was balanced by good numbers of locomotives being produced. From 1937 onwards, under the Government rearmament programme, a disused part of the works became a shell manufacturing shop, and the steel foundry output included bomb castings. The summer of 1939 saw Gorton Foundry once more in full production, with a very healthy order book and profits at a reasonable level, but September brought the outbreak of the Second World War, followed by Government control for the second time in the Company's history.

H. Wilmot.

S. Jackson.

13

The Garratt Matures,
1924-1927

Beyer, Peacock's growing business in Garratt locomotives was protected by a patent which normally would have expired in June 1923, but, on account of the interruption caused by the First World War, an extension of four and a half years was granted, deferring the expiry date to the end of 1927. The Company was determined to try to develop as much of this market as possible itself, so that it would be in a strong position when the patent terminated, although the orders for prototypes received during this period were more an investment for the future than a source of immediate profit.(1) At first, orders were slow coming in, but in the later 1920s they came from railways scattered all over the world, and to cope with the flood, the number of draughtsmen rose to about seventy. At one time sets of manufacturing drawings for five new designs of Garratt, all urgently required, were in course of preparation simultaneously. This was the busiest period for the Drawing Office in the history of the Company.

The first Garratt supplied after the First World War to a country outside Southern Africa had the distinction of being the first for the standard 4ft. 8½in. gauge, the first industrial type, and the first to work in Great Britain. It was a non-superheated 0-4-0 + 0-4-0, built in 1924 for Vivian & Sons Copper Works, Hafod, Swansea (Order 02353), with a maximum axle load of 16.5 tons, 27,880lb. Tractive Effort, and designed to operate on a 1 in 20 gradient, with many 150ft. radius curves, and one of only 97ft. The line was laid out in 1919, to link the copper works with the Great Western Railway, and was very difficult to operate, owing to the restricted area and great difference in levels. The Garratt successfully replaced two ordinary tank engines, which had been supplied new in 1919, and on test hauled 168 tons, which was 33 per cent. above the load hauled by the other engines.(2)

[Below] The first Garratt to work in Britain was also the first standard gauge and the first industrial type. It was built for Vivian & Sons Copper Works, Swansea [02353] in 1924.

Three more were built to this design, with minor modifications. One was supplied to Sneyd Collieries, Staffordshire (Order 1173) in 1932, where it had to haul empty wagons up a 1 in 18 gradient, on curves of 90ft. radius. The next (Order 1177) was built in 1934 for Guest, Keen, Baldwins Iron & Steel Company's Cardiff works, while the last (Order 1187) was supplied to Baddesley Colliery, near Atherstone, Warwickshire, in 1937. This one enabled 70 per cent. greater loads to be handled, with consequent saving in time and operational costs. It ceased working in 1963, and is now preserved at Bressingham Steam Museum, in Norfolk.

The first eight-coupled Garratt appeared at this time, a 2-8-0 + 0-8-2 built in 1924 for the metre gauge Burma Railways (Order 02396). The section for which it was ordered was on the Lashio branch, 11 miles of 1 in 25 grade, with numerous reverse curves of 330ft. radius, and no intervening tangent, or grade compensations, for curvature. Beyond this section, the ruling grade was 1 in 40. Almost from its inception, Burma Railways were forced to use articulated locomotives, first Fairlies, then

[Above] The Vivian Garratt and the tank engines it replaced.

[Heading] Tea in a Garratt boiler.

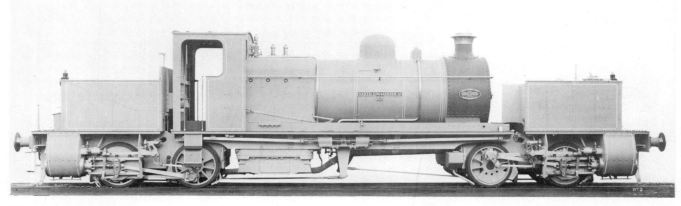

[Above] The Beyer-Garratt for Sneyd Collieries [1173] supplied in 1932.

[Below] The first 8-coupled Garratt [02396] showed its superiority over both Fairlies and Mallets on the Burma Railways.

Mallets, so the Garratt faced stiff competition. It was tested against a compound, superheated Mallet on the 1 in 25 grade and, although it was the most powerful locomotive built so far for the metre-gauge, and 40 per cent. more powerful than anything previously used on that railway, it emerged triumphant, showing a fuel economy of 18.5 per cent. and hauling a greater load.(3)

[Below] The front engine unit of the compound Garratt for the Burma Railways.

	Mallet	Garratt
Load hauled Sedaw to Thondaung [1 in 25]	145 tons	212.7 tons [max 220]
Average load hauled to Thondaung to Maymo [1 in 40]	259.4 tons	357.4 tons
Average consumption of coal per 100 ton miles	67.9lb.	55.3lb.
Average water evaporated per lb. of fuel burned	7.42lb.	9.44lb.
Coal burned per sq.ft. of grate per hour of running time	44 lb.	37 lb.
Fuel saving effected		18.5%

[4]

In 1926, a sister engine was built (Order 1119), redesigned as a compound, with two high-pressure cylinders on the rear unit and two low-pressure cylinders on the front. Little advantage was gained so, on the basis of operating experience, the simple-expansion Garratt became the standard type for Burma Railways from then onwards, and this one, and the two built for Tasmania in 1909, were the only compound Garratts ever built. The following year Burma Railways ordered three more simple Garratts (Order 1129), which were dimensionally similar to the original design of 1924, but with various detail improvements. A repeat order for ten, put out to open tender in 1929, was secured by Krupps of Essen at a time when German builders were heavily undercutting competitors' prices; by that time, of course, the basic Garratt patent had expired. This design was the basis for another batch built in the Second World War.

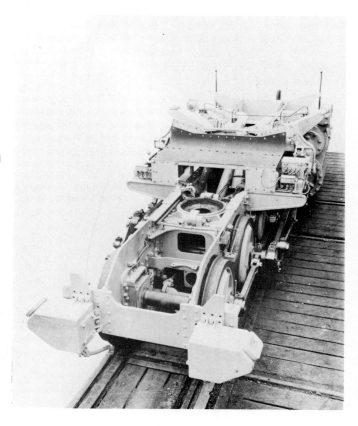

The success of the South African "GA" Garratt, followed by the performance of the Garratt for Burma, showed the superiority of this type over the Mallet, and did not pass unnoticed by other locomotive builders, who wished to participate in such a profitable venture. As Beyer, Peacock would not grant licences to other manufacturers, or certainly not in Britain, Armstrong Whitworth defied the patent in 1924 by building two 4-6-0 + 0-6-4 Garratts for the F.C. Pacifico of Columbia. A Beyer, Peacock official inspected these engines at Newcastle-upon-Tyne, and Armstrong Whitworth, after admitting that these did infringe the patent, agreed not to build any more until it had expired.(5) However, in 1928 when the patent had expired, it built two 2-6-2 + 2-6-2s for the Great Western Railway of Brazil. Both these designs were very much copies of earlier Beyer, Peacock practice.

The large diameter of the low pressure cylinders on the front bogie of this Garratt for Burma [1119] should be compared with the high pressure ones on the earlier design. The tanks on the bogies were modified considerably for this order and the next [1127].

In 1924, Goldschmidt and Weber patented the rival, Golwé design. The front tank of the Garratt was dispensed with, which allowed the front bogie unit to be moved under the boiler barrel, while the rear engine unit was retained as in the Garratt, and carried the water in a "U" shaped tank. The fuel bunker was mounted at the rear of the boiler frame, more or less concealed within the "U" of the water tank. This type was claimed to retain the advantages of a large boiler and firebox virtually unimpeded by the wheels, while having the additional advantage of being shorter. Four were built by Haine-Saint-Pierre in 1927, and sent to the Ivory Coast Railway, but the type was never repeated.(7)

Garratts were designed for exceptional circumstances where ordinary locomotives were inadequate, for one reason or another. The Garratt was an obvious choice where banking locomotives were required to assist trains up steep inclines, and the next two types to be described were intended for this purpose. On the Mush Kaf - Bolan

The only type of "Golwé" locomotive was built by Haine-St.-Pierre in 1927 for the Ivory Coast Railway.

In 1925, the North British Locomotive Company, which had supplied many Mallets to South Africa, tried to jump on the Garratt bandwagon by designing a rival articulated locomotive which was called the "Modified Fairlie". This looked very much like a Garratt, but the tanks fore and aft were mounted on the main frames and only the wheels, cylinders and their associated frames were pivoted. The North British Locomotive Company supplied a prototype "FC" class, followed by four larger "FD" class 2-6-2 + 2-6-2 locomotives, to South Africa, while Henschel won an order for eleven 2-8-2 + 2-8-2 class "HF" for the same railway, but the bigger this type of engine became, the worse its deficiencies appeared. With both front and rear tanks cantilevered out beyond the pivots, the engines did not take the curves so well as a Garratt, and there was greater pivot wear.(6)

section of the North Western Railway of India, three or four Consolidation engines were needed to handle each 160-ton train, where the gradients varied from 1 in 50 to 1 in 25. It was decided to try both Mallet and Garratt types, so the first heavy main line broad-gauge 2-6-2 + 2-6-2 Garratt (Order 111) was built as a direct comparison with a Mallet, rather than as a double one of the HGS 2-8-0 Consolidations. The Garratt started life with the disadvantage of being heavier than specified, partly due to the inclusion of many Indian State Railway standard details, but it could push 354 tons up the inclines unassisted, compared with 160 tons for the Consolidations. Some thirty large four-cylinder 2-10-0s on the Great Indian Peninsular Railway became redundant which the North Western snapped up, no doubt at a bargain price; thus no more Garratts were ever ordered, the prototype being scrapped in 1937.(8)

For similar duties, in May 1924(9) the London & North Eastern Railway ordered a 2-8-0 + 0-8-2 six-cylinder type

[Top] The 2-6-2 + 2-6-2 Garratt built in 1925 for the North Western Railway of India [111].

[Above] The London & North Eastern Railway Garratt [112] was the largest steam locomotive ever to work in the British Isles.

[Facing page] The London & North Eastern Railway Garratt being constructed at Gorton Foundry.

(Order 112), weighing 178 tons, and with 72,930lb. Tractive Effort—the most powerful steam locomotive ever built for any British railway. It was to replace pairs of Robinson 2-8-0s for banking 1,200 ton coal trains up the Worsborough incline, a 2½ mile section of 1 in 40 grade on the Wath to Penistone freight line. It originated in a 1912 project for the Great Central Railway (scheme 81865), but as discussions progressed, it gradually departed from Beyer, Peacock practice and finally incorporated most of the running gear of the Great Northern 02 Class 2-8-0, including the Gresley conjugated levers for operating the piston valve of the inside cylinder by a combination of movements of the two outside valves. Each group of cylinders drove the second coupled axle with cranks at 120 degrees.(10)

By a tremendous effort in the Drawing Office and works, the design and manufacture were completed just in time for it to run at Darlington on 2 July 1925, in the memorable procession of ancient and modern locomotives which highlighted the Centenary Celebrations of the opening of the Stockton & Darlington Railway. Mechanical stokers were then unknown on British railways (and never have been used to any great extent), so not surprisingly this mighty locomotive, with the largest diameter boiler ever used on any locomotive in Britain and with 56.5sq.ft. of grate area, was not particularly popular with firemen, but it did very well until about 1949 when the section was electrified. Later it was converted to oil-burning at the Gorton Works of the old Great Central, and transferred to the Lickey Incline for similar banking duties, but soon the policy of conversion to diesel and electric traction, plus the cost of maintaining this one-off special led to its withdrawal and scrapping in 1955.

The "Super-Garratt" which was never built.

While on the subject of giant locomotives, an ambitious design to which Beyer, Peacock gave the name "Super-Garratt" was patented (No. 230,888) in 1925. This was a hybrid of the Garratt and Mallet types, forming what might be called a "double-articulated" locomotive.(11) One of the designs proposed, possibly in conjunction with the American Locomotive Co.,—a 2-6-6-2 + 2-6-6-2 intended for railways in the U.S.A.—was estimated to weigh 460 tons in working order. With 13,330 gallons of water, 16 tons of coal, it would have had a tractive effort of 203,250lb! The boiler was to be 10ft. diamter, and the overall dimensions were 142ft. long, 16ft. 7in. high, by 12ft. wide. From intimate knowledge of the design of Beyer-Garratt locomotives, it is probably all for the best that the Super-Garratt never progressed beyond the drawing board.

One of the great advantages of the Garratt locomotive was its ability to spread the weight over a large number of axles, thus reducing the individual axle-load, and also reducing the weight per foot run. The first Garratts supplied to the Argentine went to the standard-gauge Argentine North Eastern Railway where bridges limited the axle-load to 12½ tons. In 1925, three 2-6-0 + 0-6-2s (Order 114) were built with axles widely spaced to give a very low weight per foot run. Their advent provided an increase of more than 71 per cent. in tractive effort over the line's existing locomotives, for an increase in total weight of only 21 per cent., while there was an economy of 40 per cent. in running costs. A repeat order (No. 1117) for four more was delivered in 1927, together with five for the neighbouring Entre Rios Railway (Order 1121), the latter having larger water and fuel capacity.

[Above] The wheel centres were spaced far apart on the Garratts for the Argentine North Eastern Railway [114] to distribute the weight over as large an area as possible.

[Below] Between 1925 and 1927, Beyer, Peacock modified the style of the front water tanks and also fitted self-trimming bunkers on the rear bogie, so the outline of these Garratts for the Entre Rios Railway [1121] has altered considerably compared with those for the Argentine North Eastern [114].

Identical boilers, and many other detail parts, were used on another design to meet similar conditions on the Entre Rios Railway. Five 4-4-2 + 2-4-4s (Order 1122), with 4ft. 8in. coupled wheels, intended for passenger service, were supplied in 1927. They were an immediate success, with the result that in 1930 three more were delivered to the associated Argentine North Eastern Railway (Order 1163) and all eight were converted to burn oil fuel in 1942. The only other Garratts with the Atlantic wheel arrangement were the two supplied to Tasmania (Order 0303) in 1912.

The passenger type Garratt at work on the Entre Rios Railway near Concordia soon after arrival there.

Limitations on axle-loading imposed by light track were often found on narrow-gauge lines and Garratts enabled the line capacity to be increased by hauling greater loads on existing track without the need for relaying. Good examples of this were the two 2-6-0 + 0-6-2 Garratts despatched to the Victorian Government 2ft. 6in.-gauge railways (Order 117) in April 1926. Although the axle-load was limited to 9.5 tons, they were used for hauling heavy timber traffic, and their introduction enabled a considerable reduction in train mileage to be achieved, beside a fuel economy of around 40 per cent. They could handle 255 tons on 1 in 30 grades, compared with the 68 tons of engines they replaced. One is now preserved by the Puffing Billy Preservation Society.

[Above] One of these chunky Garratts for the 2ft. 6in. gauge Victorian Government Railway [117] is now preserved in Australia.

[Below] These 2-6-2 + 2-6-2 Garratts for the Sierra Leone Government Railway [1111] were very successful and orders for many more followed.

Even more severe restrictions were placed on the first order for the Sierra Leone Government Railway, which was for three 2ft. 6in. gauge 2-6-2 + 2-6-2s (Order 1111). Owing to the 30lb. rails, and wide spacing of the sleepers, the maximum axle-load was only 5 tons, but these interesting little locomotives, built in 1926, showed what the Garratt could do to increase the capacity of railways laid with very light, poorly ballasted track. They weighed 46.65 tons yet developed 17,000lb. Tractive Effort. Three more were supplied in 1928 (Order 1135), and a further two in 1929 (Order 1149). In 1932, a basically similar

engine was supplied to the Nepal Government Railway (Order 1175) and the Sierra Leone Government Railway had a further six in 1942 (Order 11119), while the Nepal Government Railway had one more in 1947 (Order 11138). The reason for the success of this design is not hard to seek, for extensive tests were carried out with the first engines and the comparative results obtained against the performance of trains hauled by a tender and a tank locomotive speak for themselves.

	Tender Engine	Tank Engine	Engines 167 & 34 combined	Garratt Engine 51	Difference in favour of Garratt
Load tons,			184.35	182.8	
Coal consumed per engine mile [lb.]	31.44	21.22	52.66	30.6	22.06
Total coal consumed [lb.]	4,339	2,928	7,267	4,220	3,047 [1 ton, 7cwt. 23lb.]
Coal consumed per 100 ton-miles [lb.]			29.41	17.22	12.19 or 41.4%
Water consumed [gallons]	3,364	2,289	5,653	3,362	2,291
Water in lb. per lb. of coal	7.75	7.81	7.78	7.96	0.18 or 2.3%
Coal consumed per sq.ft. of grate area per hour of running time	32.87	42.58	36.19	21.07	15.12 or 41.78% [12]

The first type of Garratt locomotive for the Bengal Nagpur Railway [115] weighed 180 tons.

The massive boiler for the Bengal Nagpur Garratt.

Line capacity was also increased on standard and broad gauge lines by the use of Garratts, particularly for hauling goods trains. Frequent double heading was necessary on the Bengal Nagpur Railway in India which served a vast area, embracing no less than five coal fields, and extensive mineral deposits of iron ore, manganese and limestone, the whole yielding a heavy traffic and calling for the most efficient means of transport over mostly single track line. Such undertakings as the most important steel works in India were served by the railway and handling grain, timber, salt and cotton, besides a large pilgrim traffic, intensified the problems of operation. Therefore two 5ft. 6in. gauge 2-8-0 + 0-8-2 Garratts, weighing 180.55 tons, and with a 56,825lb. Tractive Effort, were purchased in 1925 (Order 115), to test the merits of the type for hauling heavy mineral trains unassisted. They were the heaviest Garratts built up to that date and had boilers 7ft. in diameter, and a grate area of 67.3sq. ft., designed for burning low-grade coal. The results of trials, on which they proved able to handle the 1,650 ton loads previously requiring two engines, led to further valuable orders later.

Another design for goods haulage was prepared for the Nitrate Railways (Chile) (Order 119), which ordered three massive standard-gauge 2-8-2 + 2-8-2s in 1925, the heaviest and most powerful so far. Engines built at Gorton Foundry at this period were sold virtually at cost price, and no profit was made on these.(13) They had a tractive effort of 78,370lb. and weighed 187.15 tons, with an 18-ton maximum axle-load. The coupled wheels were only 3ft. 6in. in diameter, and because of this there was the unusual condition of cylinders with bore larger than stroke (22in. x 20in.). New features for the engine units included bar frames, which were 5in. thick, cut from solid steel slabs; and radial arm bogies, instead of Cartazzi axleboxes, for the inner carrying wheels. They were the first Garratts initially designed and built for oil burning. The boiler was 7ft. 3 3/8in. in diameter with a grate area of 68.8sq. ft. and equipment included a Worthington-Simpson combined feed pump and feed water heater.

The line, which must be considered one of the most difficult in the world, rises 3,000ft. in 20 miles, with 1 in 25 gradients uncompensated, and curves of 280 to 350ft. radius, of which there were no less than 173 in the dis-

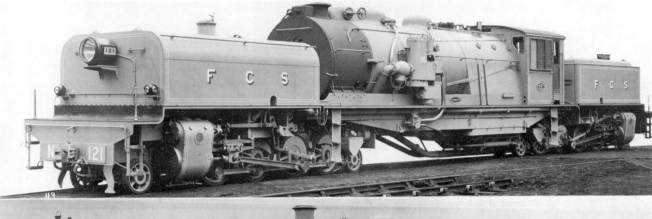

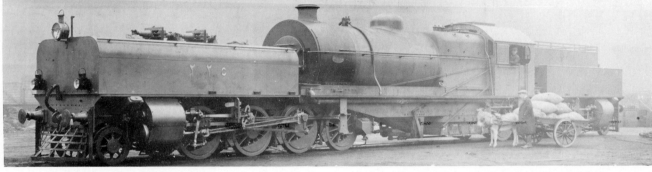

tance, making a resistance to traction equivalent to a 1 in 21 grade. Under these conditions, a high proportion of the available power was absorbed in moving the locomotive itself. In this case, the Garratt had a tractive effort of 370lb. per ton of locomotive weight, compared with 278lb. for the 4-8-4 tank engines previously used, and with a trailing load of 400 tons, compared with 180 tons for the 4-8-4T, the train weight/engine weight ratio was almost 40 per cent. higher. Three Garratts performed the work of seven tank engines, saving something like £60,000 (they cost £45,000) in running and traffic expenses in 1928 alone.(14) Three more of these giant locomotives were ordered in 1928 (Order 1133), and all six continued at work until they were replaced by diesels in 1959.

Not every prototype led to a production order, though that might have been caused by a decline in traffic through the world recession of the early 1930s, rather than any fault in the locomotive. This happened in the case of two orders which were placed in 1927, for standard-gauge Garratts to handle goods traffic. One 2-8-0 + 0-8-2 (Order 1113) was built for the Ottoman Railway (Smyrna to Aidin) which was then British owned. At the request of the railway company the design was very conservative for it was unsuperheated and had slide valves; a completely new set of drawings had therefore to be prepared for it. It

[Top and centre] Two views of the huge Garratts for the Nitrate Railway [119] on which oil-firing made the fireman's life easier.

[Bottom] The donkey cart was brought into Gorton Foundry specially to give an oriental flavour to this unofficial works photograph of the Garratt for the Ottoman Railway [1113]. Four screw lifting and traversing jacks are secured to the top of the front watertank.

worked on gradients of 1 in 36 through the Azizieh Pass but, partly through the Ottoman Railway being merged into the State system in 1935, as well as a decline in traffic, the type was never repeated.(15) The same fate befell three Garratts with the same wheel arrangement sent to the Mauritius Railway (Order 1126), where they could not be used to capacity. They had a tractive effort of 63,340lb. to cope with freight trains on 1 in 26 gradients. This contract is remembered mainly because it was delivered on time only 19 weeks from the date of order — a remarkable performance including, as it did, the preparation of a complete set of working drawings and tools.

[Top] The 2-8-0 + 0-8-2 for the Mauritius Railway [1126].

[Centre and bottom] The prototype Garratt for the London, Midland & Scottish Railway [1114].

Better fortune attended the introduction of the Garratt on the London, Midland & Scottish Railway, with three 2-6-0 + 0-6-2s (Order 1114), built for trial purposes. They were required for hauling coal trains of up to 1,500 tons on fast schedules between Toton Marshalling Yard in South Yorkshire, and Brent Sidings, in North London, and, to eliminate stops, were fitted with water scoops to pick up from the troughs. In designing these locomotives, Beyer, Peacock had to comply with the Railway's request to incorporate as many existing standard details as possible, so the engines departed from Beyer, Peacock practice in several ways, to the detriment of their performance. The insistence by the London, Midland & Scottish Railway on making certain parts the same as on the Horwich Moguls(16) led to the inclusion of relative short travel piston valves and rather undersized coupled axleboxes. Nevertheless they fulfilled their duties most creditably and led to a large batch being built in 1930.

[Top] The 2-6-2 + 2-6-2 Garratt for the Dundee Coal Co. [1118] in Natal.

[Middle] One of the Rhodesia Railways 13 Class Garratt [118] fitted with Lentz oscillatting cam poppet valves.

[Lower] The records make no mention about the enclosing of the motion, presumably to try to exclude dust and dirt, on this Rhodesia Railways 13 class Garratt.

The description "Industrial Locomotive" usually suggests 0-4-0 or 0-6-0 tank engines, but abroad it can mean something very different. In 1927, a 2-6-2 + 2-6-2 Garratt (Order 1118) weighing about 115 tons, and a tractive effort of 45,500lb., was built for the Dundee Coal Company, in Natal. This locomotive could haul 1,250 short tons on the eleven mile branch, and enabled the daily output of the colliery, about 5,000 tons, to be handled in practically half the number of trains. A similar locomotive (Order 1178) was supplied to the Consolidated Main Reef Gold Mining Company Ltd., in 1935.

Where there were long stretches of single track railway, the Garratt was particularly valuable because it could haul longer trains and increased the line capacity without increasing the numbers of trains. The success of the Garratt in South Africa led to a substantial order for twelve 2-6-2 + 2-6-2s (13th class) for the Rhodesia Railways (Order 118), which were built in 1925-26, the first of many mixed traffic types for that railway system, which extended over both Northern and Southern Rhodesia. The 13th class had a typical plate frame design of that period, similar to the South African "GD" class, but slightly larger, designed to operate on 1 in 50 grades uncompensated. Ten had piston valves, but two were fitted with Lentz oscillating cam poppet valves. The Walschaert's valve gear was designed to suit both types, and the cylinders were arranged with flanged joints on the steam ports to accommodate the alternative steam chests.

In 1926, the first of what was to become a great fleet of Garratts for mixed traffic duties was built for the metre-gauge Kenya & Uganda Railway (later East African Railways). The order (No. 1112) was for four class "EC", 4-8-2 + 2-8-4s designed for 10 tons maximum axle-load, weighing 125.35 tons and tractive effort of 40,260lb. A description of the line will be given later, in connection with subsequent orders. These engines were the first Garratts with this wheel arrangement, and at that date were the most powerful locomotives of any metre gauge railway. Many of the details of the cylinders, running gear and bogies were the same as on existing 4-8-0 tender engines, and, as built, they were designed for wood burning. Their immediate success led to orders for twenty more (Orders 1132 & 1137), the "EC1" class, with the water capacity increased by 1,000 gallons, and designed for coal firing. The original four, and two of the "EC1" class, were sold second-hand to the Yunnan Railway, in Indo-China, in 1939.

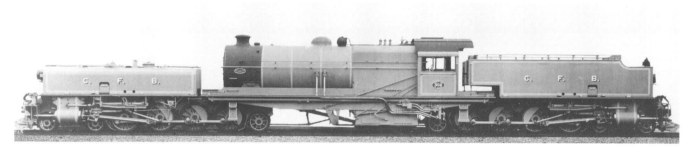

[Top] The first Garratts for East Africa were these Class EC 4-8-2 + 2-8-4 for the Kenya & Uganda Railway [1112] built in 1926.

[Middle] Garratts proved to be highly successful on the British owned Benguela Railway where the first ones were fitted with Lentz valves and burnt wood [1115].

[Lower] One of the first Garratts being erected on the Benguela Railway.

[Benguela Railway archives.]

Another design of mixed traffic Garratt with the same wheel arrangement was sent to the 3ft. 6in. gauge Benguela Railway in Angola. Six 4-8-2 + 2-8-4s (Order 1115) were built in 1927, and were the largest locomotives at that time on the 60lb rail, developing 52,360lb. Tractive Effort. The grate, which had an area of 51.5sq. ft., was designed to burn wood fuel. The bunkers could be seen piled high with eucalyptus logs, which they burned in large quantities while blasting up 1 in 40 grades on 300ft. radius curves, with a trailing load of 500 tons. The eucalyptus trees grew very fast, on Railway-owned land, alongside the track. All six engines of this class were fitted with Lentz oscillating cam poppet valves, driven by Walschaert's valve gear, of special light-weight design.

Garratts designed solely for passenger traffic were few in number, and those destined for express passenger work even fewer. In 1927 the San Paulo Railway wanted powerful locomotives to haul their express passenger trains from the head of the inclines at Alto de Serra to Jundiahy, about 70 miles, but including grades of up to 1 in 40. Six 2-6-2 + 2-6-2 Garratts (Order 1124) were built to an out-standing new design which, as speeds up to 60 mph were needed, had coupled wheels of 5ft. 6in. diameter, and developed 53,570lb. Tractive Effort. Five had piston valves, and the sixth Lentz oscillating cam poppet valves, with the valve gear designed to suit both. A Worthington-Simpson combined feed pump and feed water heater was fitted. These were the first Garratts designed for such high speeds, and after some years' service it was decided to improve the running, and increase the water capacity, by converting them to 4-6-2 + 2-6-4 in the Railway's workshop, using parts designed and supplied by Beyer, Peacock. The frames were cut off ahead of the outer coupled axles and extended in the form of a large steel casting; the cylinders and valve gear were moved bodily forward; new connecting and eccentric rods were fitted; and new four-wheeled bogies. Garratt locomotives do not easily lend themselves to graceful lines but this conversion made the appearance even more impressive, and these engines continued to work in this form until the line was electrified in 1950.

190

The casting for extending the frames of the San Paulo Railway Garratts.

Facing page

[Left top] This order [1171] for the Tanganykia Railway was similar to those for the Kenya & Uganda Railway except for the tilting front water tank to facilitate removing the boiler tubes.

[Left centre] The express passenger Garratt for the San Paulo Railway [1124] dwarfs a group of visitors alongside it.

[Bottom left] The San Paulo Railway express Garratt with passenger train.

[Bottom] Engine units for the San Paulo express Garratts ready for loading on board ship. Numbers 1 and 3 from the camera are fitted with Lentz valves, the other two, piston valves.

[Top] The loading gauge was very restricted on the Assam Bengal Railway so their Garratts [1127] had a squat appearance.

[Right] The Garratts for the Assam Bengal Railway leaving Gorton by train.

The rear engine unit for one of the Assam Bengal Railway Garratts being loaded on board ship.

The last two designs built under the original patent, in 1927, were both sent to Asia. The Assam Bengal, later Bengal Assam, Railway had a very difficult hill section between Badarpur and Lumding, a distance of 115 miles, most of which was on a gradient of 1 in 60, but one section of 11 miles was almost continuous 1 in 37, with uncompensated, unchecked curves of 440ft. radius. In addition, there were thirty-seven tunnels, some very wet, and areas of bad terrain, so that poor permanent way presented a really formidable obstacle for any locomotive. Five 2-6-2 + 2-6-2s (Order 1127) were built to a compact design which made the most of the space within the very restricted Indian metre-gauge loading limits. They enabled loads to be increased from 230 to 300 tons, and were the forerunners of later Garratts on this line.

The final design built in 1927 was a prototype 2-6-2 + 2-6-2 (Order 1128) for the mountain section of the 5ft. 6in. gauge Ceylon Government Railways. Over a stretch of 13 miles the line climbs 1,400ft., with a ruling gradient of

1 in 45 and curves of 10 chains radius. Full comparative trials were carried out against the customary pair of 4-6-0 engines. The same load was hauled by the Garratt with a saving in coal consumption of 20 per cent.(17) This was certainly a case of investing for the future, for it was not until 1946 that the Ceylon Government Railways were supplied with a further eight to this same basic design (Order 11131).

Garratt's patent expired at the end of 1927, and this chapter has shown the strides made in the development of his locomotive. The largest, the heaviest, the most powerful, are superlatives which have been used frequently to describe the engines built by Beyer, Peacock. The repeat orders have been included to demonstrate that the majority of these Garratts were well received and were able to do the tasks for which they had been designed. Such failures as occurred were more often than not due to restrictions placed on the design at the request of the railway company which was purchasing the locomotive. The words spoken by Sir Vincent Caillard at the Annual General Meeting in 1912 had proved to be a true forecast of the success of this type:

"As a last word, I should like to say that we have the possibility, I would almost say probability, of a branch of prosperity all our own in the 'Garratt' locomotive... Our anticipations... have been fully justified, the interest in it has in no way diminished, and the orders received are highly satisfactory... Our experience in the trade leads us to believe with great confidence that the 'Garratt' has come to stay, and that it is destined to supersede most existing types of articulated engines, and, indeed to extend the use of that particular type of locomotive altogether".(18)

[Below] The Ceylon Government Railways ordered this prototype Garratt [1128] in 1927 but waited eighteen years before purchasing any more.

One of the later Ceylon Government Railways Beyer-Garratts [11131] in 1973.
[L.A. Nixon]

193

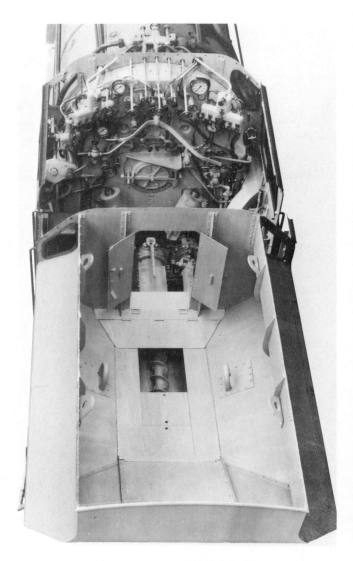

14

The Beyer-Garratt, 1928-1939.

While the Garratt had proved its superiority over the rival designs of articulated locomotives, there was another threat to the position so carefully built up by Beyer, Peacock, because, on the expiry of the patent, anybody could copy it. By long-established custom, locomotive builders had to supply complete sets of manufacturing drawings as part of the contract, and there was nothing to prevent the railway administration from subsequently putting out contracts to open tender on the basis of those drawings. From 1927 to the end of 1930, Gorton Foundry was working to capacity and, possibly through longer delivery dates given by Beyer, Peacock, as well as the fact that German firms were undercutting British prices, orders from South Africa and Burma were secured by foreign competitors. To differentiate its engines from those built by its competitors, Beyer, Peacock introduced the name ''Beyer-Garratt'' in 1928 and, with its greater experience, and the later improvements covered by other vital patents, Beyer, Peacock was able to arrange licensing agreements so that, from 1931 to 1958, all Garratts with only two exceptions were produced by Beyer, Peacock or its licensees, and therefore ought to be called ''Beyer-Garratts''.(1)

One of the later patents which helped to give Beyer, Peacock this pre-eminence was for a new form of adjustable pivot centre which was first applied in 1928 to the locomotives for New Zealand (Order 1134), and remained the standard design for this all-important part for about ten years. Inspired by the success of Gresley's three-cylinder engines, New Zealand Government Railways ordered three Beyer-Garratts for working their heavy mail trains, at speeds of up to 50 m.p.h., and tackling 1 in 40 gradients. They were built to the specifications of G.S. Lynde, Chief Mechanical Engineer, and were the first double-Pacific Beyer-Garratts, and the second and last

[Heading] Garratts came in all sizes, the large one for Peru and the small one for Ceylon.

[Below] The Beyer-Garratt locomotive for the New Zealand Government Railway [1134] was fitted with a mechanical stoker so the coal bunker was built on the boiler frame, something found to be unnecessary later.

[Above] The cab and bunker of the New Zealand Beyer-Garratt, showing the screw feed for the mechanical stoker.

design with three cylinders on each bogie, using the Gresley conjugated system of levers for operating the valves of the inside cylinders.(2) With a grate area of 58.2 sq. ft. a mechanical stoker was obviously necessary, so the coal bunker was mounted on an extension of the boiler frames. This feature, which was shown later to be unnecessary, was patented jointly by Beyer, Peacock, and the German firm of J.A. Maffei, which built one type called the "Garratt Union" for the South African Railways.(3)

With a maximum height of only 11ft. 6in., a 6ft. 6in. diameter boiler, six cylinders, 4ft. 9in. coupled wheels, mechanical stoker, Westinghouse brake equipment, etc., the Drawing Office had quite a problem fitting it all in on a 3ft. 6in. gauge locomotive. The design was a tremendous advance in power—almost too much for the standard couplers—but was a failure in service. The mechanical stokers gave constant trouble, and the engines proved to be wildly extravagant in fuel, possibly due to the stokers. In spite of many modifications, reliability and performance were not improved, so the engines were never used on passenger services. With a decline in goods traffic there were few duties which required such great power, so that in 1935 the decision was taken to rebuild them as 4-6-2 tender engines.(4)

Better fortune attended the introduction of the Garratt elsewhere. In South America, a large part of the Argentine is fairly level, but there was scope for Garratts because the track of the 5ft. 6in. gauge Buenos Ayres Great Southern Railway was lightly ballasted, and permitted an axle-load of only 12.7 tons. In 1928, twelve oil burners with 4-8-2 + 2-8-4 wheel arrangement (Order 1131) were introduced for hauling heavy freight traffic, in trains of up to 1,700 tons, over a distance of 554 km, and turn round without change. Not only did they reduce the number of trains by half, but banking was eliminated. Later, loads up to 2,300 tons were managed. On another section of the line they were able to handle the traffic in two trains instead of the previous five.

In the following years the Buenos Ayres & Pacific ordered three Beyer-Garratts with the same wheel arrangement and 5ft. diameter wheels for similar duties. (Order 1142). While weighing 191.65 tons, they developed only 50,420lb. Tractive Effort. In addition to their own 5,000 gallon tanks, a large auxiliary water tank could be coupled on for long hauls, and, with a trailing load of 1,150 tons, on a 1 in 90 gradient, these engines made an impressive sight. In 1931 at the British Empire Exhibition in Buenos Aires, a fourth was exhibited on which the fire-box was fitted with two Nicholson thermic syphons, and a steam-operated coal-pusher of American type was placed in the 10 ton bunker, to work the coal forward.(5) All four were converted to oil fuel in 1941.

Loading parts of the Beyer-Garratt for the Buenos Ayres Great Southern Railway at Mode Wheel lock on the Manchester Ship Canal.

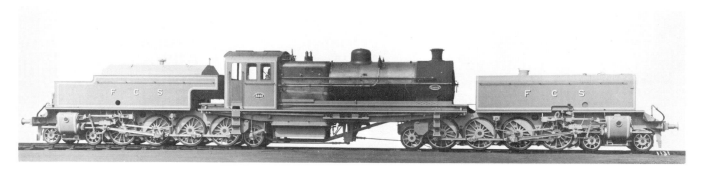

[Above] The fuel oil tank of this oil-burning Beyer-Garratt for the Buenos Ayres Great Southern Railway [1131] was situated in the rear engine unit.

[Below] The 4-8-2 + 2-8-4 Beyer-Garratt for the Buenos Ayres & Pacific Railway [1142].

[Top] The 4-8-2 + 2-8-4 Beyer-Garratt for the Buenos Ayres & Pacific Railway on display at the British Empire Exhibition at Buenos Aires in 1931.
[S. V. Blencowe Col.]

[Above] Boilers for the Buenos Ayres & Pacific Railway Beyer-Garratts leaving Gorton.

[Lower] The Buenos Ayres Midland Railway [1147] fired their engines with coal, and fitted feed water heaters and boiler feed pumps on the side of the boiler.

In 1930, an order for two Beyer-Garratt Pacifics for the Buenos Ayres Midland Railway (Order 1147) led to more extensive purchases for the Leopoldina Railway, which had two similar ones (Order 1148) in the same year. The Leopoldina Railway was the largest metre gauge line in Brazil, with nearly two thousand miles of track, which traversed, for the most part, very mountainous country, with the consequent heavy grades and curvature. These engines were 60 per cent. more powerful than any other owned by the Railway, and were used with immediate success to operate the heavy night passenger service between Campos and Victoria, a distance of 323 km, with a ruling grade of 1 in 33, and 250ft. radius curves. Not only could they burn low grade fuel, but also hauled loads 75 per cent. greater than the ordinary Pacifics, at improved speeds, so a further six were built in 1937 (Order 1191), and another eight in 1946 (Order 11118).(6)

On the other side of South America, in the Andes, are to be found some of the most difficult to work railways in the world. On the 1 in 33 gradients of the Antofagasta & Bolivia Railway, where the axle-load was restricted to 13 tons, ordinary eight coupled locomotives were limited to a train of 234 tons. Experience with Garratts on other mountainous railways suggested that they would be superior to the Kitson Meyers, and provide the solution

of obtaining increased power. The three 4-8-2 + 2-8-4 Beyer-Garratts (Order 1138) delivered in 1929 had a 55,190lb. Tractive Effort (greater than those of the Buenos Ayres & Pacific), and could haul 424 tons over the worst sections, at a speed of 12 km.p.h. They were the most powerful metre gauge locomotives in the world at that time, and had a slight American air with a large bell. During the Second World War they were used extensively to haul metal ore trains when they were joined by Garratts from near-by railways to help out. In 1950, the original three were augmented by a further six (Order 11145), built to a slightly modernised design. It is interesting to note that this railway passes through Condor station, at 15,814ft. the highest in the world. Also in 1929 locomotives of almost identical design were built for the Cordoba Central Railway (Order 1144), but they were originally coal burners.(7)

The Cordoba Beyer-Garratts being loaded on board the ship. All available space on board was filled by the locomotives.

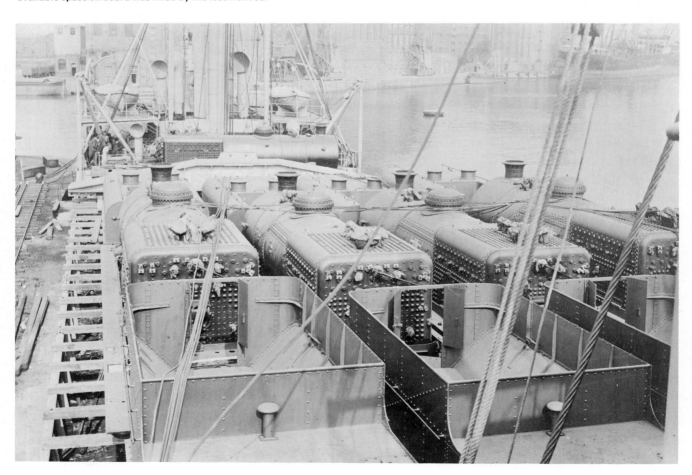

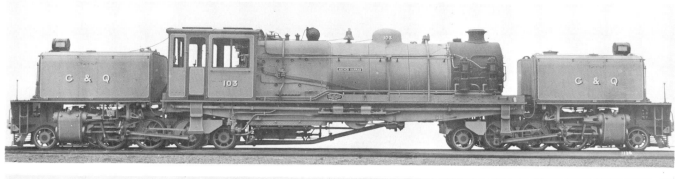

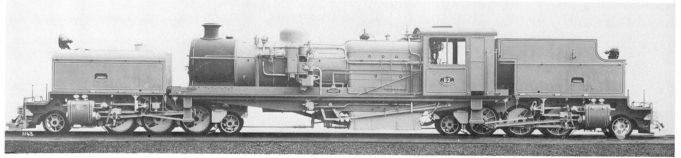

The 3ft. 6in. Guayaquil & Quito Railway, in Equador, is noteworthy for the exceptional nature of its line, being one of the steepest adhesion railways in the world. In 48 miles, it rises 9,650ft. with a ruling grade of 1 in 18 uncompensated, or 1 in 15 compensated. The total curvature amounts to 16,000 degrees, or the equivalent of 45 complete circles, mainly of 200ft. radius. To combine high power with extreme flexibility on curves, a 2-6-2 + 2-6-2 (Order 1139) was designed, with wheels only 3ft. 2in. in diameter, on a rigid wheelbase of 7ft. 3in., developing 42,990lb. Tractive Effort, and weighing 120.5 tons.

In that same year 1929, four 2-6-2 + 2-6-2s were sent to the metre-gauge Argentine Transandine Railway (Order 1143), which rose over 4,500ft. in 80 miles to the beginning of the rack section over the Andes themselves, and it was on the first part where these Beyer-Garratts worked.

[Top] To cope with the 1 in 15 gradients, the Beyer-Garratts for the Guayaquil & Quito Railway [1139] were built with large boilers and small diameter driving wheels.

[Centre] The Argentine Transandine Railway [1143] 2-6-2 + 2-6-2 Beyer-Garratts were used on inclines of 1 in 14.

[Above] An Argentine Transandine Railway Beyer-Garratt with passenger train soon after being put in service.

However in 1934, floods put the railway completely out of action, leaving two of the Garratts stranded for about five years. For a time some worked between Guemes and La Quiaca, where there was an 11 km section of rack, with a maximum grade of 1 in 14. Here the Garratts banked the rack locomotives, so that 380 tons instead of 180 could be hauled. In 1911 a scheme for a Garratt with rack mechanism on the front bogie had been prepared for this line, but none was ever built.(8)

[Above] The oil-fired Beyer-Garratt reached the highest point of any standard gauge railway at Callao, 15,693ft., on the Central Railway of Peru [1157].

[Below] The Rhodesia Railways 14th class Beyer-Garratt [1136] built in 1928 which incorporated all the latest improvements.

[Above] One of the Rhodesia Railways 14th class Beyer-Garratts piloting a goods train in 1975. [T. Middlemas Col.]

[Below] The Rhodesia Railways 16th class [1146] firmly established the Garratt in that country.

The last design of Beyer-Garratt for the Andes was ordered by the Central Railway of Peru, which received two 2-8-2 + 2-8-2 (Tractive Effort 64,790lb.) in 1930 (Order 1157), and a further one in 1932 (Order 1174). This railway reaches the highest point of any standard gauge main line in the world, where it passes through Callao, at an altitude of 15,693ft. In reaching this height, 61 tunnels, 41 bridges and 13 zig-zag reversing stations are encountered, and the ruling gradient is 1 in 22 uncompensated, with curves of 328ft. radius. It is probably the most spectacular adhesion railway in the world, but the zig-zags proved to be the undoing of the Garratts. On some sections, they could haul loads which were longer than could be accommodated in the reversing sidings and, with the ends of one or two lines already either built out over the side of the mountain on trestles or into the mountain wall itself, the zig-zags could not be lengthened. So the Garratts had to double-shunt their trains, which proved to be an operating nightmare. It was claimed that maintenance was higher than on two single engines, but the Corporation thought sufficiently highly of them to consider the purchase of standard Garratts for their Central and Southern Railways in 1955, although no order was ever placed.(9) The original three were used until 1966, when diesels took over.

The Beyer-Garratt was becoming well established in other parts of the world too for, as a result of the good performance of their first ones, the Rhodesia Railways ordered sixteen in 1928 and 1929 (Orders 1136 & 1156) of what became their 14 Class, which was a modernised version of the earlier ones, with all the latest improvements. They had open-back cabs, a feature found only on the Rhodesia and Benguela Railways. The Railway then ordered a 2-8-2 + 2-8-2 (Order 1146), designated the 16th Class, which produced 34 per cent. more power than the previous ones. Eight were built in 1929 and a further twelve in 1938 (Orders 1194 & 1197). These engines firmly established the Garratt on Rhodesia Railways for their running costs over the years proved to be lower than the standard 4-8-2 tender engines per ton mile. The maximum

permitted loads for these Beyer-Garratts over the section between Umtali and Salisbury, which has a ruling gradient of 1 in 60, were 520 tons for passenger trains, as against 395 for straight eight-coupled engines, and 700 tons for goods, as against 480 tons.

Spain, another mountainous country, was the home of many Garratts, but most were built in that country under licence. One exception was the pair of locomotives built by Beyer, Peacock in 1929 for the Rio Tinto Railway (Order 1145), to haul pyrites and sulphur 52 miles to the port of Huelva. Luckily the load was all in the downhill direction, so trains of 2,000 tons were sent down to the port while the Beyer-Garratts had to haul the empties back up, weighing only 550 tons. This was a new design, but another 3ft. 6in. gauge industrial railway, the Emu Bay Railway, of the Electrolytic Zinc Company of Tasmania, had three Beyer-Garratts (Order 1151) based on the Kenya & Uganda "EC" class for their 88 mile line.(10)

Then in 1929 two Beyer-Garratts which were the largest and most powerful yet produced, the mighty "GL" class, were completed for the South African Railways (Order 1141). Only the single Beyer-Garratt sent to the U.S.S.R. ever exceeded them in power and weight. These huge 4-8-2 + 2-8-4 locomotives weighed 214.1 tons and had a tractive effort of 89,130lb. Their massive bar frames were 5in. thick, and the 7ft. 3 3/8in. diameter boiler weighed 36 tons when empty. Two Nicholson thermic syphons were fitted in the firebox, and a fifty-element superheater, with multiple-valve regulator in the smokebox. This class incorporated the first full scale application to Garratts of mechanical stokers, in this case an American Duplex type.(11)

[Below] An industrial Beyer-Garratt for the Rio Tinto mineral railway [1145] in Spain.

[Foot] More Garratts for Tasmania. The Australian Electrolytic Zinc Company purchased for their Emu Bay Railway three Beyer-Garratts [1151] similar to those supplied to the Kenya & Uganda Railway.

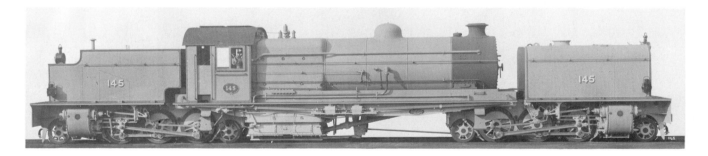

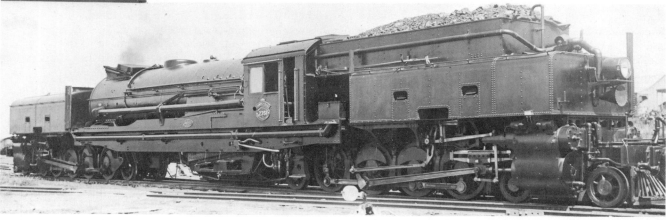

[Above] The South African Railways "GL" class [1141] was the most powerful Garratt ever built, developing 89,130lb. Tractive Effort. Very few South African Railway locomotives were named, and so calling this one "Princess Alice" was a great honour.

[Left] The South African Railways "GM" class was a very important design because its success led to many more orders later. Special track was laid out at Gorton to test the front hemispherical pivot, which allowed the front bogie to tilt relative to the rest of of the engine.

This South African Railways "GM" class was photographed with white boards behind it at either end to aid the photographer later when "touching out" [Order Nos. 1195 & 1196].

In Natal, the line from the port of Durban to the Transvaal and Johannesburg, via Pietermaritzburg, was one of the most important in the whole of South Africa, and carried heavy traffic in both directions. The 171 mile section beyond Pietermaritzburg had been electrified, but the heavily graded section of 73 miles from there down to Durban was still operated by steam. Although a new route, with 38 miles at 1 in 66, had been opened in 1921 to replace the old one, which had many miles at 1 in 30 and 300ft. radius curves, the Beyer-Garratts had to be designed to work over either line. Therefore they had to meet the same conditions as the existing Class "14" Mountain type tender engines, and had the same size wheels, cylinder bore and stroke. Thus they were double the power of the existing locomotives and 40 per cent. more powerful than any other engine in South Africa, yet they weighed only 214 tons, compared with 280 tons for a pair of ordinary engines. The great gain lay in the boiler, which had a grate area of 74.5 sq. ft., or larger than the combined Mountains and, incidentally, larger than any engine then running on the 5ft. 6in. gauge railways, yet weighed considerably less than the pair of Mountain boilers. The Garratt boiler, at 36 tons, was 35 per cent. lighter than the pair of Mountains at 56 tons, but was more efficient through its inherently better design, for it produced the same tractive effort, yet its evaporative heating surface was only 3,376 sq. ft. compared with 4,724 sq. ft. The Garratt also gained when comparing the tractive effort against weight for it produced 349lb. per ton against the 267lb. of the Mountains.(12)

The Class "14" locomotives hauled 500 tons at 14.5 m.p.h. up the new deviation towards Pietermaritzburg. On test runs, the first Beyer-Garratt was gradually worked up to 1,117 tons at a speed of 16.4 m.p.h. However, it was decided to restrict the load to 950 tons, which was the limit the electric locomotives could manage on the section beyond. So successful were these two Beyer-Garratts that after working for only seven weeks, an order (1162) for six more was cabled to Gorton. In 1930, the Governor-General of South Africa, the Earl of Athlone, wished to travel from Durban to Pietermaritzburg. One of the mighty "GL" class was assigned to the duty because the load of fourteen bogie carriages was too much for the ordinary locomotives to handle. One of the cases belonging to His Excellency was mislaid and, so that the train could be searched at the first stop, the driver speeded up the engine and gained thirteen minutes on schedule. Then in spite of two additional stops to enable His Excellency and Her Royal Highness Princess Alice to travel on the footplate, the train arrived at Pietermaritzburg on schedule, having averaged 26 instead of 22 m.p.h. (13)

Much more could be written about these remarkable locomotives, and how they have been moved from one set of arduous duties to another as electrification was gradually extended, but it is necessary to concentrate on the Beyer-Garratt story and move ahead to 1938, when the South African Railways faced power problems in handling the increasing traffic on the Johannesburg-Zeerust-Mafeking line, which was laid with 60lb. rail and had extensive sections of 1 in 40. Using the experience gained with the "GL" class, the "GM" was evolved (Orders 1195 & 1196). Both classes had hemispherical pivot bearings on the front bogies to give greater flexibility, and both had similar designs of boilers, with mechanical stokers, but, to reduce weight, the "GM" boiler was smaller, and the water capacity drastically reduced, so that coal only was carried on the rear unit, while the front carried a tank with just sufficient water for shunting purposes. The main water supply was carried in an auxiliary water tank mounted on bogies.(14)

In order to obtain 68,800lb. Tractive Effort on the 60lb. rail, the Civil Engineer permitted a maximum axle-load on the "GM" class of 15 tons on the driving wheels, subject to severe restrictions and lower loadings on the bogie axles, and certain restrictions on balancing. Roller bearings on all bogie axles, grease lubrication throughout except for cylinders and slide bars, and other features combined to reduce time and labour in servicing. These locomotives gave a 50 per cent. increase in power on a line where other Garratts such as the "GE" class were already in use, and gave an immediate increase in line capacity from 500 to 750 tons without relaying. With a coupled wheel diameter of 4ft. 6in. they could be used on passenger trains at speeds up to 45 m.p.h. They were the heaviest and most powerful locomotives ever placed on such a rail weight, and were remarkably successful, leading to further orders which were delayed by the Second World War.

In complete contrast to the South African locomotives was a "one-off" special 2ft. 6in. gauge 2-4-0 + 0-4-2, weighing only 39 tons, built in 1930 for a branch line on the Ceylon Government Railways (Order 1158). It replaced two 0-4-2 tank engines and enabled an increase of up to 83 per cent. in the weight of trains, with economies in coal consumption per ton mile of 17 per cent.

The two original Garratts on the Bengal Nagpur Railway had proved their value, for in 1930 a major order was fulfilled comprising sixteen class "N" 4-8-0 + 0-8-4s (Orders

1152, 1153, 1154), which ranked among the largest and most powerful Garratts ever built. They had a tractive effort of 69,660lb., and weighed 234 tons in working order, with 14 tons of coal and 10,000 gallons of water. On test they hauled 2,400 tons on the 1 in 100 ruling gradient. The 7ft. 0in. diameter boiler, designed to burn low grade fuel, had a grate area of 70 sq. ft. and, labour being cheap, they had two firemen, otherwise mechanical stokers would have been essential. The cab was exceptionally roomy, being 10ft. wide by 9ft. 6in. long.

The first ten had piston valves and Walschaert's valve gear, the next three Lentz rotary cam poppet valves, and the last three Caprotti poppet valves. Designing the frames to suit all these variations was quite an exercise. In addition all sixteen locomotives were fitted with a patented arrangement of built-in worm-geared lifting screws, whereby the front tank could be tilted to facilitate removal of the boiler tubes. Normally front tanks were formed with a recess at the inner end for this purpose, but in this case the tank had to hold 6,300 gallons of water, so to get the weight distribution right and also to be able to take out the tubes, which were 15ft. long, without removing the tank, the tank was designed to tilt.

[Above] The 2ft. 6in. gauge Ceylon Government Railways Beyer-Garratt [1158] being tested at Gorton.

[Facing page, upper centre] These 4-8-0 + 0-8-4 locomotives for the Bengal Nagpur Railway [1152] were amongst the largest Garratts ever built.

[Facing page, top] The mamoth floating crane loading parts of the Bengal Nagpur Beyer-Garratts.

[Facing page, lower centre] The next order for Beyer-Garratts on the Bengal Nagpur Railway [1166] was fitted with Lentz valves and reduced water and fuel capacity to bring the axle loading down to 17 tons.

[Facing page, foot] The final order for Beyer-Garratts for the Bengal Nagpur Railway [11113] was changed into a 4-8-2 + 2-8-4 type to improve the tracking qualities and also enable more coal and water to be carried while the axle loading of 17 tons remained the same.

This order was in turn followed by two (Orders 1166 & 1167) for ten ''NM'' class, which were built in 1930-31. To lower the axle loading from 20 to 17 tons, so that these engines could work over the more lightly-laid branch lines, the cylinder diameter and the boiler capacity were both slightly reduced, as were the water and coal capacities, to 6,000 gallons and 8 tons respectively. With a total weight of only 204 tons, they could haul 1,800 tons on a 1 in 100 grade. The experiments with different forms of valve gears were continued by having all ten of the class fitted with Lentz oscillating cam poppet valves and Walschaert's valve gear. Two had Nicholson thermic syphons in the fireboxes.

The story of the Beyer-Garrats on the Bengal Nagpur Railway is concluded with an order (No. 11113) for four ''P'' class, which were delivered in 1940. They were essentially the same as the ''NM'' class, but to enable them to work on the branch section to Chirmiri, which had numerous curves, and 54 miles long, they were built as 4-8-2 + 2-8-4. The trailing wheels helped them to take the curves better and also enabled the coal and water capacities to be increased, yet the axle loading remained the same at 17 tons. In this way, 3,000 more pounds of tractive effort could be introduced, and the need to relay the track with 90 instead of 75lb. rail was avoided. Once again no mechanical stoker was fitted, in spite of the grate area of 70 sq. ft., so that two firemen were carried, while a return had been made to piston valves.(15)

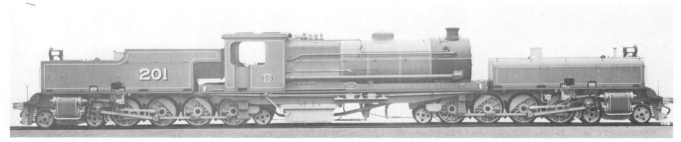

Normally the designs for new orders were up-dated with the latest technical features, and in 1930 an order (No. 1155) for fourteen locomotives for the Benguela Railway was no exception. These "10B" class were similar to the "10A", but had bar frames, which increased the weight to 168.4 tons. Also they had piston valves, "Alligator" crossheads, and longer connecting rods, driving the third coupled axle. Wood was still the fuel, but twenty years later they were converted to oil burning.

Moving further north in Africa, 1930 saw the first of a very successful range of Beyer-Garratts built for Nigeria. Here was a typical Garratt problem, for many weights of rail had been used in the construction of the lines, and on the Jebba to Minna section a rail of only 45lb. had been used, compared with 80lb. on an adjoining part. The axle-load was fixed at 9½ tons, yet Beyer, Peacock managed to produce two 4-8-2 + 2-8-4 Beyer-Garratts (Order 1159) that developed 39,920lb. Tractive Effort, and were the most powerful design ever built for this weight of rail. They were of conventional construction with plate frames, piston valves, Walschaert's valve gear, and Belpaire boilers.

These Beyer-Garratts proved their value, and indeed were capable of hauling a heavier train than could be taken over the 60lb. track on another section by the existing locomotives so, after an exhaustive examination that lasted twelve months, the Chief Engineer decided that the axle load could be increased to 9.75 tons, and a new design

[Top] The 10B class for the Benguela Railway [1155] was modernised with connecting rod drive to the third coupled axle, latest pivot design, etc., but still wood-burning.

[Centre] The first Beyer-Garratt design for the Nigerian Railways [1159] was a 4-8-2 + 2-8-4 so it could travel over 45lb. rail.

[Above] The next design for the Nigerian Railways [1179] was a 4-6-2 + 2-6-4. These engines could haul the same load on the lightly laid sections which conventional engines could manage on other parts of the line.

was ordered. A 4-6-2 + 2-6-4 Beyer-Garratt which produced 33,600lb. Tractive Effort and was 5 per cent. more powerful than the standard locomotives working on the 60lb. rail was preferred to a 2-10-4 conventional locomotive. Four (Order 1179) were built in 1935, to an up-to-date design with roller bearings on all bogie axles, and grease lubrication throughout, except for cylinders and slide bars. Two more were finished in 1936 (Order 1185), six in 1937 (Order 1192), four in 1939 (Order 11112), and six in 1943 (Order 11121). The Nigerian Railways became vitally important during the Second World War in connection with the North African campaign. Engine mileage, which in 1939-40 totalled 4,438,000 miles, rose to 7,076,000 miles in 1944-45, and in spite of the difficulties in the supply of spares, the Beyer-Garratts averaged nearly 3,000 miles per month for all engines of this class.(16)

The largest order for Garratts up to that time was received in 1930 when the London Midland & Scottish Railway ordered thirty 2-6-0 + 0-6-2s (Orders 1164 & 1165), to basically the same design as the three originally built in 1927. The whole thirty-three continued to handle the heavy coal traffic between South Yorkshire and London throughout their working life. The grate area of 44.5 sq. ft. meant fairly hard work for the fireman, and with that in mind one of the batch was fitted experimentally with a rotary bunker, patented (No. 319052) by Samuel Jackson. It was in the form of a conical drum, mounted with the bottom side sloping down towards the front, and the top horizontal. On top were quick release doors for filling. It was rotated by a two-cylinder steam engine, driving a worm shaft engaging with a toothed ring encircling the drum. Rotating it periodically brought the coal forward to the shovelling plate, saving the fireman having to do this chore. The enclosure of the coal in this special bunker prevented coal dust being blown into the cab when running bunker first. Following trials, all but for two were brought back and fitted with rotary bunkers. It was an ingenious device, but recalling the array of parts required, and that the fireman still had to shovel the coal, it was unfortunate that the opportunity was not taken to go the whole hog and try a mechanical stoker.(17)

[Top] One of the London, Midland & Scottish Railway Beyer-Garratts [1164] ordered in 1930 was fitted experimentally with Spencer's coal pusher and canvas cover to the bunker.

[Right] All but two of the Garratts on the London, Midland & Scottish Railway were fitted with a rotating bunker, designed to save the fireman bringing the coal forward. The driving mechanism for the rotating bunker can be seen in the rear bogie.

[Below] One of the London, Midland & Scottish Railway Garratts showing the rotating bunker.

[Top] No. 7968 climbing Hope Bank, with an Avenue Sidings to Gowhole coal train, in June 1948. [K. Boulter]

Facing page

[Top left] The L.M.S. Beyer-Garratt with the coal-pusher in the bunker hauling a coal train.

[Centre left] No. 4986 fitted with a rotating bunker.

[Bottom left] No. 7993 near Avenue Sidings, on an up coal train. [J.C. Naylor]

[Below] The Sierra Leone Development Corporation Railway [1172] used only Beyer-Garratt locomotives to handle all its traffic.

The years 1929, 1930 and early 1931 were a boom period at Gorton, but by the end of 1930 the lack of new orders was already affecting the Drawing Office. The shortage of work there was temporarily alleviated by a contract to prepare a complete set of manufacturing drawings for the large new express passenger Garratt for the Algerian Railways, which is described in Appendix VII.(18) The worsening trade depression brought unemployment in its wake, first in the Drawing Office, and then in the works. Ninety-two Beyer-Garratts were built in 1930, but only five in 1931, and six in 1932. Two of those in 1932 were almost identical to the 2-8-2 + 2-8-2 ''GE'' class for the South African Railways and were designed for Sierra Leone Development Corporation Railway (Order 1172). This railway was planned in 1930 to exploit the iron ore deposits at Marampa, which was 52 miles from the coast, and these Garratts were chosen to handle all the traffic. One more was built in 1935 (Order 1181), and another in 1937 (Order 1188); the line remained unique in being operated entirely by Beyer-Garratt locomotives.

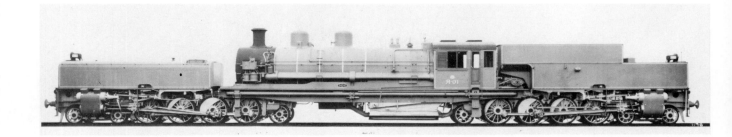

[Above] The Beyer-Garratt for Russia [1176] was the largest ever made. It is seen here [below] with a standard gauge 0-4-0 tank engine ''Pontadawe'' for W. Gilbertson & Co. [1411].

[Left] The immense size of the Beyer-Garratt for Russia is only appreciated when men are standing on it.

[Below and facing] The two bogies and boiler unit for the Russian Beyer-Garratt [1176].

The last Beyer-Garratt in 1932 was the monster 4-8-2 + 2-8-4 (Order 1176) for the 5ft. gauge railways of the U.S.S.R. This one-off new design had the distinction of being the largest and heaviest of this type ever made (Tractive Effort 89,200lb., weight 262.5 tons) and also of any steam locomotive built outside the U.S.A. The photograph does not give a true impression of its size because the Russian engineers requested that the chimney and domes should be extended to the full height of their loading gauge, which was 17ft. 1 7/8in. The overall length was 107ft. 9½in., and width 10ft. 6in., while the boiler was 7ft. 7in. in diameter, with grate area 85.5 sq. ft., and weighed 40 tons empty; it was fired by a ''Standard'' B.K. mechanical stoker. The extra dome housed a special cascade type of water purifier. The engine units had bar frames 5in. thick, and the cylinders were of cast steel. Very special attention was paid to prevent freezing, as the locomotive had to be designed to work in ambient temperatures down to minus 30°C. Locomotives in the U.S.S.R. at that time were a mixture of Russian, German and American practice, some of which was imposed on this very British locomotive. Unfortunately there was no follow-up, for the Russians decided to build large conventional locomotives and the Beyer-Garratt disappeared into Siberia, never to be heard of again, although under test it hauled a load of 2,700 tons at about 10 m.p.h. up a 1 in 111 gradient.

No Beyer-Garratts were built in 1933, and in 1934, when the Company's affairs were at their lowest ebb, the total output was one of their 0-4-0 + 0-4-0 industrial Garratts, for Guest Keen Baldwin's Iron and Steel Co., Cardiff,

(Order 1177). In 1935, a new Garratt design appeared, that for the Nigerian Railways (Order 1179), and two other Garratts were built to earlier drawings. The following year was a little better, when again two locomotives were built for the Nigerian Railways (Order 1185), and one each for Australian Portland Cement (Order 1183), and the San Paulo Railways (Order 1184), to existing designs, but new types were prepared and built for the Iranian State and the Sudan Government Railways. The turning point had been reached, for more orders began to come in, and the workshops at Gorton started to fill.

The Iranian State Railways ordered four heavy 4-8-2 + 2-8-4s (Order 1182) to operate on the severe mountainous section in the Elburz, where the line climbed nearly 7,000ft., with a ruling grade of 1 in 36 for nearly 40 miles. To scale the northern escarpment, which was very abrupt, there were ten spiral loops, with many tunnels on the spirals of up to a mile in length. The locomotives were designed to tackle the 1 in 36 grades at speed, and so were constructed with a boiler of large steaming capacity, which was oil fired. The fuel burnt was the naphtha residue from their own refineries. The Anglo Iranian Oil Company sent two trainee drivers to Gorton to study the engines, and see their construction. Then Beyer, Peacock was asked to send someone to Iran as a Locomotive Driver/Inspector until their own drivers had had some experience of handling these locomotives. W.R. Major, who had recently been the Chief Mechanical Engineer of the Central Railway of Peru, was appointed as Locomotive Engineer in North Iran for two years.(19)

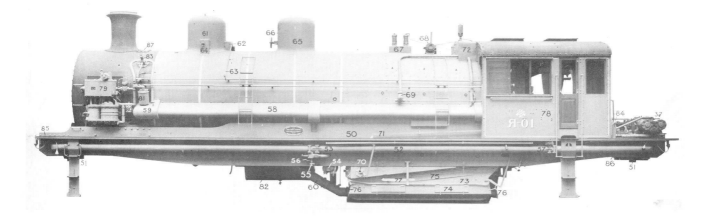

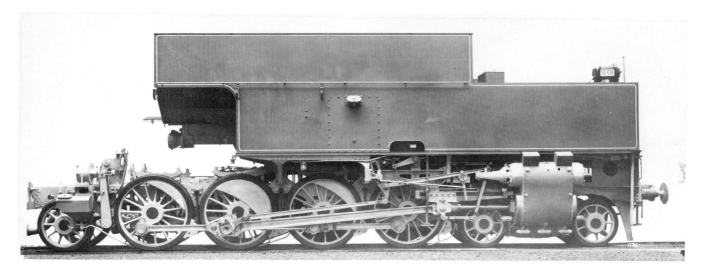

[Above] The industrial 0-4-0 + 0-4-0 Beyer Garratt for Guest Keen & Baldwin's Iron and Steel Co. built in 1934.
[Below] The Beyer-Garratt for Iran [1182] undergoing trials at Gorton.

[Foot] One of the Iranian Garratts in the Elburz mountains.

The other new design built in 1936 was a 4-6-4 + 4-6-4 for the 3ft. 6in. Sudan Government Railways (Order 1186). It was the first Garratt to have this particular wheel arrangement, which was necessary to carry the required amount of water for operating over long stretches of waterless desert, where the track was only 50lb., and the maximum axle-load 12½ tons. The initial order was for four locomotives, one being built in 1936 and three in 1937, followed by six more (Order 1193) later that year. These engines worked trains from Atbara through Khartoum to Wad Medani, a distance of 300 miles, thus obviating a change of engines at Khartoum. This run was caboose worked, making a round trip of 600 miles. At the time of their introduction, they were the most powerful engines to operate on the 50lb. rail, for they developed 43,520lb. Tractive Effort.

They had bar frames and, as originally built, the springs of all the coupled wheels and the inner four-wheeled bogie were equalised in one group. This involved supporting the inner bogie on the bottom of a vertical sliding pillar, linked by a central equalizing beam and a cross beam to the coupled spring group, whereby the system was also cross-equalised. After a time some trouble was experienced due to the extremely sandy conditions, because the front power bogie stirred up the dust which found its way into the moving parts of the rear unit. Through this, the unusual suspension system did not function as well as expected and at the end of the Second World War, all the engines were out of service. Design modifications were made but the Railway's policy had changed, and the engines were offered for sale. They were bought by the

Rhodesia Railways in 1949, at the instigation of Frank Hough, who was then the Chief Mechanical Engineer. He altered the couplers and put them to work successfully as the Rhodesia Railways "17th class". Finally they passed to the Mozambique Railway, and worked on the Beira section, which was taken over from the Rhodesia Railways in 1949; a chequered history with a happy ending.

The output of Beyer-Garratts increased to twenty-five in 1937. The only new design that year was for two 4-6-2 + 2-6-4s for the Dorada Railway, in Colombia (Order 1189). This was a compact bar-framed oil burner, which had the distinction of being the only Garratt for the 3ft. gauge. The following year was a most important one in the history of the Garratt, for it saw the beginning of large and valuable orders, which were interrupted only briefly during the Second World War, and continued to the end of the steam era. For example, Rhodesia Railways ordered twelve more of their "16th class" (Orders 1194 & 1197), and there was the order for the sixteen "GM" class for South Africa.

Of the twenty-three Beyer-Garratts built in 1939, the most important new design was that of the six built for the Kenya & Uganda Railway, as its EC3" class (Order 1198). This railway climbed nearly 5,500 ft. in 330 miles from Mombasa to Nairobi, then a further 3,500ft. to the summit, before dropping again to an altitude of just under

[Above] The Beyer-Garratts for the Dorada Railway [1189] were the only 3ft. gauge Garratts ever constructed by Beyer, Peacock.

[Below] The first Garratts with a 4-8-4 + 4-8-4 wheel arrangement were built for the Kenya & Uganda Railway [1198] as its class "EC3" in 1939.

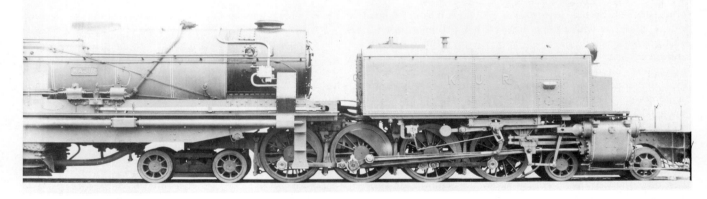

[Lower] The "drifting valve" fitted to the Beyer-Garratts on the Kenya & Uganda Railway.

4,000ft. at Kampala, a total distance of 879 miles. As far as Nairobi the line was laid with 80lb. rail, but the final section was on 50lb. rail, which created a severe bottleneck, as the line was severely graded, with long stretches of 1 in 50 uncompensated, and, of course, with severe curves. The train and engine mileage had increased from 3,000,000 miles in 1934 to 4,000,000 in 1939, and the existing Garratts were unable to handle the loads.

The 50lb. rail limited the axle loading to only 11.75 tons, and therefore a 4-8-4 + 4-8-4 was designed, which was not only the first locomotive with this wheel arrangement, but was also the most powerful on the 50lb. rail, developing 46,100lb. Tractive Effort. To fit such a locomotive onto the

metre gauge was quite an achievement, even if there had been no limitation imposed by the strength of the rail. The Railway Gazette compared these engines with those in Great Britain:

"On this light rail—half the weight of the rail in Great Britain—and on a gauge 1ft. 5 1/8in. less with more difficult grade and curvature conditions, the tractive effort of the engine is equal to the biggest passenger engines in Great Britain while the boiler is practically equal in horsepower, having a similar size grate and an even larger barrel diameter despite the total height to chimney top from rail level of 12ft. 5½in., which is nearly a foot

The Kenya & Uganda Railway "EC3" class [1198] in the erecting shop at Gorton.

lower than the highest British dimension. The locomotive further weighs roughly 20 tons more than the largest British types, the width over the running board is 9ft. 6in., and the footplate area is considerably larger than that of many standard gauge engines."(20)

Despite their great length of over 90ft., they were able to traverse curves of 275ft. radius in sidings (the outer coupled wheels had wide flangeless tyres), and their top speed was increased because their driving wheels were 4ft. 6in. in diameter, compared with the 3ft. 7in. of the earlier locomotives. The boiler pressure was 220lb. per sq. in. They had "Butterfly" air-operated firedoors, thermic syphons, self-emptying hopper ashpans, roller bearings on all carrying axles, and grease lubrication for all the axle boxes and valve gear. One application of soft grease to the valve gear lasted for 2,000-3,000 miles, while the pads of hard grease fitted to the axle boxes of the coupled wheels provided lubrication for 20,000-30,000 miles. Mechanical and hydrostatic lubrication elsewhere enabled these locomotives to operate with a minimum of servicing and maintenance on duties which included round trips of 1,100 miles.(21)

Another patented design of adjustable pivot centre had its first application on these locomotives. This used a horizontal wedge, with a simple screw adjustment to take up the wear, while the pivot was inverted, with the male portion on the bogie to exclude dirt. It was, of course, mechanically lubricated. Spring suspension was modelled on the Sudan arrangement, but was later modified by eliminating the equalizing beam between the inner bogies and coupled springs. The drive was taken to the third coupled axle to reduce the forces on the crossheads, which were of the Laird type, underslung from twin slidebars, which became the standard practice in East Africa. Another new feature was the alteration of the valve gear to bring the quadrant block links of each engine unit to the same position for whichever direction the engine was running. Previous to this, one engine had always to be in back gear. Special by-pass and air relief valves were fitted to enable the engines to coast down the long grades, particularly on one section where there were "momentum" grades like a switchback.

The Kenya & Uganda Railway, and its successor the East African Railways, was, and still is, a metre gauge line, but on this order, and on all subsequent ones, provision had to be made for possible conversion to 3ft. 6in. gauge, and also for replacing their A.B.C. couplers with automatic couplers and draw gear at the same height as those on the Rhodesia and South African Railways. The gauge conversion was catered for by special design of the wheels, so that different tyres could be fitted and with brake-hangers that could be changed from one side to the other. These locomotives were probably the most successful Garratts on these lines, and a further batch of six was built in 1940 (Order 11116), to be followed by eighteen more in 1949 (Order 11142). During the Second World War, when train mileage increased and spares were difficult to find, the class of twelve engines put up some remarkable performances.

	1942	1943	1944	1945
Total mileage for 12 engines	671,257	681,184	696,079	710,300
Average miles per engine per annum	55,938	56,765	58,007	59,192
Total number of days in Shops, i.e. not available for traffic	613	377	435	504
Average number of engines available for traffic	10.32	10.97	10.81	10.62
Average miles per month per engine available	5,420	5,174	5,366	5,573
Average miles per day per engine available	178.2	170.4	175.9	183.26 (22)

The high mileages were maintained month after month, and year after year. Hot bearings were unknown, and the

Chief Mechanical Engineer reported that after the second general overhaul, that is after 400,000 miles of running, it was not considered necessary to remove the boiler from the cradle for repairs. On engine No. 87, it was reported:

"This engine was put on the line on 25th February, 1941, and run up to 27th April, 1944, before entering Shops for Heavy Repairs. During this period of thirty-eight months the engine ran 211,630 miles, an average of 5,569 miles per month; the actual maximum and minimum mileages were 6,775 and 4,030. During this time the engine did not enter shops for repairs of any kind whatever, nor did the coupled wheels come out for turning of tyres, but the bogie wheels were moved to different positions and turned left to right on several occasions. These results have been obtained under the stress of wartime conditions." (23)

These engines gave thirty years of hard service, frequently having to make all-out assaults on the steep gradients. Some were fitted with Giesl ejectors, which may have improved their performance, but probably hastened their end. The freer running thus obtained put a greater strain on the boilers, which deteriorated rapidly and led to the withdrawal of most of the locomotives before 1973.

The Beyer-Garratt story up to 1939 ends with the construction of eight 2ft. gauge "NG/G16" class 2-6-2 + 2-6-2 for the South African Railways (Order 1199). This was a slightly modified repeat order of the original four of the class built under licence by John Cockerill & Co., Belgium, in 1937. They were the largest and most powerful locomotives on any 2ft. gauge railway. So ended the period between the wars, with the Company restored to health, and with good prospects ahead after the lean years it had experienced.

Side and rear views of the 2ft. gauge "NG/G16" class for the South African Railways [1199].

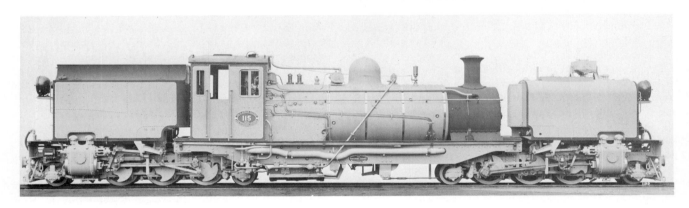

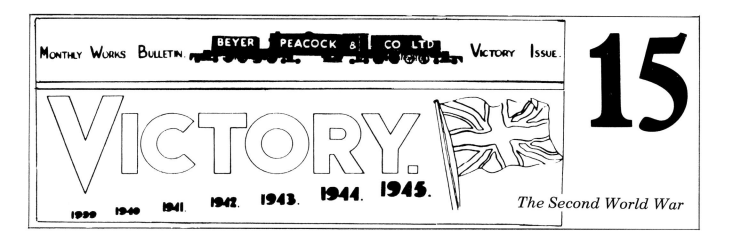

With the Nation once more at war, Gorton Foundry came under Government direction for the second time in its history, but fortunately the need for locomotives was so great that they continued to be built throughout the war. A wide variety of other products, such as tanks, shells, bombs and guns was undertaken, so the works contained a series of little "empires", each with its special stores and offices for inspectors from the various departments of the armed services involved. The planning, equipping and staffing of these various semi-separate departments threw a tremendous strain on the management, headed by the Works Director, Samuel Jackson. His assistant, James Hadfield, achieved special distinction for the skill and energy which he displayed. Recollections of that hectic period bring fresh appreciation of the amazing adapt-

ability of the people involved, and of the remarkable results achieved in rapid production of war material other than locomotives.

Tanks

The production of tanks lasted for a comparatively short time because, later in the war, the greater part of Gorton Foundry was required for building locomotives. After the fall of France, it was realised that the Germans would try to invade England, and a larger, heavier tank was designed by Vauxhall Motors Ltd. to meet this threat. Beyer, Peacock was invited to undertake the manufacture of a number of hulls and other components, and to be responsible for assembling, testing and final trials. Such was the urgency that this design, originally known as the "A22",

[Heading] Victory issue of the Works Bulletin.

Tanks under construction.

but later as the "Churchill" tank, was produced without previous experimental work. On 20 July 1940, it was agreed to go into production, and the pilot model was running on 12 December 1940. Production began to flow in May 1941, and by the autumn 400 were available for battle.

Part of the works had to be reorganised to undertake this production, which meant moving machine tools and clearing floor space. The tank chassis, or hull, was a fairly straight-forward boiler-shop job, but there were problems with shaping the armour plate and turret on equipment normally designed for mild-steel. Also welding techniques had to be revised to cope with different materials.

The final assembly of these tanks required unusual thoroughness and precision, for the parts had to be installed in the correct sequence, and there was little space inside. Beyer, Peacock's own maintenance electricians fitted the wiring in the interior, which included the power and light, as well as telephone communication and radio installation. A 20-acre brick-field was leased as a trial ground, where the tanks could be tested before being sent out to fight.

Guns

The demand for guns of every type was enormous. Beyer, Peacock had been approached in 1937, for it was clear that locomotive builders had the equipment, and could rapidly acquire the technique for constructing gun carriages and mountings.(1) This work was soon subcontracted to various manufacturers, each one specialising in a particular part, and Gorton became responsible for the steel castings and assembly of the carriage. The steel castings consisted of upper and lower racer plates, forming the base of the mounting, the large gun cradle,

[Above] Four tanks on railway flats about to leave Gorton Foundry.

[Left] Another view of tanks under construction.

[Below] Beyer, Peacock A.R.P. unit in 1939.

gear boxes and a number of other details. The construction of the carriage necessitated the employment of highly skilled boilermakers, and also required machining and fitting with a degree of precision quite beyond anything normally called for in locomotive construction. This in turn demanded a number of accurate jigs, and a considerable amount of measuring equipment for use by the inspection department. Most of this work was concentrated on production of 4.5in. anti-aircraft gun cradles, but a number were supplied for 9.2in. howitzers.

Much of the war-time effort was co-ordinated with the factory of Richard Garrett, at Leiston. Gun mountings for the naval 12-pounders were made there, and it was decided to set up a duplicate line at Gorton in case one or

[Top] Mountings for 12 pounder guns.

[Right] Gun barrels being bored.

[Below] The machine shop where the breech mechanisms were made.

other should be bombed. The locomotive packing shop was allocated to their manufacture, and hundreds came off the production lines, made to a great extent by female trainees. Manufacture of the new 4in. twin naval mounting was duplicated similarly. Many hundred mountings were produced for the 20mm. Oerlikon cannons, which were fitted to ships of all types. Gun mountings were being produced in such numbers that a shortage of barrels was feared. Normally gun barrels are made on very special lathes designed solely for that purpose. To have obtained new machines from the usual manufacturers would have caused long delays, so Beyer, Peacock offered to design and manufacture the gun-making machinery. The machines themselves were designed and made at Leiston, but once more a duplicate production line was set up at Gorton.

Having solved the problems of manufacturing mountings and barrels, a bottle-neck appeared in the production of breech mechanisms. The breech mechanism of a gun is normally regarded as the most intricate item of precision engineering in the whole unit. The production techniques were far removed from anything associated with locomotive engineering, for many small parts were involved requiring a high degree of accuracy. Normal manufacturing procedures demanded a large amount of skilled fitters' time after the parts left their final machining operations, and skilled fitters were very scarce in Manchester during the war. By improving the tooling, and providing specialised fixtures and jigs, a production line was established which, in the hands of female trainees, manufactured the component parts to such a high degree of accuracy that fitting was virtually eliminated. Final assembly was mated to a special gun breech in which the limits had been so fixed that, if mating were possible, then that breech mechanism would fit any standard 12-pounder breech which had been manufactured within the prescribed tolerances. This ensured complete interchangeability and also reduced manufacturing costs to something less than one-third.

[Top] The component parts of a breech mechanism.

[Right] Weighing a finished shell.

[Below] The shop were shells were machined.

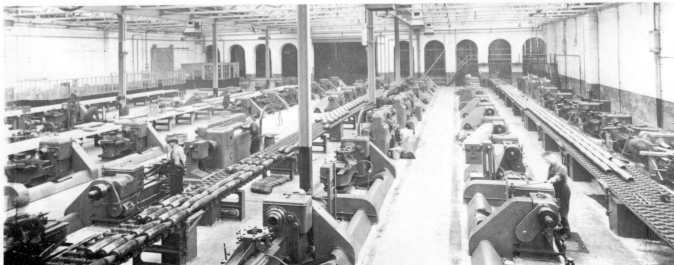

Shells and Bombs

Even before the outbreak of war, a production line for shells had been set up in part of Gorton Foundry. There were between thirty and forty machining operations to turn the pierced billet, which weighed 180lb., into a varnished shell, weighing 80lb., ready for filling. As the only lathes available were of German origin, it was decided that Richard Garrett should design a line of production machines at Leiston. Because conventional lathes were soon jammed by the volume of turnings, those built at Leiston were inverted, so that the swarf fell down into bins underneath, from where it could easily be removed. The production line at Gorton was set up to manufacture 6in. shells entirely by female labour, so all sorts of lifting devices were installed to help handle the shells with the minimum of fatigue. Forgings flowed on roller conveyors from the stock bank down the production line, and at each operation the removal from the conveyor to the machine and back again was accomplished by easy lifting devices designed and made in Gorton. The machine tools were painted blue-green to make them appear as attractive as possible.

As Beyer, Peacock possessed a steel foundry, the firm had been asked as early as 1936 to manufacture cast steel bombs. The bulk of the production was casings for the 1,000lb. type.(2) Casting a bomb was an intricate operation because the casing had to be thick enough to withstand the impact on landing, yet thin enough to en-sure the correct degree of fragmentation on explosion. Also it had to be made with the weight in exactly the right places, so that it had the greatest possible degree of accuracy in dropping. Numerous experiments had to be made to discover the best method of casting so that the metal, only about ½in. in thickness, did not "freeze", and the subsequent annealing temperature was critical too.

The machining of these bombs was done on semi-mass-production lines, and runways with small electric hoists were laid down to move the bombs through the various production stages. The Ministry of Aircraft Production arranged for single-purpose machinery to be designed and manufactured for the various machining operations, which were done on a somewhat novel basis. The bomb was inserted in a pot-jig, which was a component part of each of the various machines, then hoisted from one machine to the next, and only removed when the machining operations had been completed. Once again women operatives were quickly trained to manage these machines and hoists.

* * * * *

Women operating the bomb manufacturing lathes.

Locomotives

"We must regard the locomotive just as much a munition of war as the gun, tank, or shell."

Such was an extract from a letter written by the Controller-General of Munitions Production, stressing the imperative necessity of locomotive production for war purposes. In contrast with the previous holocaust, Beyer, Peacock continued to make locomotives throughout the whole of the Second World War, to meet the unparalleled demands for transport that arose in many countries. Often this traffic was far beyond anything envisaged when the railways were built so the Garratt locomotives assumed an important role in helping to increase a line's capacity, but many ordinary engines were built as well.

Nineteen different designs were delivered, covering the following gauges: 2ft. 6in., metre, 3ft. 6in., 4ft. 8½in., 5ft. 3in., and 5ft. 6in. They were sent to Brazil, the Burma Front, Ceylon, France, French Equatorial Africa, the Gold Coast, India, Iran, Kenya, the Near East, Nigeria, Sierra Leone and South Africa.

When war was declared in 1939, orders which had already been received included Beyer-Garratts for Rhodesia, East Africa and Brazil together with batches of large tender engines for Turkey and Iran. The order for Turkey was already in hand in the works, but was held up until after the war. Design work continued for some time on the contract for Iran, which was for twenty-four powerful 3-cylinder 2-10-2 oil-burning tender engines of entirely new design, but eventually this too was suspended. However, Iran was to some extent compensated, for six 2-10-2 tender engines, built by Friedrich Krupp of Essen, were intercepted in Eastern waters and diverted there. Beyer, Peacock was asked to make these locomotives

suitable for service on the Trans-Iranian Railway and, with very few drawings available, had to redesign the outer structure to fit the loading gauge, to alter the buffing and draw-gear, provide oil-firing, and a number of other incidentals. This job was carried out at high speed and the parts shipped to Iran, where the engines were modified on the spot without difficulty, and proved a welcome addition to the hard pressed motive power department.

The 4ft. 8½in. gauge locomotives for France and the Near East were standard Ministry of Supply war locomotives, based on the London, Midland & Scottish 8F class 2-8-0 tender engines,(3) as this design had been selected for rapid production by a number of builders. Beyer, Peacock built a total of fifty (Orders 1544, 1545 and 1546), delivered during 1940-41, the later ones being converted to oil burning, and with other modifications, for operation in Egypt and Iran. In the latter country they were used on the Trans-Iranian Railway to haul supplies of war material to the U.S.S.R.

In 1942 Nobel Industries at Capetown received an 0-8-0 tank engine (Order 1424) for shunting in their gunpowder works, and some 4-6-2 tank engines for suburban passenger traffic were sent to the Leopoldina Railway (Order 1423) in the same year. These engines presented a considerable problem at Gorton, as £48,000 had been spent on various orders for that Railway, and the engines had been finished to clear space in the works, but there was no shipping space, and storage at Gorton was out of the question. Finally, shipping space was allocated and the engines despatched, but four were lost at sea.(4)

[Below] The standard London, Midland & Scottish Railway 2-8-0 goods engine [1544] was chosen for mass-production to help the war effort.

[Foot] The 0-8-0 tank engine for the Nobel Industries [1424] built in 1942 was the same as the "Dan Fraser" supplied in 1927 [145].

The Great Western Railway of Brazil likewise had to wait for its order for Beyer-Garratts, but the Rhodesia Railways were lucky, and took delivery in 1940 of four engines (Order 11115) built to a new 4-6-4 + 4-6-4 design.(5) They were intended principally to operate the passenger service between Bulawayo and Mafeking, a distance of 484 miles, which they worked as a round trip, with a caboose for the crew and the minimum of servicing for the engines. Such conditions of sustained performance demanded the utmost reliability. The use of roller bearings throughout, and grease lubrication, meant that servicing became the duty of shed staff and not the enginemen, so bearing trouble on the road became a very rare occurrence.

These Rhodesian locomotives were similar in design to those ordered by the Sudan, and had the same system of spring suspension (subsequently modified). The boiler was larger, for it was almost identical with the Rhodesian ''16th'' class, and the cylinders were bigger, so these engines, with their 4ft. 9in. diameter coupled wheels, and 42,750lb. Tractive Effort, became the most powerful locomotives at that time on the 60lb. rail, having an axleload of 13.25 tons. While this type of locomotive works equally well in either direction, they were generally operated chimney first because there were convenient triangles for turning at either end. Therefore the front tank was streamlined, and the back of it fitted with a

removable plate to assist in the withdrawal of boiler tubes. These engines were capable of speeds up to 60 miles an hour, and could haul passenger loads of 500 tons and goods-trains of 1,050 tons, yet were economical in fuel and maintenence.

The next orders for Beyer-Garratts, which included those for the Kenya & Uganda, Sierra Leone, and Nigerian Government Railways, were all for existing types. Then in 1942 came four small 2-4-2 + 2-4-2 Beyer-Garratts of a new design (Order 11117) for the Leopoldina Railway, to work on the Cantagallo branch, which was 77km. in length, with a ruling gradient of 1 in 30 uncompensated, and with such severe curvature, poor ballast, and light rails, that only four coupled engines could work on it. There was a further complication, for the engines had to be able to burn Brazilian coal, which had a low calorific content and an ash content of 40 per cent. The Garratt, with its wide, deep firebox was able to meet all these requirements, and to double the loads hauled as well.

[Below] Because there were triangles at the ends of the lines on the Rhodesia Railways where these Beyer-Garratts [11115] worked, they were normally run chimney first so the front tank was streamlined and the cab had no back.

[Below centre] The 2-4-2 + 2-4-2 Beyer-Garratts for the Leopoldina Railway [11117] were fitted with Lentz valves.

[Foot] The first order [11122] received from the War Department for Beyer-Garratts for the Far East war zone was so urgent that it was built as a 2-8-0 + 0-8-2 type based on those supplied to Burma in 1927.

In the middle of July 1942, an Emergency Board Meeting was called to consider a request from the Government to extend the locomotive building programme.

"So far as this Company was concerned... the extent of change-over from our present production to locomotive production was so considerable and the locomotive programme so large that, in consultation with the Managing Director, it had been decided that it was advisable that an Emergency Board should be called immediately to review the situation...

"The Government are today considering the locomotive not only as a transportation vehicle, but in every way as important to the war effort as a tank or any other fighting weapon...

"The Minister and the Director of Royal Engineer Equipment had stated that it was imperative that the largest number of locomotives be produced in the quickest possible time, and that these locomotives should have the widest possible degree of availability over different railways, and from the point of design the Government were intending to standardise as far as possible. So far as Beyer, Peacock is concerned the Managing Director reported that preliminary investigation had been made as to the possibility of undertaking a total of 137 Garratts (including the 12 already on order for Sierra Leone and Nigeria) for completion by December 31st. 1943, and that this investigation had clearly shown that unless most exceptional steps were immediately taken and a most aggressive policy adopted, irrespective of commercial and peacetime practices, the programme could not be fulfilled."(6)

Production of these locomotives was just getting well under way when, in March 1942, an urgent demand was received for Garratts for Burma, in the Far East war zone. Such was the urgency for these engines, to help stem the advance of the Japanese(7) that there was no time to work out a new design, so the first ten were supplied as 2-8-0 + 0-8-2s (Order 11122), basically the same as those built for Burma Railways in 1927. In view of subsequent developments, Beyer, Peacock had a strong aversion to duplicating that 16-year old design, and by a tremendous effort it was brought up to date and the first locomotive steamed only 17 weeks after the receipt of the order; all were delivered in 1943.

The design was built originally with this wheel arrangement so that the maximum amount of tractive effort would be available to haul the largest possible load on the 1 in 25 grades, but the inside coupled wheels came in for severe punishment. In the meantime drawings were prepared for building the remaining fourteen locomotives of this order (No. 11123) as 2-8-2 + 2-8-2s to carry more coal and water, and also to promote smoother running on the curves. This order was considered of such overriding importance that other work had to be relegated to second place. From the date of receiving the official instruction, the designing, procuring of materials, and manufacturing processes were completed, and the first engine in steam, within 118 days - 4 days ahead of programme. Although intended for Burma, twelve* were diverted to the Bengal Assam Railway, where they did spectacular work on the heaviest section between Badarpur and Lumding, with its notorious hill section. They played a vital role in the 14th Army's re-conquest of Burma, for they enabled much heavier trains to be hauled over the hill section.

The Chief Mechanical Engineer of the Bengal Assam Railway wrote:

"I should like to place on record my appreciation of the work done by your Beyer-Garratt Locomotives during a very critical phase in the history of this Railway...

*two were lost at sea

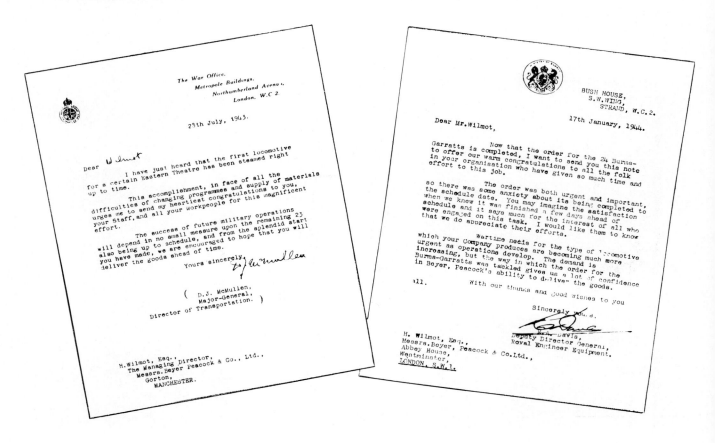

"The 2-8-0 + 0-8-2 Garratts worked heavy petrol and stone trains... The length of these trains was governed by the length of the station loops... The military situation at the time demanded increased lifts over this section [Badarpur and Lumding]. Your 2-8-2 + 2-8-2 Garratts provided the answer and with them the average lift was stepped up to 420 tons. Markedly lower coal consumption was achieved at the same time, as the Garratts burned only 60 per cent of the coal per 1,000 Gross Ton Miles consumed by the 4-8-0 class previously used on that service.

"These Garratts have proved mechanically reliable and have resulted in reduced engine maintenance, the footplate staff like them because they can take a considerable amount of punishment without attendant failures. The detail design is good and the braking system is the only satisfactory one we have had on the hill section up to date.

"It can be truly stated that without these engines we would have been unable to handle the inflated military traffic which passed over that section of the Railway, thereby contributing to the success of the 14th Army in Burma."(8)

[Below] The next order of Beyer-Garratts for Burma [11123] was constructed as a 2-8-2 + 2-8-2 to carry more coal and water as well as taking the curves better. The first one was completed in 118 days from receipt of order.

[Foot] 2-8-0 + 0-8-2 No. 825 and 2-8-2 + 2-8-2 No. 835 Beyer-Garratts supplied to the Burma Railways during the war are pictured here at Thazi Jet shed in 1975. [H. Ballantyne]

Work was already in hand for the Ministry of Supply, on two new designs of Beyer-Garratt, which were to be suitable for use on many railways abroad. These bore the codenames "SHEG" (Standard Heavy Garratt) and "STALIG" (Standard Light Garratt). The SHEG type had to be suitable for use on all important 3ft. 6in. gauge railways in Africa, with rail sections of 60lb. per yard or over, maximum axle-load 13 tons, for gradients up to 1 in 30, and with maximum possible tractive effort, employing an eight-coupled design. This resolved into a 2-8-2 + 2-8-2,(9) built to a composite of many loading gauges, and with due regard to minimum radius of curves. The base design selected was the South African "GE" class, last built 13 years earlier, which was transformed, as far as the urgency of the requirements and wartime austerity of construction permitted to bring it up-to-date. The SHEGS had 3ft. 9½in. diameter wheels, a tractive effort of 58,260lb., and carried 9 tons of coal and 4,600 gallons of water. Plate frames were employed on all Ministry of Supply orders for SHEGS and STALIGS, for economy of material, and speed of construction.

Eighteen of the SHEGS were delivered in 1943-44, and were allocated by the Ministry of Supply to the Gold Coast (6) (Order 11125), the Congo-Ocean (Pointe Noire to Brazzaville) (3) (Order 11125), and Rhodesia Railways (9) (Order 11126), all 3ft. 6in. in gauge. This caused one problem, for it involved making provision for three different types and heights of couplers and draw gear, with a

minimum of alteration. The nine for the Rhodesia Railways (later their "18th" class) and the three for the Congo-Ocean Railway, were eventually sold to the Mozambique Railways in 1959, where they were still operating in 1976.

Seven more were built in 1944, nominally classified as SHEGS, (Order 11127) but with considerable modifications. They had a 4-8-2 + 2-8-4 wheel arangement, to accommodate 12 tons of coal and 6,000 gallons of water, and were allocated to the Kenya & Uganda Railway (their "EC4" class, later the East African Railways "54" class). Therefore they were metre gauge, but convertible to 3ft. 6in. gauge. They were fitted with Westinghouse brake equipment instead of vacuum, and with that Railway's standard ABC couplers, but with provision for conversion to automatic couplers and draw gear. In later years they were converted to oil burning. In service they were at a disadvantage, with comparatively small coupled wheels of 3ft. 9in. diameter and the plate frames did not stand up to heavy pounding which they received, but they were of course built under the extremely difficult conditions of wartime shortages.

In June 1943, while work on the Ministry of Supply contracts was at its peak, Samuel Jackson, the Works Director and Chief Designer, died suddenly.(10) In his 43 years with the Company his strong personality made a deep impression on all who knew him. There was a touch of the dictator in his attitude to the whole engineering side of the business, and he was not good at delegating authority, a trait which may even have hastened his untimely death. His involvement with the Garratt locomotive at its inception has already been mentioned, and he was the dominant figure in its development during his lifetime.

Following Jackson's death, his Technical Assistant, James Hadfield, was appointed Technical Manager, which included overall authority over Drawing Office and works. He was an all-round engineer of great ability and immense energy, which enabled him to cope with the many problems of the period when he assumed control. Under his personal direction, a general reappraisal of the design of Beyer-Garratt locomotives was undertaken, with due regard to records of performance in service of the many already built, and in the light of the latest advances in engineering. Numerous improvements were introduced, and the results will be evident in the concluding chapters, for he laid the basis of the final evolution of this remarkable type of locomotive.

The commercial affairs of the Company continued to be controlled by Harold Wilmot, as Managing Director, from his office in London, for he had the responsibility of looking after the affairs of the other companies in the group as well. He was assisted by Leslie T. Dawes, who was then Commercial Manager at Gorton. In the London office, there was also that well-known figure in locomotive circles, W. Cyril Williams, who became the Sales Director in 1945. His assistant was Maurice A. Crane, who joined the sales staff in 1942. These men saw the Company through the last difficult years of the war, and laid the foundations of its prosperity in the equally difficult years after the war had ended.

[Top] The Kenya & Uganda Railway had seven SHEGS built as 4-8-2 + 2-8-4 which became their EC4 class.

[Above centre] The standard light type of Beyer-Garratt or STALIG [11124] was designed to fit on most metre gauge lines and became the prototype for many post-war orders.

[Above] One of the STALIGS for the Kenya & Uganda Railway was finished on 7 May 1945, the day the Germans surrendered unconditionally, so it was fitted with a special plaque, inset.

The inset plaque reads:

BEYER, PEACOCK & CO LTD
MANCHESTER
BEYER-GARRATT LOCOMOTIVE
PATENTS 298422-51825
PROGRESSIVE No 7156.
———
THIS LOCOMOTIVE WAS COMPLETED
ON THE DAY OF GERMANY'S
UNCONDITIONAL SURRENDER.
7TH MAY 1945

L. T. Dawes

One of the STALIG Beyer-Garratts originally sent to Burma at work
on the East African Railways in 1970. [H. Ballantyne]

Although evolved during the war, the STALIG helped in
the post-war recovery, for it became the basis of engines
built for metre gauge railways in four continents. Many
locomotives were required for the various phases of the
war in the Far East and, in addition to normal types, more
powerful engines were required for dealing with the
heavily graded lines, the gauge of which was predominantly metre. In view of the considerable mileage of
light track of 50lb. per yard, a maximum axle-load of 10
tons was selected and naturally the engine would have to
conform to the smallest loading gauge, namely the Indian
standard, which restricted the maximum height and width
to 11ft. 3in. and 8ft. 6in. respectively. As certain railways
in India could take a height of 11ft. 9in., removable strips
were fitted all round the cab so that the height of the roof
could be either 11ft. 3in. or 11ft. 9in.

Within these limitations of a fairly restricted loading
gauge, Beyer, Peacock had a free hand with the design,
so it was based on their latest practice, subject to certain
wartime material economies. A 4-8-2 + 2-8-4 type was
evolved which gave reasonable fuel and water capacities.
The 4ft. 0in. diameter driving wheels made these locomotives suitable for all types of traffic with speeds up to
40 mph being possible, yet economical on 1 in 40 gradients. The outer coupled wheels were flangeless, to
facilitate passage through severe curves. The 6ft. diameter boiler, with 49sq. ft. grate area was one of the
largest placed on so light a rail and the 43,520lb. Tractive
Effort produced made these the most powerful metre
gauge locomotives in the Far East. Reinforced plate
frames were used to help reduce the weight.(11)

Delivery of these engines commenced towards the end
of 1944. By that time the Japanese were being pushed
back on all fronts, so the 2-8-2 + 2-8-2 Garratts on the
Bengal Assam Railway were transferred to their intended
destination of Burma, while nine STALIGS (Order 11124)
were sent to the notorious hill section between Badarpur
and Lumding instead. Here these new engines performed
very well, although they had a slightly lighter axle-load
than the 2-8-2 + 2-8-2 type. Nine were sent straight to

Burma (Order 11129), where they were used as a general
purpose type on the main lines, and were not confined to
the hill sections. Two more engines were delivered to the
Kenya & Uganda Railway (Order 11129), where they had
to be fitted with the Westinghouse brake. Here their
4ft. diameter coupled wheels gave them an advantage over
the earliest Garratts, which had wheels of only 3ft. 7in.
diameter.

In 1944, thirty huge general purpose 4-8-2 tender
engines of the "15F" class were supplied to the South
African Railways (Orders 1554 & 1555) where they were
urgently required to cope with the tremendous increase
in traffic.(12) Not only were the industrial resources of
South Africa important, but, because the Mediterranean
was closed to shipping, all the convoys to the East had to
pass by the Cape. In this connection, the mining of coal in
South Africa, and the moving of it to the ports for bunker-
ing and export, increased in a fantastic manner. Total coal
transported by the South African Railways in 1939 was 13
million tons. This had risen in 1944 to nearly 18½ million
tons. The delivery of these locomotives was therefore a
very welcome addition to South African engine-power.

The next order for Beyer-Garratts was for the Ceylon
Government Railways (Order 11131) and eight 2-6-2 +
2-6-2s were built in 1945 to an up-dated version of the prototype of 1927.(13) One important feature was added, for
these locomotives were the first to be fitted with the
Hadfield Power Reverse Gear. On such large engines as
these Beyer-Garratts, some form of power reversing gear
was necessary, but the traditional type tended to "creep"
in service. The Hadfield power reverse gear provided a
positive lock and was fitted to all subsequent large
Beyer-Garratts, and many other locomotives as well.

[Above] The massive 15F class 4-8-2 tender engine for the South African Railways [1554].

[Below] The order for eight 2-6-2 + 2-6-2 Beyer-Garratts for the Ceylon Government Railways [11131] in 1945 was the first to be fitted with the Hadfield power reverse gear.

The last of the Ministry of Supply wartime contracts was for fifty 4-8-2 + 2-8-4 Beyer-Garratts for the South African Railways (Order 11132, 11133, 11134, 11135).(14) Deliveries commenced in 1945 and extended through 1946. The South African Railways saw fit to call these locomotives class "GEA" implying some connection with their class "GE," but apart from both being eight-coupled, there was no resemblance. The fact that fifty locomotives of a new design were ordered at once implied great faith in the builders and this order was, incidentally, not only the largest single order for one type of Garratt, but also the largest for articulated locomotives ever placed in the world.

The design was for a general purpose locomotive with a tractive effort of 63,030lb. to work on the 60lb. rail. The axle loading was unusual, for the weights decreased towards the extremities of the units, reaching a maximum of nearly 15 tons on the driving axle, instead of a normal 13 or 13½ tons. With 4ft. diameter coupled wheels (all of which had flanges) these locomotives had a wider availability than the "GM" class and, as more weight was allowed on the bogies, carried more coal and water, so did not need the auxiliary tank. With full grease lubrication and roller bearings in the bogies, the drivers' duties in the preparation of these locomotives at the running sheds were considerably reduced.

[Above] Fifty of these 4-8-2 + 2-8-4 "GEA" Beyer-Garratts were purchased by the South African Railways [11132] in 1945, which was probably the largest order ever placed at one time for articulated locomotives. Here is one leaving Oudtshoorn for Mossel Bay in 1972.

[L.A. Nixon]

These locomotives put up splendid performances and proved very reliable in service. To give but two examples, on the Mossel Bay - Oudtshoorn section, which climbed to 2,490ft. in 33 miles, with long gradients of 1 in 40 and many curves, these engines could haul 14 bogie coaches which previously needed to be double-headed by class "GD" Garratts. Then on the severely graded and curved branch from Pietermaritzburg to Donnybrook and Franklin, these engines took in a single load the passenger trains which previously had been split in two, each hauled by a six-coupled Garratt. All these class "GEA" Garratts were fitted with steam chest pressure gauges in the cab, indicating the pressures at the front and hind cylinders. They revealed that, in the first place, there was no difference between the pressures recorded in the front and hind engines, and secondly, the drop in steam pressure on long banks was often nil, and never exceeded 3 to 5lb., in spite of the long steam pipes.

Although not part of the Beyer, Peacock story, a note must be included about the Australian Standard Garratt, which was designed in 1943 for their 3ft. 6in. gauge lines. Because Garratts could not be obtained from Britain, a new design was prepared independently of Beyer, Peacock. The engines, built in Australia, proved to be rough riding, and so liable to derailment that some of the drivers refused to work them. This culminated in the appointment of a Royal Commission to inquire into their design and construction.(15) After the war they were all withdrawn on the Queensland and South Australian Railways, but survived longer on the Western Australian Government Railways. There was concern at Gorton lest the troubles of these Garratts should reflect on the reputation of the Beyer-Garratts, but this proved to be unfounded.

[Below] The Garratt designed and built in Australia during the Second World War was not a success.

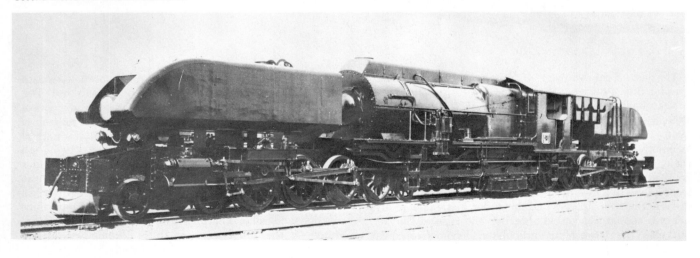

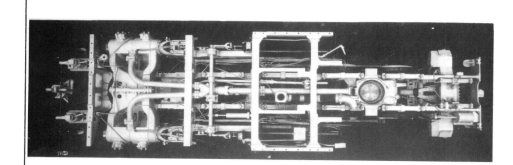

Developments in Design

The building of Garratt locomotives covered a span of fifty years, from 1908 to 1958, and during that period there were many changes in detail design, arising from operating experience, increasing size, weight, and power of locomotives, various inventions by the Company's engineers, for which patents were obtained, and general advances in metallurgy, and the art of locomotive engineering. This chapter examines those changes which originated at Gorton, and were applied principally to the Garratts, for this is where Beyer, Peacock made its most important contributions to the general progress of locomotive design.

Pivot Centres

In reviewing these developments, it is fitting to start with the pivot centres, since this vital part of an articulated locomotive must withstand all the traction and buffing forces, with a minimum of wear and maintenance, while providing for all the relevant movements between the engines and boiler unit.

In the early designs, the pivot centres were generally similar to those of four-wheeled bogies on locomotives (See fig. 1). The upper was the male portion and was perfectly cylindrical in shape, with a flat bottom. It was formed on a steel casting, which was itself incorporated in a plate structure forming a stretcher between the main

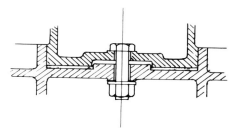

Fig. 1 First pivot.

[Heading] One power unit for the Benguela Railway Beyer-Garratt [11151] built in 1952.

[Below] The front bogie for the first Garratt for the Tasmanian Railways [9954] with the low pressure cylinders.

frames of the boiler unit. At either side, flat bearers, normally not in contact, were provided to check any excessive roll, and central keeper pins ensured that the pivots did not separate during violent buffing, or other abnormal conditions. Vertical loads were taken care of by a single flat phosphor bronze plate, secured to the lower, female, half of the bearing by recessed screws. The steel upper half rested on it, and the weight of the boiler unit was quite sufficient to keep the two parts permanently in contact. The plates had a pattern of oil channels milled on their faces, and in service these proved to give adequate lubrication for the duration of their working lives. Such wear as there was was automatically taken up by the upper unit sinking deeper into the joint of its own weight. The only exception to the straight-faced pivot was the use of a hemispherical type, at the front end only, applied in those cases where extreme track curve transitions made it necessary, because of the degree of lateral tilting of one engine unit relative to the other.

In later designs the structure spanning the gap between the boiler unit frames became a one-piece steel casting, incorporating the male part of the pivot, and provision for peripheral wear was made by shrinking on a renewable steel ring, mating with a ring liner in the lower pivot. Safety clips were provided, because the steam ball joint was now attached to the bottom of a projection on the top casting which passed down through the centre of the lower casting. This method of construction continued in use until 1928 (See fig. 2). The increasing size, weight, and tractive effort of the locomotives, however, accelerated the peripheral wear, resulting in undesirable fore-and-aft knocking in the pivots, under running conditions.

In an endeavour to eliminate this source of trouble, Patent 298,422 (See fig. 3) was taken out for an adjustable design, which was first applied in 1928 on Order No. 1134 for the New Zealand Government Railways. The bottom pivot centre now had sectional bearing blocks fore and aft, and flat liners which could be replaced, or shimmed, after measuring the required thickness with the locomotive backed hard up against the buffer stops, or to an-

[Below] The bogie unit from the Russian Beyer-Garratt [1176], showing the bolts for adjusting the pivot bearing surfaces.

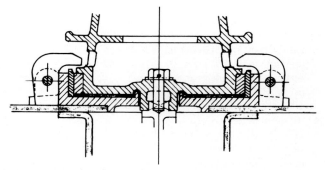

Fig. 2 Improved pivot.

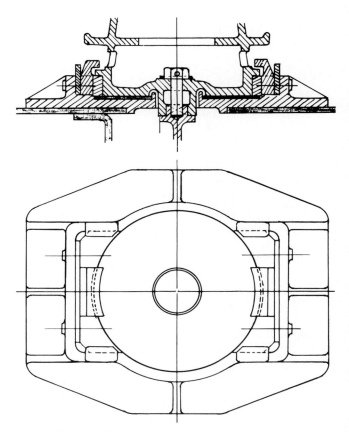

Fig. 3 Adjustable pivot.

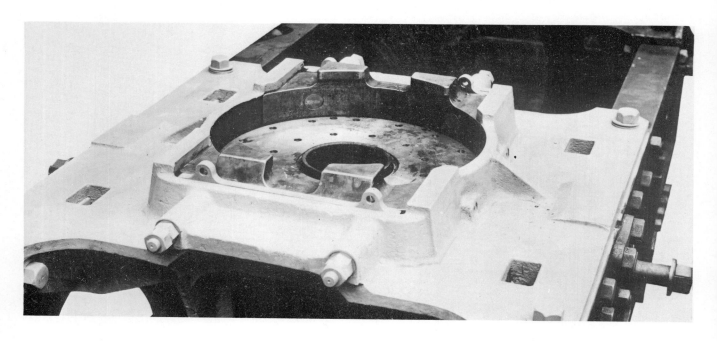

other locomotive. This first adjustable pivot centre made a considerable improvement, but still had some disadvantages. The presence of dirt made it difficult to gauge accurately how much wear had to be taken up, and the confined space at that point made measuring and fitting an unpleasant and troublesome operation. This in turn made the preparation and fitting of new liners, or shims, expensive in terms of time taken by skilled labour, nor was it easy to ensure just the right clearance for possible rolling and tilting, without there being enough space to allow appreciable knocking.

These considerations, plus the realisation that under normal operating conditions it was impossible to prevent accumulation of dirt and moisture in and around the pivot centres, led to another new design, Patent No. 518,251 (See fig. 4) of 1938. In this the adjustment was much simpler. Just one stout captive screw, accessible from one side of the locomotive, operated a horizontal wedge behind one of the pivot bearing blocks. The wedge was tightened solid and then slackened by a prescribed small amount. The other new feature was that the entire pivot was inverted to prevent ingress of dirt or water. Oil was fed to the flat bearing liner and allowed to spill over a lip onto the peripheral faces. This inverted adjustable pivot centre was first applied in 1939 on Order 1198 for the Kenya & Uganda EC3 class engines. By this time the main steam pipes had been rearranged and the steam ball joint was in a tunnel through the top pivot casting. Also roller type side bearers had been developed. Samuel Jackson was responsible for these two patented arrangements, the second of which continued in use until 1948, some time after his death.

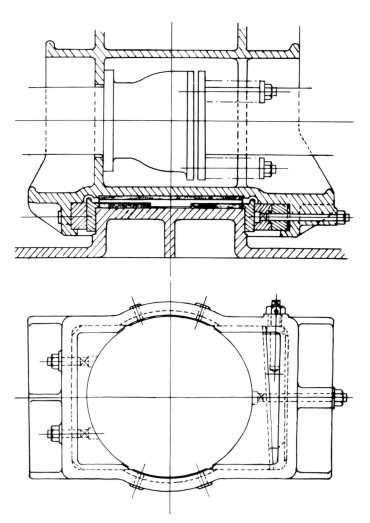

[Below] The inverted type of pivot on the South African Railways "GEA" class [11132].

Fig. 4 Inverted adjustable pivot.

When James Hadfield took over as Technical Manager, in 1943, and was discussing future design policy, the pivot centre was very much in mind. Hadfield's target was to produce a design which would allow complete freedom of movement for longitudinal tilting and lateral rolling, without having to provide any running clearance, and simultaneously to have a self-adjusting arrangement to compensate for wear. By this means, 'knock' would be eliminated and wear reduced, and they would work for very long periods without attention. Pivots of cylindrical form always had to have sufficient clearance to prevent binding when traversing abrupt changes of grade (sometimes referred to as 'vertical curvature') with which locomotives have to contend. Experience showed that it was necessary to allow for a longitudinal tilt of about 1 in 35 of the engine unit relative to the boiler unit.

With the new self-adjusting type of pivot centre patented by Hadfield (No. 647,476), (See fig. 5) the mating faces were made to a special contour and were held permanently in contact by a vertical wedge under the action of two long coil springs. The wedge had to be reversible in action, i.e. capable of being forced back against the spring load by applying sufficient horizontal pressure to the pivot adjusting block as happens when lowering the boiler unit into position and to a very slight extent in extreme conditions of tilting. The spring load on the wedge was carefully determined to ensure that the

wedge would not back out under the maximum tractive force being transmitted. To prove the calculations and the material selected for the mating parts, lengthy tests were made with a 'mock-up' on a hydraulic press.

[Above] The top unit of the self-adjusting pivot patented in 1949, with the spring loaded side bearers.

[Below] The bottom unit and parts of the self-adjusting pivot.

The first application of this new self-adjusting pivot centre was in 1949, on Order 11136, built for the Burma Railways, and it became standard from then on. At first the inverted form was retained, but it was very soon changed back to the opposite arrangement, with all parts enclosed in a carefully sealed oil bath (Patents 647,480 and 647,519) (See above). Associated with this latest pivot design was a new form of side bearer, comprising a spring-loaded friction pad with limited vertical travel to check any excessive lateral roll. The Beyer, Peacock self-adjusting pivot proved to be one of the most important

Fig. 5 Latest self-adjusting pivot.

improvements in articulated locomotive design, for the wear was extremely small and it did not have to be dismantled for inspection even when the locomotive was shopped for general repairs.

Steam and Exhaust System

When Beyer, Peacock introduced the Garratt locomotive, superheating was in its infancy, and a number of the earliest types were built with saturated steam boilers. There appears to have been a policy of excessive caution in several of the earliest designs, such as the provision of two regulator valves in the boiler, one for the steam supply to each engine unit, normally operated together, but with means for using one only if required. With the introduction of superheaters, only one regulator could be used, but the same idea persisted for a short time in a different form by fitting a shut-off valve on each main steam pipe. Perhaps it was regarded as a selling point that a breakdown on one engine unit would not immobilise the locomotive, or perhaps they were a little sensitive about the reliability of the steam ball joints. If the latter were the case, their fears proved groundless.

Perhaps one of the most remarkable records of the entire Garratt saga was that of the steam ball joint, whose design remained basically unaltered for the whole fifty years. Although the diameter, working pressure and steam temperature increased substantially over the years, the same metal-to-metal spherical joint, with its spring-loaded cover, self-adjusting for wear, and with the same arrangements for mechanical lubrication, proved equal to all demands. The illustration (See fig. 6) shows a three-point spring-loading, but eventually four springs were fitted on large diameter joints. An overflow oil outlet was provided to ensure that the ball could not be unseated from the socket by oil pressure, and this overflow was commonly used as a feed to the exhaust steam ball joint. The exhaust ball joint also functioned as an expansion joint and was spring-loaded, and self-adjusting for wear.

[Right] Exhaust ball joint for the Queensland Railways Beyer-Garratts showing the various parts.

Fig. 6 H.W. Garratt's drawing of the steam ball joint, 1910.
[Garratt Archives]

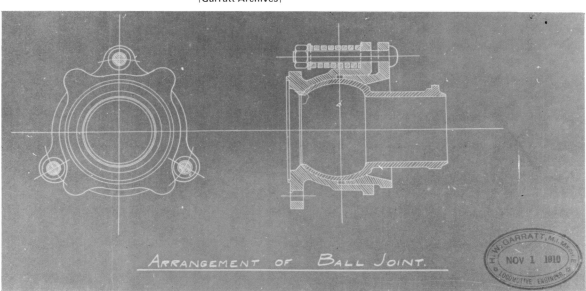

ARRANGEMENT OF BALL JOINT.

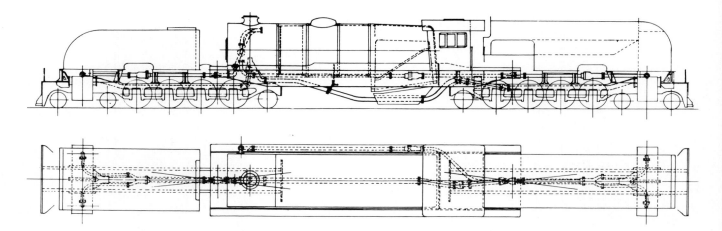

Fig. 7 Later arrangement of steam and exhaust pipes.

Thermal expansion of the steam and exhaust pipes was considerable, making expansion joints essential. Their design progressed from old-fashioned and inefficient asbestos-packed glands to the final arrangement using first-class specialist soft packing rings, lightly spring-loaded, sealing on a precision-ground stainless steel sleeve, welded onto the end of the pipe, and lubricated. Early designs had rather too many bends in some pipes, and it was quite usual to have the exhaust pipes passing below some of the axles, which impeded quick removal of wheel sets. This layout was improved as time went on, and finally the designers tried to achieve straight runs of steam pipes into expansion joints wherever possible, with easy accessibility from ground level, and simple procedures for separating the engine and boiler units, and un-wheeling the engine units (See fig. 7).

The arrangement of exhaust outlet and blast nozzle was at first subject to two schools of thought—those who favoured discharging the exhaust from both engine units through a single orifice, and those who thought that the steam from one engine should exhaust through a central orifice, and from the other through an annular orifice concentric with it. Initially the latter arrangement was favoured, but it proved to be unsatisfactory and unnecessarily complicated, and very soon gave place to the single orifice (See fig. 8). Of course there were many variations of the single combined orifice, including patented exhaust systems like the 'Kylchap', jumper top nozzles, etc., but the most common arrangement was the plain orifice with four 'Goodfellow' tips (vee-shaped bars projecting partly over the orifice). The Giesl blast pipe and chimney have been substituted in later years on many of the East African Railways Beyer-Garratts, and considerable success was claimed for them at first.

[Below] The packings and tubes for an expansion joint.

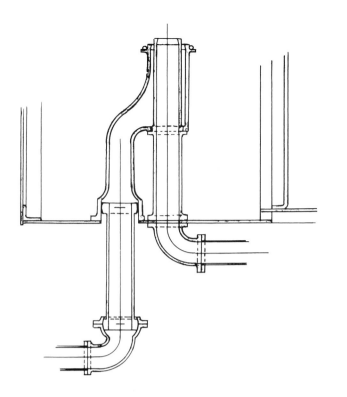

Fig. 8 Double blast pipe with concentric outer orifice.

[Above] The inside of the smokebox on a Rhodesia Railways 16A class built in 1952.

[Below] An East African Railways 60 class Beyer-Garratt with Giesl ejector and chimney, at work in 1976 on the Nauyuki branch at Thika.　　　　　　　　　　　　　　　　[Photo H. Ballantyne]

The Engine Units

Up to 1908, almost all the engine units on articulated locomotives had only driving wheels and, except for the Mallet, the pivots were in the middle. Garratt's original conception, shown in his 0-4-0 + 0-4-0 picture, followed this pattern and this was how the first Tasmanian Garratt (Order 9954) evolved. But the drawing in the Complete Specification for his patent has a 2-4-0 + 0-4-2, so that the extra carrying wheels could help to give guidance. With this longer wheelbase, the pivot centres have been moved away from the centres of the engine units and, possibly to help the balance, the cylinders have been placed at the outer ends, features found on all subsequent Garratts.

It is difficult to determine precisely when it was realised that carrying wheels at both ends of the engine units were essential to help the tracking qualities (especially at the high speeds at which Garratts could run), because they ran equally well travelling in either direction. The four-wheeled bogies at the outer ends, and the pair of trailing wheels, with Cartazzi axle-boxes, at the inner ends of the Tasmanian 4-4-2 + 2-4-4 Garratts (Order 0303), in 1912, may have been designed primarily to achieve a low weight per foot of length, for both the express South African ''GG'' class (Order 113), and the San Paulo ones built in 1927 (Order 1124), were designed as 2-6-2 + 2-6-2s. The San Paulo ones were improved later by having a four-wheeled bogie substituted at the front which was followed on all subsequent high-speed Garratts.

The trials of the South African 2-6-0 + 0-6-2 heavy Garratt (Order 0941) in 1921 suggest that the vital importance of the inner carrying wheels, even for slower engines, had not been appreciated. All Garratts designed after 1930 had inner carrying wheels.

Up to about 1927, the inner carrying wheels were positioned close to the adjacent coupled wheels, and the small amount of side-play of up to about 1in. each way, required to traverse the specified minimum radius of curvature, was provided by a straight lateral movement of the axle-boxes in the guides. The control force resisting this displacement was provided by a Cartazzi inclined plane block on top of the axle-box, a device commonly used in those days (See fig. 9). .

Later the carrying wheels gave place to a radial truck with spring side control, which provided better running characteristics and reduced tyre wear (See fig. 10). The axle-boxes on radial two-wheeled trucks had to withstand high thrusts, arising from the lateral pressure between wheel and rail, and axle deflection had to be catered for. On the Beyer-Garratts, these progressed from a pair of rigid bearings built into the truck frame, to rocking brasses, and finally to complete axle-boxes with curved crowns, with either plain or roller bearings, the latter being by far the most satisfactory. Another variation (East African Railways ''59'' class) had a combined truck frame and 'cannon' type roller bearing axle-boxes.

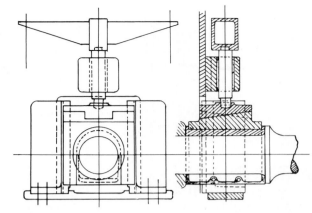

Fig. 9 Cartazzi inclined plane.

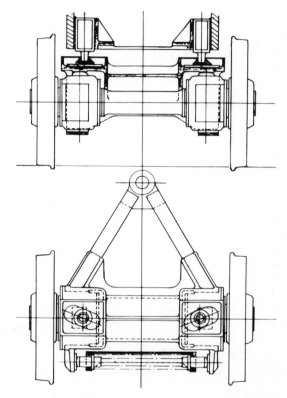

Fig. 10 Radial truck.

The pony truck for the East African Railways 59 class [11164].

238

Cylinders and Valve Gear

When Garratts first appeared, the use of piston valves was only in its infancy, and for a long time such valves were used with the short travel and cranked ports more normally associated with slide valves. There was a gradual change to straight-ported cylinders and piston valves with longer travel, eventually with some streamlining for the steam and exhaust flows.

Very special care was taken in laying out the valve gear to produce valve events which were almost equally uniform in both forward and backward directions—unlike tender engines for which it was usual to give preference to the forward gear. On a massive skeleton model at the end of the Drawing Office, every valve gear design was set up full size after patiently plotting it out on the drawing board. Wherever possible it became the general practice

[Above] The motion of the South African Railways "GEA" class [11132] built in 1945, with long connecting rods to the third driving axle.

to have long connecting rods driving the third coupled axle, which helped to produce uniform valve events by reducing the angularity effect on the out-stroke relative to the in-stroke. More important than that, of course, the long connecting rods reduced the vertical pressure on the slide-bars and promoted steadier running.

A small point about the skeleton valve gear model in the Drawing Office, which incidentally could cope with 'Stephenson Link' and 'Joy' gear as well as 'Walschaert', was that all the nuts and bolts on it were to a system of Beyer, Peacock spanner sizes dating from well before the introduction of Whitworth standards!

[Below] The valve gear model in the Drawing Office.

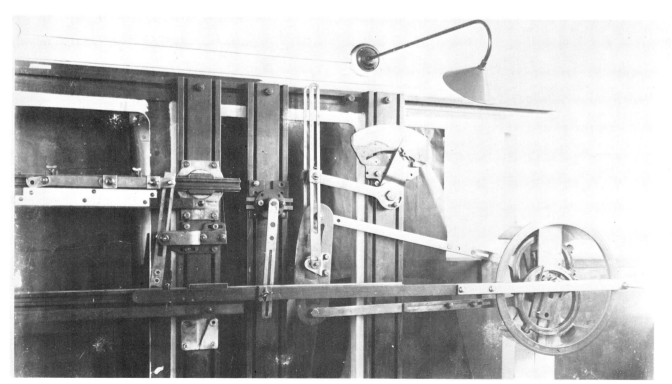

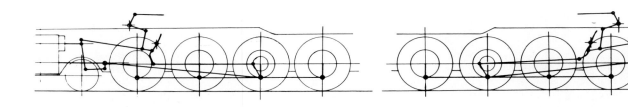

Fig. 11 Walschaert valve gear as arranged on later Beyer-Garratts.

The two complete engine units were, as far as possible, identical, but facing in opposite directions. Since the valve gear was also identical, the die-block was in the lower half of the reversing link on the front unit and in the upper half on the hind unit when running forward, hence the emphasis on uniform performance in forward and backward gear. But many customers preferred to run the locomotives chimney first as much as possible, having convenient triangle tracks for turning, and it was decided to modify the valve gear so that the dieblocks on both engine units could be at the bottom of the reversing links when in forward gear, which gave a more direct drive to the valve and less load and wear on the reversing link trunnions, the gear being designed so that most of the 'slip' was in the top, or indirect, half of the links.

This was achieved with a layout which located the return crank at exactly 90° behind the main crank on the front engine unit. The identical wheel set transposed straight back to the hind engine unit, but not reversed as with the earlier valve gear arrangement, brought the return crank to the desired position on that engine unit, i.e. 90° behind the main crank when running forward. To obtain the 90° setting of the return crank relative to the main crank, the tail pin on the reversing link must lie on a line joining the mid-point of the crosshead travel to the centre of the driving axle when the main crank is in the 'dead-centre' positions (See fig. 11)

This description of a piece of geometrical juggling is included because thereby hangs a tale. A draughtsman accidentally omitted a special note on the crankpin assembly drawing concerning this arrangement, and the works reverted to the earlier standard procedure. The locomotive was steamed, and panic ensued when she flatly refused to move in either direction! A 'clanger' of the first magnitude, or so it seemed, but fortunately not difficult to rectify when it was tracked down. However, through all the years that followed at Gorton, executive colleagues never allowed David Patrick to forget this incident, insisting that he personally was the genius who designed a locomotive to travel in both directions at the same time, which is what it was trying to do.

Power Reverse Gear

The smaller Beyer-Garratts had hand reverse gear, usually the screw type, but with two sets of valve gear to control, it is not surprising that power reverse gear was fitted on the majority. With very few exceptions, the earlier reversers were an adaptation of Sterling's steam-operated type already used on British locomotives. As first applied on the Garratts, they were mounted on the side of the boiler frame and consisted of a steam cylinder coupled in tandem to an oil-filled cylinder, with the piston rod passing through both and extended at each end to

A draughtsman at work.

couple up to the reversing rods. The controls in the cab comprised a lever linked to a slide valve on the steam cylinder and to a 'cataract' valve in the ports connecting the two ends of the hydraulic cylinder, with a cut-off indicator connected to the reversing rod.

To operate the reverser, the driver moved the control lever forward or back as appropriate to open the valves, and by watching the movement of the indicator he had to judge the appropriate moment to snatch the control back to the closed position. The function of the hydraulic cylinder was to lock the gear at any desired cut-off when the cataract valve closed and also to damp down the speed of operation. A variation of this, which was adopted later, was to mount the reverser on top of the boiler frame and drive through a vertical lever connected to the piston rod between the steam and oil cylinders.

That was the practice right up to 1945, when a new design, known as the Hadfield Power Reverse Gear, was introduced and patented by James Hadfield (Patent No. 582,396, October 1944). This emerged from studies of the existing type which did not lend itself to precise control, and had a tendency to creep away from the supposedly locked position. The hydraulic cylinder must be completely filled with oil and remain so, but as constructed on the old type, it was impossible to avoid air being trapped when filling it. Also the plug type cataract valve was difficult to maintain as a positive lock.

[Above] The Hadfield power reverse gear fitted to the East African Railways 60 class Beyer-Garratts [11161].

Water Tanks

On the Hadfield reverser, the hydraulic cylinder was redesigned with cam-operated spring-loaded poppet valves giving a really positive lock. The cylinder was filled from the bottom, thus expelling all air, and the oil was pumped in by a spring-loaded ram submerged in a small oil reservoir to ensure automatic make-up of any oil loss at the glands. Finally, precise selection of cut-off was obtained by using a light handwheel and screw control, and the vertical floating lever on the reverser ensured that if any creep did take place due to leakage past the piston, the valves would open and reset the gear. It was first fitted on Order No. 11131 for the Ceylon Government Railways built in 1945. From then on, it was fitted to practically all Beyer-Garratts built by Beyer, Peacock & Co. and by its licensees and was also supplied for a large number of tender engines built at home and abroad, thus becoming a very profitable patent for Beyer, Peacock. One notable side benefit was that considerable savings in coal consumption were obtained.

Various means were evolved over the years for replacing boiler tubes without having to remove the front tank. Where the overall design and weight distribution permitted, this was provided for by forming a U-shaped recess on the inner end of the tank. However, on many designs it was important to use this space for water, and three other means of facilitating boiler tube removal were devised and patented by Samuel Jackson. One method was to move the tank forward horizontally on rollers, pulled by a screw at the front. This was used, in 1929, on Order No. 1145 for the Rio Tinto Railway, and also by the Compania Eskalduna on the Beyer-Garratts built by them for the Compania Sierra Menera. Another method, used on the large Beyer-Garratts (Order Nos. 1152/3/4 and 1166/7) for the Bengal Nagpur Railway, was to anchor the tank to the frame at the front by two substantial pivot pins and elevate it to an angle of about 30° through a pair of built-in jacking screws, worm-driven and operated from the side of the locomotive (Patent 290,137). Both methods were fairly hard work to operate, but quite effective. The third method, applied to many of the Beyer-Garratts for Rhodesia, East Africa and elsewhere, was to fit a series of bulkhead doors across the inner end of the tank.

[Below] The front tank pulled forward on the Beyer-Garratt for the Rio Tinto Railway [1145] to allow more working space in the smoke box.

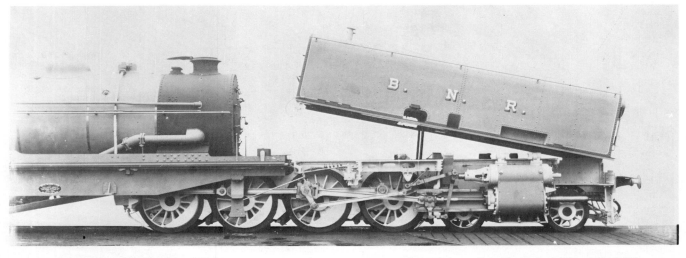

The front tank of a Bengal Nagpur Railway Beyer-Garratt [1152], raised up by screw jacks to allow easier access to the boiler tubes.

Tank and bunker design came in for a lot of attention. Early designs were uncompromisingly rectangular and square-cornered, while bunkers were like those on tenders of the period. From about 1926 onwards self-trimming bunkers were provided on most designs, while tanks changed to more pleasing top contours and eventually to a well-rounded shape, the latter being done mainly to improve the appearance. Fashions in tank construction came and went too—the all-riveted job with visible snap-head rivets was sometimes varied by making all rivets flush on the outside to produce a smooth exterior. Then came the upsurge of electric welding and tanks were fully welded, but finally a judicious combination of riveting and welding prevailed, because in fact a locomotive frame can never form a really rigid foundation. An all-welded tank with the internal baffle plates welded in position has many stresses locked up in it before it ever experiences the severe working strains in service, due to surging, acceleration, braking, and vibration from the 'live' power unit on which it is mounted.

[Left] Front and rear tanks on the original order [02405] in 1924 for the South African Railways "GE" class.

[Below] The modified front and rear tanks of the later order [1169] in 1930, for the South African Railways "GE" class.

242

Proof of this last point was the fact that when tank walls sometimes cracked it was very often at points adjacent to the attachment of angles or brackets. Studies of this led to a patented arrangement (Patent No. 723,321) of tank fastening, first applied in 1951 on Order No. 11151 for the Benguela Railway. The new design comprised stepped shoes on the tank across the outer end, and on each side at the inner end, fitted at assembly to engage with substantial brackets on the frame at these points, thus locating the tank positively in the longitudinal and lateral directions. The holding-down bolts were in clearance holes and spring-loaded, their only function being to secure the tank from dislodgement vertically. The springs provided flexibility to allow the engine frame to deflect slightly without affecting the light plate structure of the tank.

[Above] The stream-lined front tank for the Rhodesia Railways 15 class [11151] Beyer-Garratts built in 1940.

[Above] The final evolution of front tank design with the upper parts of the sides tapering in, seen as two East African Railways 59 class [11164] pass at Embakasi Station in 1976.   [Photo H. Ballantyne]

[Below] The tanks on the Rhodesia Railways 20 class were mounted on the frames with Beyer, Peacock's patent fastening system.

243

Locomotive Brake Equipment

On the first two designs, space was found for separate vacuum brake cylinders on each engine unit, but on the third type for the Western Australian Government Railway (Order 0246) a single vacuum brake cylinder was placed on the boiler frame connected by shafts and rods to the engine units. This became the preferred arrangement with either vacuum, steam or compressed air for most railways. The brake shaft was in fixed bearings and equalisation of the braking force on the front and hind engine units depended on the care devoted to adjusting the pull rods to take up wear—in those days brake rigging was remarkable for its stark simplicity. That layout was greatly improved later by making the shaft bearings in the form of sliding blocks, mounted in slotted brackets, which gave equalisation fore and aft, but still retained the ability to brake one unit if a pin or pull rod broke on the other. By that time, equalisers were also fitted throughout the rigging, so ensuring equal pressure on every brake block (See fig. 12).

That arrangement of brake shaft was still rather clumsy and sometimes not easy to accommodate, so it was abandoned in favour of a separate brake cylinder and shaft on each engine unit, with the hand brake applied to the hind unit only. Where vacuum brakes were used on the train, it was usual for many years to apply steam brakes on the locomotive, the control including a 'proportional valve' to regulate the intensity of the application on the locomotive in proportion to that on the train. Later still, for Rhodesia and South African Railways, vacuum brake cylinders were fitted on the front engine unit and a steam brake cylinder on the hind unit, all tending to smooth braking as a whole. The last move for the South African Railways was to fit vacuum brake cylinders on both engine units (GMAM and GO class), as on the very first Garratts!

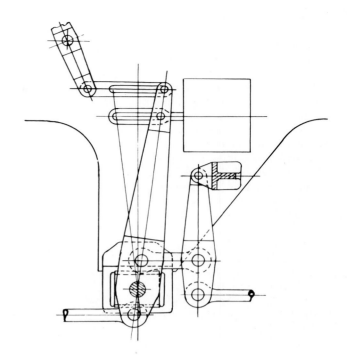

Fig. 12 Brake rod compensation system.

[Below] The South African Railways ''GL'' class was designed with the vacuum brake cylinders on the bogies.

These were the principal developments in detail design affecting parts other than those which were common to all types of steam locomotives. In the latter field, Beyer, Peacock was always abreast of the latest practice at home and abroad, and was sometimes even ahead of British railways in certain ways, as were also the other private locomotive builders. Beyer, Peacock had, of course, to comply with a much greater variety of operating requirements in the conduct of a world-wide export business. Rocking and drop gates of various types were fitted from early days, with dual power and hand operation. The old slide valve regulators were superseded by various designs of balanced valves and later by multiple-valve regulators integral with the superheaters. Smokeboxes and drafting arrangements were greatly improved over the years, from their original simplicity up to the most sophisticated layout based on practice in the United States. The final type was 'self-cleaning', with its system of deflector plates, spark arrestor screen and carefully calculated gas areas all the way from firebox to chimney. Ash ejectors were fitted on the bottom of the smokeboxes, operated by a pressure water jet from the boiler. A highly successful design of self-emptying hopper ashpan was also developed at Gorton.

At first, the crossheads were the single-bar or the double-bar 'Alligator' type, but later the 'Laird' type became standard, with its single slipper block working between twin slide-bars above the cylinder centre line. Grease lubrication for motion pins and connecting and coupling rod bearings became universal, with the rod bearings in the form of perforated floating bushes of bronze, or special alloy cast iron, working in fixed steel bushes. Coupled axle-boxes were often of solid bronze, with automatic hard grease lubricators in the keeps, and later came roller-bearing axle-boxes. Welded steel fireboxes, many with 'Nicholson' thermic syphons, steam-operated butterfly doors, the most advanced mechanical stokers—all these new features, and many more, were included during the fifty years of building Garratt locomotives.

Thermic syphon ready for fitting in a boiler.

[Below] The main frames for the Russian Beyer-Garratt [1176], in the erecting shop.

The Turkish State Railways 2-10-0 engines in the paint shop.

The Last Years of Steam,
1946-1958

The transition to peace-time conditions in 1946 was much easier than it had been in 1919, since locomotives were an important part of Beyer, Peacock's war production from 1940 onwards, and had become the major part by 1945. The first necessity was to finish those orders which were still outstanding and, in 1946, Gorton Foundry was filled to capacity with producing another twenty-six of the South African "GEA" class, and a repeat order for ten 2-8-0 tender engines for the Peruvian Corporation (Orders 1551 & 1553). Another pre-war order was finished also when eight Beyer-Garratts of the type supplied in 1930 and 1937 were dispatched to the Leopoldina Railway (Order 11118). In the following year this railway received

four 4-6-2 tank engines (Order 1426) to replace those lost at sea, while the remaining fourteen of the "GEA" class were delivered to South Africa in 1947.

Still outstanding were two large orders for tender engines which had been received in 1939, but were held up on Government instructions. The first, on which construction had already started, was for fifteen heavy 2-10-0s for the Turkish State Railways (Orders 1542 & 1543). They were almost identical with the German State Railway "I.E." type, having bar frames, with under-hung springs, "Krauss-Helmholtz" leading trucks, and the sophisticated "Riggenbach" back-pressure braking system. They

[Heading] The Turkish engines en-route to the docks.

[Below] One of the 2-10-0 engines for the Turkish State Railways [1542] being lowered onto its wheels.

[Above] The Turkish engines awaiting shipment.

were the only 10-coupled locomotives ever constructed at Gorton Foundry, and were eventually finished in 1948. They made an impressive sight in the streets of Manchester in transit by road to Liverpool, for they were shipped fully erected. The other order was for twenty-four very large, oil-fired, 3-cylinder 2-10-2 engines, of entirely new design, for the Iranian State Railways. The drawings were in hand when work on them was suspended in 1940, but after the war, they were subcontracted to Vulcan Foundry Ltd. to clear the way for the increasing output of Beyer-Garratts. They were completed in 1953, after redesign with only two cylinders, and as part of a much larger contract.

The post-war outlook for the locomotive building industry was good, through the need to rehabilitate railways which had been ravaged during hostilities, through supplying overdue replacements, and through proposed railway extensions in under-developed countries. James Hadfield, who had joined the Board as Technical Director, made a valuable tour of railways abroad, while in 1947, Cyril Williams made a round-the-world trip, visiting India, Burma, Ceylon, the Malay States, Australia, Tasmania and returning via the U.S.A. The following year he went to South Africa, Rhodesia and Portuguese East Africa.(1) The demand for Garratt locomotives was growing, and the unusual position arose of railways "reserving space" ahead in the building programme for their anticipated requirements, in one case for locomotives of a new design still to be discussed. Such moments were rare in the history of a company building locomotives.

Ordinary Locomotives

While many orders for tender and tank engines were repeats of earlier ones, in 1948 the Great Northern Railway of Ireland received five 4-4-0 express tender engines to a new design. To gain as much power as possible within the restrictions imposed, they were 3-cylinder simples (Order 1558), and for the first time enabled non-stop running between Belfast and Dublin. They were the last to be sent to this Irish company. The last tank engines built at Gorton Foundry also went to Ireland in 1951. They were one 4-4-2T for the Belfast & County Down (Order 1425), and two 0-6-4Ts for the Sligo, Leitrim & Northern Counties Railway (Order 1427). The Sligo, Leitrim & Northern Counties Railway could not afford to pay for its, but Beyer, Peacock realised there was no point in starting legal proceedings for breach of contract, because the Railway had no money to pay compensation. The locomotives were offered first to the Great Northern of Ireland, and then to the Ulster Transport Authority. Neither wanted them, so they were offered to the Victorian and South Australian Railways, with no better success. Then it was suggested that the Sligo, Leitrim & Northern counties Railway might like to take the locomotives on hire purchase and, after some haggling, Beyer, Peacock agreed to accept £3,000 as a deposit, and £500 per annum, so the engines were sent to Ireland nearly 18 months late. A special plate was fixed to their sides stating that they remained the property of Beyer, Peacock. This was not the end of the story, for the Railway closed early in 1958 and Beyer, Peacock resumed possession, only to sell them to the Ulster Transport Authority.(2)

[Top right] The 4-4-2 tank engine built in 1951 for the Belfast & County Down Railway [1425] was the same as those built in 1924 [02417].

[Centre] The Sligo, Leitrim & Northern Counties Railway 0-6-4 ''Lough Erne'' [1427] was the last tank engine erected at Gorton.

[Below] The last 4-4-0 for the Great Northern Railway of Ireland [1558] was a three-cylinder simple design.

[Top] The streamlined casing, originally designed for, but not used, on the Western Australian Government Railways locomotives, was included on those for the Silverton Tramways [1563].

[Above] Some of the Western Australian Government Railways 4-8-2's [1561] in the yard at Gorton ready for shipping.

[Right] The boiler for the Western Australian Government Railways 4-8-2.

[Lower right] R. Stephenson & Hawthorn built the 2-8-2 class "V" which Beyer, Peacock had designed for the Western Australian Government Railways [1567].

The Western Australian Railways received two new designs of tender engine, designed to burn their low-grade Collie coal. The first type, a 4-8-2 class "N", had to run over routes with 45lb. rails on the 3ft. 6in. gauge, yet produced 21,760lb. Tractive Effort. Sixty were built in 1951-2 (Orders 1561 & 1564), and another four were supplied to the Silverton Tramways (Order 1563), with chimney, dome, sandbox, etc. enclosed in a long casing, which made a striking change in their appearance. The outstanding feature on these engines, as well as on a design for a heavier class "V" 2-8-2, was the boiler, which had a firebox of very large proportions, and steeply sloping door plate and front, leading into a combustion chamber, to provide for the slow burning and full-flame length of the poor coal.(3) Twenty-four of the 2-8-2s (Order 1567) were built at Darlington, under sub-contract by the firm of Robert Stephenson & Hawthorn Ltd., because, although designed by Beyer, Peacock, the volume of work at Gorton Foundry was such that not only entire orders such as this, but also parts for engines being built in Manchester had to be contracted out. Both classes of engines were well received in Australia and performed successfully.

The last tender engines to be built at Gorton Foundry (Order 1569) were three standard gauge 2-8-0s in 1957, for the Cerro de Pasco Copper Corporation, whose private lines linked up to the Peruvian Corporation system. Between 1936 and the end of the steam era, forty-nine of these engines were supplied to the Peruvian Corporation, and a further eight to the Cerro de Pasco, a total of fifty-seven, making them one of the most successful of Beyer, Peacock's later designs.

[Below] The last ordinary engines built at Gorton were three 2-8-0's for the Cerro de Pasco [1569] in Peru.

[Foot] Beyer, Peacock 2-8-0's at Ovaya shed on the Central Railway of Peru in 1955.   [Photo V.F. Sampson]

The Wartime Standard Light Garratt

The wartime Standard Light Garratt was used as the basis for five designs supplied to six railway companies in four continents, suitably modernised and adapted for each. The first was an order in 1949 for ten for the Burma Railways (Order 11136), which had the same 4-8-2 + 2-8-4 wheel arrangement common to all, and the same power characteristics, but differed from the war ones by having Belpaire fireboxes, streamlined tanks and bunker, 4½ tons more coal, roller bearings on all carrying axles, and a maximum axle load 11½ tons. Owing to the disruption of the railway by terrorists, only four actually went to Burma, and they were sold later to the Assam-Bengal Railway through lack of work for them. The other six were fitted with Westinghouse air brake equipment and shipped direct to the East African Railways, becoming their ''56'' class. Also in 1949, the 3ft. 6in. gauge Luanda Railway in Angola had six (Order 11147) very similar to those for Burma, but fitted for oil-burning, and carrying 1,500 gallons of oil and 5,500 gallons of water.

The third design was for the Queensland Government Railways, where a 25-year expansion programme was in hand, based on the widening market for their agricultural, pastoral and forestry products, as well as coal and other mining developments. With 6,567 miles of line, Queensland's railways ranked as second only to the South African as the largest 3ft. 6in. system in the world. These Garratts were adapted to the more spacious loading gauge, but the axle-weight was restricted to 9.65 tons by the many wooden bridges. They were intended to haul heavy freight trains, as well as the ''Sunshine Express'' between Brisbane and Cairns, a distance of 1,043 miles. Thirty were ordered, and the first ten were built in 1950 at Manchester (Order 11146), but the last twenty (Orders 11153 & 11154) were sub-contracted to the Société Franco-Belge in order to speed up delivery. Their tractive effort of 32,770lb. was nearly 50 per cent. higher than the most powerful engines then in service in Queensland.(4)

In 1952, the Great Western of Brazil received six oil-burners, similar to those for the Luanda Railway, which were sub-contracted to Henschel. In the following year, the Société Franco-Belge supplied ten to the South Australian Government Railways, which were the last steam locomotives in regular service in that State at the end of 1969.(5) The last design was delivered in 1954 to the East African Railways, where twenty-four were sent to the Kenya & Uganda section (Order 11161, twelve built at Gorton; and Order 11167, twelve built by the Société Franco-Belge, under sub-contract) and another five went to the Tanganyika section (Order 11171, built at Gorton). They were constructed as oil-burners from the outset, and so were designated the ''60'' class, being generally like the ''56'' class, but adapted specifically to East African requirements, with their ample loading gauge, instead of the restricted Indian limits for which the ''55'' and ''56'' classes were prepared originally.

[Below] The larger loading gauge on the Luanda Railway [11147] allowed the chimney and dome to be built higher on this ''standard light Garratt''.

[Foot] The Queensland Railways ''standard light Garratt'' [11146] under steam at Gorton.

[Above] Burma Railways received the first of the post-war ''standard light Garratt'' designs [11136] in 1949.

[Above] The motion of a Queensland Railways ''standard light Garratt''.

[Below] East African Railways 60 class Beyer-Garratt soon after entering service.

Other Beyer-Garratts for the East African Railways

In addition to the "56" and "60" classes, Beyer, Peacock supplied two other designs of Beyer-Garratt to the East African Railways after the war. The earlier was based on the "EC3" 4-8-4 + 4-8-4 supplied to the Kenya & Uganda Railway in 1939, and became the E.A.R. "58" class (Order 11142). They were built as oil-burners with larger diameter cylinders, so had a tractive effort increased to 49,030lb., while various improvements included the latest self-adjusting pivot centres and the Hadfield power reverse gear. One locomotive had dual vacuum and Westinghouse brake equipment, with a proportional valve to control air pressure in the locomotive brake cylinders, when making a vacuum application of the train brakes. This was intended for future trials with vacuum braking. Between 1939 and 1950, a total of thirty, including the earlier "EC 3" ("57" class) and the "58" class, was built, all giving excellent service.(6)

[Above] The 4-8-4 + 4-8-4 East African Railways 57 class Beyer-Garratt [11142] was one of the most successful ever built.

[Below] Looking along the cab and boiler unit of an East African Railways 57 class.

[Below] One of the East African Railways 59 class being prepared for shipping.

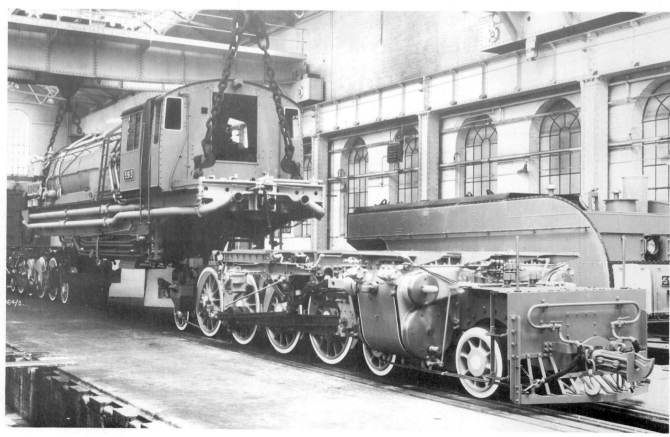

254

Discussions had been continuing concerning a completely new design. This was produced in 1955, when thirty-four 4-8-2 + 2-8-4s, of class "59", were completed (Orders 11164 & 11168). These spectacular engines—the largest and most powerful by far of any steam engines built for a metre-gauge railway, and 43 per cent. more powerful than any other East African Railways locomotive— were designed for the steeply graded main line from the port of Mombasa to Nairobi, which had been relaid with heavier track. A maximum axle-load of 21 tons, tapering off towards the outer and inner bogies of each unit, was permitted, subject to certain restrictions on the balancing of reciprocating parts. These mighty locomotives, which weighed 251.7 tons, were over 100ft. long, by 10ft. wide, and 13ft. 5½in. high, and had a tractive effort of 83,350lb. Except for the height, these dimensions were only a little less than those of the Beyer-Garratt built for the Russian 5ft. gauge.

These monsters were oil-fired, by twin burners. The 7ft. 6in. diameter boiler, with a grate area of 72 sq. ft., round-top firebox, and working pressure of 225lb. per square inch, was the second largest of all Garratt boilers, and its accommodation on so narrow a gauge is a resounding proof of the claims originally made by H.W. Garratt in 1907. The reversion to a round-top boiler was to give the driver a better view, for the boiler nearly filled the loading gauge. All axles had Timken "Cannon"-type roller bearing axle-boxes, and roller bearings also on the driving crank pins for the connecting rod big ends, and coupling rod main bearings. Equipment of the most up-to-date type included Beyer, Peacock patented pivot centres, reverse gear and tank fastening system. To meet East African requirements, in addition to the usual crop of provisions for future conversions—to 3ft. 6in. gauge, the change to Alliance couplers and the provision for vacuum braking— there was allowance for possible reversion to coal burning by designing the firebox, bunker, etc. so that a mechanical stoker could be fitted. It was almost like designing the engine twice.

The "58" class could haul 700 tons at 10 m.p.h. on 1.5 per cent. gradients, but the "59" class managed 1,200 tons at 14 m.p.h. on the same stretches, as well as being more economical. The "59" class did their job so well that within a year of entering service, the back-log of traffic at Mombasa had been cleared and traffic was functioning normally.(7) In a way this was almost a pity, for the East African Railways were discussing with Beyer, Peacock the design of a 4-8-4 + 4-8-4, with a 26-ton axle-load, a boiler of 8ft. 3in. diameter and 110,000lb. Tractive Effort. This metre gauge class "61" would have been bigger than most of the locomotives in the United States, but it was never to be, for the next locomotives purchased by the East African Railways were diesels.

New South Wales

Meanwhile another spectacular design had been prepared for the New South Wales Government Railways (Order 11155), in 1952. Initially it was for twenty-five AD60 class standard gauge 4-8-4 + 4-8-4s, with maximum axle-loads of 16 tons, tractive effort of 59,560lb, and weighing 254.8 tons, with 14 tons of coal and 9,200 gallons of water. The most powerful locomotives in New South Wales at that time were the "D58" Mountain type, with 56,000lb. Tractive Effort, but with axle-loads of 22½ tons, which restricted them to certain heavily laid lines, while the Garratts could traverse almost the whole of the system.(8)

[Above] The East African Railways 59 class Beyer-Garratt was the largest locomotive ever built for the metre-gauge, with a length of 104ft.

[Below] The AD 60 class Beyer-Garratt for New South Wales was one of the most modern designs ever produced and weighed 254.8 tons in working order.

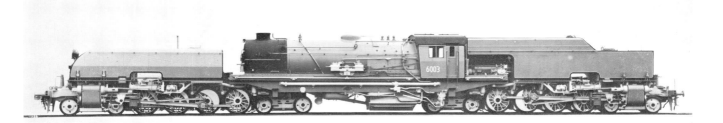

These were some of the most modern and lavishly equipped Garratts ever constructed, designed for intensive main-line operation, with an absolute minimum of servicing. Roller bearings were fitted on all axles and on the main crankpins. Mechanical lubrication of a very sophisticated kind was provided for the cylinders, steam chests, piston rods, valve spindles, slide bars, axlebox guides, pivot centres, reversing link trunnions and shafts, steam and exhaust ball joints, and stoker telescopic and ball joints, with grease lubrications for motion, brake and spring gear. The 7ft. 3in. diameter boiler, with grate area of 63.4 sq. ft. was fired by a "Standard" HT mechanical stoker made by Beyer, Peacock under licence. Other boiler equipment included the latest multiple valve regulator, a "Melesco" steam dryer, and a "Waugh" table fire grate. The superheater consisted of fifty elements made from solid-drawn steel tubes, with integrally forged return bends, and ball joints which gave a surface area of 750 sq. ft. The first engines were fitted with five 3in. diameter steel arch tubes in the firebox, but a later order had two thermic syphons.

At the request of the railway authority, the engine frames were one-piece "Cast Steel Beds"—the first Beyer-Garratts with this American feature—which provided an interesting exercise in design collaboration at long distance. The cast steel bed was a single casting incorporating the cylinders, steam chests, axlebox guides, bottom pivot centres, draw gear, tank supports, bogie centres, and brackets for valve, reverse, spring and brake gears. They were cast and machined by the General Steel Castings Corporation, in their huge special-purpose plant at Granite City. Beyer, Peacock prepared detail drawings and skeleton assemblies of all the parts to be accommodated, and General Steel Castings designed the frame around them. While the cast steel bed eliminated a large number of bolted connections, it was a more expensive and somewhat heavier construction, which Beyer, Peacock never regarded as being really necessary on Garratt locomotives. Their purchase created difficulties because dollars had to be obtained to pay for them, and delivery was delayed, causing hold-ups in production.(9)

[Below] A cast steel bed for the AD 60 class partly machined.

[Foot] One of the engine units with a cast steel bed for the AD 60 class about to leave Gorton.

An order for another twenty-five was received, of which twelve were dispatched in 1954 (Order 11158), and a further five in 1956 (Orders 11173 & 11174), but American companies were promoting the introduction of diesel-electric locomotives—which a new Chief Mechanical Engineer favoured instead of steam—and teething troubles with the Garratts, because the drivers and maintenance men had no previous experience of this type, provided the excuse for the Government to order work to be stopped on the remaining locomotives. An assortment of parts which already had been made for the remainder was shipped, and eventually used to complete one more engine in Australia.(10) The loss of part of this order at Gorton Foundry was offset to some extent by New South Wales placing a large order for electric locomotives with Metropolitan-Vickers Ltd.; these were built at the Stockton works of Metropolitan-Vickers - Beyer, Peacock Ltd. These forty-two huge Beyer-Garratts were the last of a grand total of six-hundred and seventeen steam locomotives built by Beyer, Peacock & Co. for the New South Wales Government Railways, from 1865 onwards. They proved to be extremely versatile and useful locomotives with a draw-bar pull unequalled by any single diesel, and were the last steam locomotives in regular service in Australia, working until March 1973.(11)

[Below] This final design of the 10 D class for the Benguela Railway delivered in 1956 [11165] shows many detail improvements as well as the change to oil firing.

[Foot] It was a remarkable achievement to have produced so powerful an engine on so narrow a gauge, 2ft. 6in., on so light an axle load, 5 tons, as these Beyer-Garratts for the Sierra Leone Railway [11169].

Benguela and Sierra Leone

In 1951 and 1952, eighteen class ''10 C'' Beyer-Garratts were built for the Benguela Railway (Order 11151); these were an updated version of the ''10B'' class, built in 1930. The cab was widened to the limit of the loading gauge to provide the floor space necessary when firing with wood. On the severe gradients, the eucalyptus logs had to be fed in almost continuously to keep up steam pressure. Then in 1956 another ten were supplied (Order 11165), designated the ''10 D'' class, because they were built as oil-burners, and equipment was supplied to convert the earlier ones. The life of the firemen must have been improved out of all recognition by this, compared with heaving such masses of wood into the firebox, but the smell of the oil burning did not have the same aroma as the eucalyptus. These were the last Garratts for the Benguela Railway, making a total of forty-two of the four classes.

The 5 ton axle-load limit was still in force on the Sierra Leone Government Railways in 1955 when a 4-8-2 + 2-8-4 (Order 11169) was designed, to give a tractive effort of 23,000lb., compared with the 17,000lb. of the earlier Garratts. These fourteen were certainly the most powerful steam engines ever built for such light rails on the 2ft. 6in. gauge. Through these limitations, they were as remarkable a design as the East African Railways ''59'' class, and coming immediately after those giants, the degree of mental adjustment needed by the design staff in dealing with these engines, which weighed only 66.5 tons, can well be appreciated. The Railway was very pleased with the performance of these engines.

257

Rhodesia

The early examples had firmly established the Garratt concept on the railways of Rhodesia, so as soon as possible after the war, many more were ordered. Between 1947 and 1950, sixty of their "15" class 4-6-4 + 4-6-4s were supplied,(12) with some being built as the "15 A" class, which had their boiler pressure raised to 200lb. per square inch, and the bunker capacity increased to 12 tons. Then in 1952 delivery began of thirty "16 A" class (Orders 11156 & 11157), which were the latest version of the "16" class 2-8-2 + 2-8-2s built in 1929 and 1938.(13) The maximum axle-load allowed was now 14½ tons, so an additional 500 gallons of water and 2½ tons of coal could be carried. Boiler pressure was raised to 200lb. per square inch, which increased the tractive effort to 55,270lb., and the details and styling now matched the "15 A" class. Ten were fitted with roller-bearing bogie axle boxes, and twenty with plain bearings which were interchangeable. The gain in performance of these latest locomotives, compared with the original type introduced in 1929, and also the improved version in 1938, was most marked. The superior riding qualities, freer steaming of the boiler, modern valve gear and greater cab comfort were important features. In all, fifty of the "16" and "16 A" classes were built.

[Top] The final development of the Rhodesia Railways 15 class [11139].

[Above] 15 class 4-6-4 + 4-6-4 No. 356 blasts up grade from Victoria Falls Bridge to the station after collecting wagons off the bridge from Zambia in October 1974.   [Photo H. Ballantyne]

[Below] Zambia Railways, formerly Rhodesia Railways, 16A class No. 646 and 15 class No. 401 leaving Chambishi in 1972.
[Photo E. Talbot]

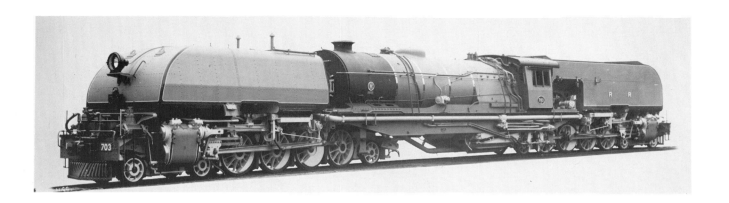

[Top] The 4-8-2 + 2-8-4 20 class was a fitting climax to steam loco-motives on the Rhodesia Railways [11166].

[Above] One of the 14A class "baby" Beyer-Garratts for the Rho-desia Railways [11162], again a fully modernised design.

In 1953, they were followed by eighteen of the "14 A" class (Order 11162) a complete redesign of the "14" class 2-6-2 + 2-6-2s, built in 1929-30, but with the same power characteristics. These forty-eight "14 A" and "16 A" Beyer-Garratts represented over 2,500,00lb. of extra trac-tive effort on the Rhodesia Railways. The "14 A" class was modernised throughout, and embodied the latest practice of both builders and Railway. Improvements to give a more robust design included the chassis, with its cast steel cross stays, the massive pivot casting, the con-struction and design of the tanks, which were mounted on special fittings so the frames could move beneath them, and the generous proportions and location of the details of the machine as a whole. The majority of the lubrication points were brought to the outside to facilitate the work of the drivers and running shed staff. Compared with the original "13" class, the perfection of these latest designs was readily apparent, for they were simpler to operate, had lower maintenance costs and a longer life.(14)

In 1954, fifteen powerful new "20" class 4-8-2 + 2-8-4s (Order 11166) were supplied; these weighed 223.4 tons, carrying 14 tons of coal and 8,000 gallons of water on a maximum axle-load of 17 tons, and had a tractive effort of 69,330lb. In the seven years before their introduction,

traffic had increased from 2,250,000 to just under 4,000,000 train miles annually, and the lines had almost reached full capacity, but by relaying with 80lb. rail and strengthening the track, these large locomotives, which had an increase in power of 25 per cent. over any previous Rhodesian engine, could haul much heavier loads, taking 1,400 tons over the 1 in 64 gradient between Kafue and Broken Hill. Embodying all the latest Beyer, Peacock design features and lavishly equipped, they were among the greatest of all Garratts.(15) They were the first for Rhodesia to have mechanical stokers, and another special feature was the provision in the cylinder design for possible connection to a separate condensing unit, coupled behind the locomotive, to recover some of the water by condensing the exhaust from one engine unit. This idea (never carried out) was inspired no doubt by the experi-ments on the South African Railways with their class "25" tender engines. After the successful introduction of the first ones, orders were placed for forty-six more (Orders 11182, 11183 and 11184). The final forty were designated "20 A" class, and had the outer bogie wheels increased in diameter from 2ft. 4½in. to 2ft. 9in. All these engines performed so well that a provisional order was placed for another thirty-four, to be built in 1958, but declining traffic through the world slump in that year meant that they were not necessary, and the order was never confirmed. Between 1925 and 1958, one hundred & seventy-nine Garratts of all types were supplied to Rhodesia, many of which were still working in 1978. The "20" class were a fitting climax to these years of develop-ment, and showed what could be done with a modern steam locomotive.(16)

259

South Africa

Except for seven of their 2ft. gauge 2-6-2 + 2-6-2s, built in 1951 (Order 11152), no Beyer-Garratts were delivered to South Africa between 1947 and 1952, when there was a long period of discussion about project designs and specifications in which Henschel & Sohn became involved jointly with Beyer, Peacock. The basic design was the "GM" class, built in 1938, and these new engines had the same wheel diameter and power characteristics, but differed greatly in detail. The first order for five "GMA" and twenty "GMAM" class 4-8-2 + 2-8-4s was placed with Henschels, who prepared all the manufacturing drawings, incorporating the latest Beyer, Peacock patent self-adjusting pivot centres, Hadfield power reverse gear, and tank fastening system. Beyer, Peacock manufactured the mechanical stokers and reverse gear, as well as providing general technical collaboration. The "GMA" class carried 14 tons of coal and 2,100 gallons of water, compared with 11.6 tons and 1,650 gallons on the "GMAM" class, otherwise they were identical. Henschel built thirty more "GMAM" class in 1954, and in the same year twenty-five "GO" class, which were generally similar to the "GMAM", but with smaller boiler and cylinders, and reduced fuel and water supplies.

Following a period in service of the Henschel-built "GMAM" class, in December 1955 South African Railways ordered thirty-five more from Beyer, Peacock, on condition that delivery commenced within seven months:

> "On the face of it this seemed impossible. Only by straining to the utmost our friendly relationship with suppliers and by the adoption of unconventional methods in the manufacture of certain essential components were we able to meet our obligations. The first locomotive was in steam and

South African Railways "GMA" class Beyer-Garratts Nos. 4080 and 4167 leaving Albert Falls on a freight to Pietermaritzburg in June 1971. [Photo E. Talbot]

under test at our Manchester factory one month before contract date and we were happy to have the General Manager of the South African Railways and Harbours at Manchester to witness this achievement."(17)

In order to help meet the tight delivery dates, the construction of twelve of them (Order 11181) was sublet to the North British Locomotive Company.

Then, in 1956, an order for sixty more "GMAM" class was won against fierce competition from other locomotive builders, as well as different types of power. In view of South Africa's urgent need, twenty of the first thirty were subcontracted to North British, and all the final thirty went to Henschel, so Beyer, Peacock itself only built ten at Gorton (Order 11186). For all these locomotives, the South African Railways had specified Commonwealth Cast Steel Beds and bogie frames, manufactured in the United States. "Cannon"-type S.K.F. bearings were fitted on all axles, and S.K.F. bearings on the driving crank pins. The outer firebox shell, inner firebox and the U-shaped pressed steel foundation ring were of all-welded construction. Mechanical lubrication was employed comprehensively, plus grease lubrication for all running gear. The boiler frames, in the form of girders, were fabricated by welding. Both engine units were vacuum braked. Like the original "GM" class, they carried only enough water for engine movements, the main water supply being drawn from an auxiliary tank which could be coupled to either end. The "GMA" class carried only 17½ cwt. more supplies than the original "GM" class, but was over 11 tons heavier—such was the effect of the cast steel beds and other refinements!

A South African Railways 2ft. gauge NG/G16 class Beyer-Garratt still working hard in the early 1970's.   [Photo L.A. Nixon]

It was noted in the Board Minutes for 25 November 1958 that:

> "The last of the seven NG/G16 Beyer-Garratt Locomotives for the Tsumeb Corporation had now been dispatched and this completed current orders for Steam Locomotives."(18)

These were almost the same as the South African Railways 2ft. gauge 2-6-2 + 2-6-2 Beyer-Garratts but with more space for coal and less for water. These last Beyer-Garratts were delivered to the South African Railways following the decision to convert the Corporation's track to 3ft. 6in. gauge. The building programme for 1958 had been nine of the Rhodesia Railways "20 A" class, the last ten of the South African Railways "GMAM" class, and these seven for Tsumeb Corporation. In the busy post-war years, Beyer, Peacock had built over 130 tender and tank engines in addition to 449 Beyer-Garratts at Gorton, and sublet or licensed a further 235 Beyer-Garratts for construction by other companies.

[Below] The first and last orders for Garratt locomotives built at Gorton Foundry happened to be for the 2ft. gauge, the final ones being ordered by the Tsumeb Corporation in Southern Africa [11188], but were delivered to the South African Railways.

Problems and Profits

The volume of work passing through Gorton Foundry steadily increased, from 6,214 tons per annum in 1947, to 10,376 tons in 1956, when the value of work produced was £3,123,025.(19) In October 1950, the Order Book exceeded £10,000,000 so careful planning was essential to ensure that maximum production was attained without delays. For a long period, shift working, both day and night, for seven days a week, was in operation to try to meet the demand. Deliveries of steel caused serious problems, because it was in great demand from other industries as well as the locomotive builders. Quality too was sometimes poor and this caused production problems. On the East African Railways "59" class, several slabs of steel for the bar frames had to be rejected after machining, due to defects, and this upset the whole production schedules.(20)

One particularly acute problem with the growing size and numbers of the Beyer-Garratts was planing the bar frames. The existing planing machines at Gorton Foundry did not have enough capacity, so some of the work had to be contracted out, and therefore in July 1954, four large planing machines were ordered, at a cost of approximately £50,000.(21) In January 1955, over £30,000 was spent on a heavy-duty railway wheel lathe and two vertical turning and boring machines, and such was the confidence of the directors in the future of the steam locomotive that they ordered more machine tools to the value of £70,000 during that year. However, the machine tool builders were so busy that a planing machine ordered then was delivered after the last steam locomotive had been finished.

As well as having problems with the supply of materials, there was also a shortage of skilled men in the early post-war years. While the efficiency of Gorton Foundry was steadily improved, so that greater production was achieved with the same number of personnel, the Chairman's Annual Reports constantly had to point out that even better figures would have been reached if they had been able to recruit all the men they had needed. Yet, in spite of all these problems, the Chairman was able to report that in 1954, the centenary year of Beyer, Peacock & Co., "total sales and total gross profits should both have reached new record high levels".(22)

[Above] The works in 1947.

[Below] Drilling a slab of steel for a main frame.

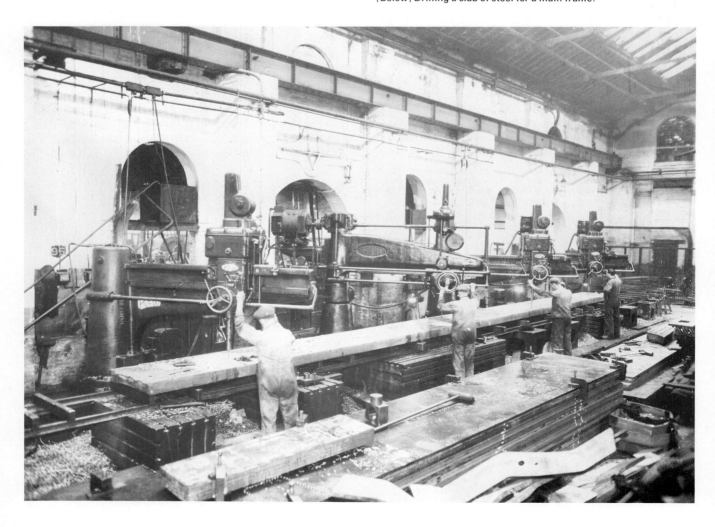

These post-war years were the most profitable for Beyer, Peacock, certainly since the formation of the Private Limited Company in 1882. Although towards the end of this period, profits from the other associated companies began to swell the figures, the dividends of 10 per cent. or over were the highest recorded in the Company's history for such a long run of years. The level would have been even higher if the number of shares had not been increased. With such heavy demand and such good results, it would have been folly for the Directors to consider changing production from the steam locomotive and more especially the Beyer-Garratt.

The End of Steam

The ways in which the Directors sought to broaden the base of Beyer, Peacock & Co. and to diversify its products will be discussed in the next chapter. They had of course long been aware of the increasing threat to the steam locomotive from alternative forms of power, such as the electric locomotive, or the diesel in its various combinations. They therefore took the decision that Gorton Foundry should not be expanded to cope with the growing demand for Garratt locomotives, but that extra capacity could best be obtained by subcontracting or licensing. Various French and Belgian locomotive builders were visited after the war by James Hadfield and agreements were concluded with Société Franco-Belge, at Raisemes in France (a continuation of a previous agreement in their case), and with Forges Usines et Fonderies, at Haine-Saint-Pierre in Belgium. Similar arrangements with Henschel & Sohn in Germany came later.(23) The following work was subcontracted:-

1949	Franco-Belge	38	"HT" Boilers	-	Indian Store Dept.
1949	Henschel	6	Garratts	-	Gt. West. of Brazil
1949	Vulcan Fdry	24	Engines & Tend.	-	Iranian St. Rlys.
1950	Franco-Belge	20	Garratts	-	Queensland Gvt. Rlys.
1950	" "	10	Garratts	-	South Aust.Rlys.
1950	" "	10	Garratts	-	Rhodesia Rlys.
1951	Anglo-F.Belge	10	Tenders	-	Western Aust. Gvt. Rlys.
1951	R. Stephenson	24	Engines & Tend.	-	" " "
1952	Franco-Belge	12	Garratts	-	East African Rlys.
1956	North British	12	Garratts	-	South African Rlys
1957	North British	20	Garratts	-	" " "

The following work was licensed:-

1951	Henschel	5	Garratts GMA	-	South African Rlys
1951	"	20	Garratts GMAM	-	" " "
1951	"	6	Garratts	-	Mocamedes Rlys.
1951	Haine-St Pierre	12	Garratts	-	Beira Railway
1953	"	12	Garratts	-	Katanga Rlys.
1953	Henschel	5	Garratts	-	Beira Rlys.
1954	"	30	Garratts GMAM	-	South African Rlys
1954	"	25	Garratts GO	-	" " "
1956	"	30	Garratts GMAM	-	" " "

[Below A scheme for a 4-8-2 + 2-8-4 Beyer-Garratt for the Indian Government Railways [Scheme 133969] was the last produced for a steam locomotive.

Such a policy ran the dangers not only of giving the "know-how" of the Garratt locomotive to competitors, but also of filling their factories with orders. However, it was felt better to run these risks, and meet the demand by controlling it in this way, so that when orders fell off the customers would most likely turn to Beyer, Peacock and keep Gorton Foundry busy. In 1956, Beyer, Peacock Directors confidently expected that:

> "...steam locomotives of the Beyer-Garratt type will be required by a reducing number of customers in a reducing field for a number of years. If it is possible to 'phase' the demand in such a measure as to eliminate the necessity for either licensing or sub-contracting and yet keep our Manchester production facilities fully occupied, that is the theoretical ideal we should strive to attain."(24)

This was written a year after the publication by British Railways of their modernization plan which envisaged the scrapping of their steam locomotives. Why were the Beyer, Peacock management so confident when other private locomotive builders were facing difficulties?

In 1954, Beyer, Peacock had made a tentative offer to take-over Vulcan Foundry Ltd., including Robert Stephenson & Hawthorns Ltd., but refused to enter into an auction when outbid by English Electric Co. At Hunslet's it seemed, on Edgar Alcock's death in 1951, that orders for steam locomotives would be received for at least another 25 years, and it continued to build steam and diesel engines in equal numbers for the next three years. The position totally changed after the decision by British Railways.

> "Between October 1955, when a small 2ft. gauge steam locomotive was ordered for Natal, and July 1956, no steam orders were received by the Company and throughout the whole of the following winter only one new steam locomotive was built. Apart from the orders for spares, for boiler repairs and for replacement boilers, the production picture was transformed to almost 100 per cent. diesel practically overnight. Seldom has any technical revolution come about with such dramatic speed."
>
> (25)

The North British Locomotive Co. had spare capacity at the end of 1955 when it agreed to subcontract the twelve "GMAM" Beyer-Garratts for the South African Railways. Part of the bargain was that North British would not compete with Beyer, Peacock for Garratt orders for the next fifteen years. North British built its last steam locomotive in February 1958 and went into liquidation in 1962. Henschel too was in financial difficulties by 1957.

In 1954, Beyer, Peacock had failed to win an order for Garratt locomotives in India because German and Japanese competitors could build two "WG" class ordinary locomotives more cheaply than one Garratt. India re-

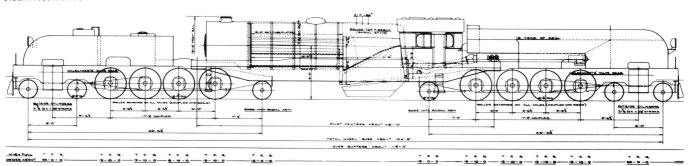

mained seriously interested in buying or themselves building Garratts until well after 1958. Similarly, between 1954 and 1958 China, Angola and Mozambique all expressed great interest in purchasing Garratts. In 1955, quotations for Garratts were submitted to Jordan, Nigeria and Nepal, while the Dehri-Rohtas Railway in India purchased ordinary locomotives from Krauss Maffei instead of Garratts. In that same year, James Hadfield went to Peru and reached agreement with the Peruvian Corporation for a new type of Garratt locomotive, and design work was started on it at Gorton, while orders were actually received for thirty-five "GMAM" class for the South African Railways and forty-five "20" class for the Rhodesia Railways.

In 1956, a further order from the South African Railways was received and it seemed that Bolivia and Mexico might place orders too. In 1957, the Rhodesia Railways were expected to confirm an order for thirty-four of their "20" class in August, but this was never placed as a result of the decline in the price of copper, and the diminishing of traffic on their lines. The slump in world trade similarly affected South Africa, where the demand for coal dropped, and traffic on the East African Railways also fell away. The railways in these countries, as well as in many others, delayed ordering new locomotives, and the very few that were ordered were for some form of diesel, to try out this type. Requests for steam locomotive quotations continued into 1959, but they were so few that they could be counted on the fingers of one hand.(26) The demand for Garratt locomotives remained bouyant until at least the early part of 1956, and the Beyer, Peacock management seem justified in concluding it was a matter of trying to marshall that demand to keep an even production and output, but the world recession killed this.

Then the decision to abandon steam locomotives, which was taken by British Railways in 1955, changed the policy of the boards of many overseas railways too, for it was a case of "when father turns, we all turn". As long as steam was good enough for Britain it was good enough for those railways overseas with strong British connections, whose officers were largely recruited from British Railways. These people had no intention of being left behind in any modernization programme, so British Railways decision had a dramatic effect on the world market. The management of Beyer, Peacock did not anticipate this, and it is doubtful if they could have realised the sudden change that would come, because it was intensified by the world recession. This meant that virtually no orders for any types of locomotives were placed anywhere and, at the end of 1958 Beyer, Peacock was forced to close down the greater part of its facilities for building steam locomotives.

South African Railways "GMA" class Beyer-Garratt No. 4080 climbing to Lootsberg summit with the Mossel Bay to Pretoria passenger train on 16 June 1978.   [Photo E. Talbot]

The Technical Officers of Beyer, Peacock had long been aware of the growing interest in diesel locomotion among railway companies, for as far back as 1931 three schemes for diesel-electric locomotives were drawn up, two for the London, Midland & Scottish Railway, and one for the Silverton Tramway, in Australia.(1) In January 1946, the Managing Director stated that:

> "We are now receiving numerous enquiries for mechanical parts for Electric and Diesel Electric Locomotives. The suggestion was put by Mr. Wilmot that we should make some form of agreement for a period of ten years with English Electric Company whereby B.P. & Co. would collaborate in the design etc. and be responsible for the manufacture of the chassis and bogies."(2)

Nothing came of this because English Electric declined the offer, but in May 1947 negotiations began with Metropolitan-Vickers of Trafford Park, Manchester, which led in 1949 to the establishment of a separate company, Metropolitan-Vickers - Beyer, Peacock Ltd., to build "Locomotives other than Steam" at the Bowesfield Works, Stockton-on-Tees. The history of this Company is told in Appendix VII. Its existence was one of the reasons why no diesel locomotives were built at Gorton Foundry until after 1958, but, because the staff at Gorton were responsible for running Bowesfield, they gained valuable experience in designing and producing both diesel and electric locomotives.

The threat to the predominance of the steam locomotive caused the Directors of Beyer, Peacock to diversify their manufacturing interests, first by expanding the Company, by purchasing controlling interests in other firms, and then by finding alternative work for Gorton Foundry. By 1953, to the pre-war acquisition of Richard Garrett Engineering Works at Leiston had been added Denings of Chard, makers of agricultural machinery, Fyna Industries Ltd., makers of milling machinery, Theramic Ltd., of Deal, makers originally of thermic syphons for locomotives, Maiuri Refrigeration Patents, Low Temperature Developments Ltd., and some other companies concerned with sales, such as Rail Traction Supplies Ltd. The profits from these subsidiary companies gradually came to assume increasing significance in the balance-sheet of Beyer, Peacock & Co. Ltd.

After 1955 it became obvious that it would be necessary to find alternative work to keep Gorton Foundry fully active in case the demand for Garratt locomotives fell, and was unable to keep the work force fully occupied.

[Heading] The Beyer, Peacock "Hymek" Bo-Bo diesel-hydraulic locomotive.

[Below] The scheme [111463] proposed in 1931 for a diesel electric locomotive for the London, Midland & Scottish Railway.

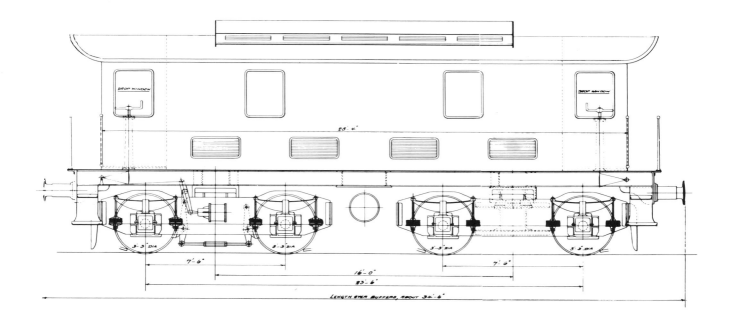

The first new product intended to take the place of the Beyer-Garratt was a range of track maintenance machines, built under a licence agreement with the Railway Maintenance Corporation, of Pittsburg, U.S.A., and marketed under a new subsidiary company named Beyer, Peacock Railway Equipment Ltd., formed in 1956.(3) A vast amount of design and development work was put into this project, since the drawings supplied were of machines designed for the 4ft. 8½in. gauge only, and for American conditions, using American equipment. Six types of machines were involved—a large sixteen-tool tamper, spot tamper, mole ballast cleaner, ballast distributor, linemaster and spike-master. These were redesigned to incorporate power units, hydraulic and pneumatic equipment, all of British manufacture, with models for metre, 3ft. 6in., 4ft. 8½in., and 5ft. 6in. gauges. Prototype machines were built and demonstrated, but only a few were sold, because they were in competition with the excellent products of two well-established European makers, who introduced innovations which made the Beyer, Peacock designs out of date. This project had been abandoned by the end of 1962.

[Top right] Tool tamper.

[Upper middle right] Jack tamper.

[Middle right] Ballast distributor.

[Foot right] Ditching machine.

[Below] Linemaster spot tamper.

Another new project taken up in 1956 was the design and building of diesel-electric shunting locomotives, in collaboration with Brush Electrical Engineering Co. Ltd., Beyer, Peacock being responsible for the mechanical parts and complete erection.(4) A batch of six 200hp 0-4-0 standard type was built and orders came from various quarters. Between 1958 and 1964, a total of twenty-six was constructed with various diesel engines, including twelve built in 1960 for Park Gate Iron & Steel Works. A standard 400hp 0-6-0 was also designed, but only one prototype was produced in 1962. The last shunters built were six 275hp 0-4-0s for Skopje Steel Works in Jugoslavia; which were delivered in 1964. While it had been realised that production of this type of locomotive would never replace the Garratt, the results of this collaboration fell far short of expectations, but the design work on these and on the track maintenance machines did ensure that staff were available in the Drawing Office to tackle the design of other projects, in particular diesel-hydraulic locomotives.

[Above] A pair of 0-4-0 diesel-electric shunting engines working in tandem for the Skopje Steel Works.

[Above] The diesel engine and generator inside one of the 0-4-0 diesel-electric shunting engines.

[Below] The prototype 0-6-0 diesel-electric shunting engine which was used by the Brush Electrical Engineering Co. at Loughborough.

There was another angle to the association with Brush Electrical Engineering Co. during those years—the production of complete fabricated underframes, wheel sets, and complete bogies for the long run of Brush A-1-A + A-1-A Type 2 diesel-electric locomotives for British Railways. About two hundred sets of these parts were supplied between 1957 and 1962. One more new product embarked upon in 1957 was the manufacture of a new design of 2,000 c.f.m. two-stage, double-acting air compressor for Broom & Wade Ltd., for which all the working drawings were prepared, under its supervision. The prototype was completed in 1958, but what had been envisaged as a batch of twenty, to be part manufactured and assembled as called for, ended with only eight, as the price proved uneconomic.

It became increasingly obvious that this amount of work would not keep the factory busy and the Board made strenuous efforts to find alternative products. At a meeting held in March 1957,

> "The Chairman outlined his discussions with the Deputy Chairman of John Brown & Co. Ltd. with a view to acquiring a financial interest, by exchange of shares, in one of the subsidiaries for the John Brown Group—Craven Carriage and Wagon Co. Ltd., a company which produces inter alia Rail Cars and train sets.
>
> "The Chairman stated that in his opinion there would be a considerable increase in the demand for Rail Cars etc., and on his instructions, Mr. Crane and Mr. Hatz (Rail Traction Supplies) had visited de Dietrich, Strasbourg, who were pioneers in this type of railway equipment. . .
>
> "The Chairman also referred to discussions with Mr. L.W. Robson, Chairman of Associated British Engineering, on the proposal to form an association with that Company, who hold rights to the free piston engine to apply that principle in railway locomotive construction.
>
> "In this connection and in association with Mr. Hadfield, the Chairman stated that he had lodged an application for a master patent for a Beyer-Garratt Locomotive to be driven by gas other than steam. He considered that this technical development could prove important to the Company."(5)

None of these projects, and many others which were discussed, ever developed into anything.

In October, 1957, the decision was taken to investigate the manufacture of diesel-hydraulic locomotives.(6) The diesel-hydraulic system of transmission had made much progress in Germany and was considered to have great possibilities for the future. Another factor in the decision was that there was no prospect of competing on level terms for building main-line diesel-electric locomotives, since the other principal British locomotive builders had facilities within their own group organisations for producing power units and all the electrical equipment. It would have been uneconomical for Beyer, Peacock to have built this equipment so this would have to be sub-contracted.

Numerous project designs of diesel-hydraulic locomotives were prepared and submitted with tenders in response to enquiries received from many overseas railways, but, with sometimes as many as twenty-eight competitors from Germany, France, U.S.A., Italy, Japan, Australia and elsewhere, no orders were secured. The diesel-hydraulic was regarded by many as still being in the experimental stage, but in 1958 the decision by the Western Region of British Railways to use this type of

[Above] The Broom & Wade air compressor.

[Below] The Maybach high-speed diesel engine manufactured by Bristol Siddeley.

[Below] The hydraulic transmission manufactured by J. Stone & Co.

[Above] Hymek D7000 hauling a goods train.

locomotive made the future seem brighter. Swindon Works was building the 2,100hp D800 class, closely following the design of the German V22, built by Krauss-Maffei, which had Maybach high-speed diesel engines and Maybach-Mekydro transmissions. The design which Beyer, Peacock decided to follow used the same basic equipment and a new company, Beyer, Peacock (Hymek) Ltd. was formed to market these locomotives. This was a consortium with Bristol Siddeley Engines Ltd. which had a manufacturing licence for the engines, for which a new plant was set up at Coventry, while J. Stone & Co. (Deptford) Ltd. had a licence for manufacturing the transmissions.

In the latter half of 1958, the Western Region placed an order for forty-five Beyer, Peacock (Hymek) Bo-Bo twin-cab single-engined 1,700hp locomotives, and subsequently increased the order to a total of a hundred and one, which carried the numbers D7000 to D7100.(7) The power unit was a Maybach MD 870 16-cylinder supercharged engine, conservatively rated for this application at 1,700hp and built at the Ansty Works near Coventry. The Maybach-Mekydro transmission was made at Deptford, and comprised a single special torque convertor combined with a four-speed automatic gearbox and with final drive gearboxes on each axle, all linked by Cardan shafts. The locomotive was designed for a starting tractive effort of 45,750lb. and a maximum speed of 90mph. Equipment included an oil-fired train heating boiler. As on all British Railways main-line diesels, there was no space to spare once all the equipment was on board.

[Above] The front of a Hymek locomotive.

It had been hoped to retain some facilities to manufacture steam locomotives, should the demand arise, and boiler-making capacity was retained for some time. Indeed some boilers were made for Rhodesia and other railways. However, production in the iron and steel foundries ceased as it was reckoned that any castings needed could be supplied from outside. The foundries were converted into an excellent fabricating shop for the underframes and body sections of the diesel locomotives, which were fed across a short track into the input end of a new assembly shop, created in the old boiler shop. Inside the high bays of the boiler shop, twenty diesel locomotives could be

[Top] The yard in front of the ''new'' boiler shop as it was in the days of steam locomotive construction, filled with flanging plates, patterns, etc.

[Above] The ''new'' boiler shop fitted with doors and the traverser in front of it ready for building diesel locomotives.

erected on a new assembly line. They were placed crosswise in the shop, on temporary bogies, which ran on tracks through doors to a traverser, installed outside, whereby they could be moved progressively down the shop. At the final station, a set of four synchronised jacks was installed to raise the complete superstructure and run the finished bogies under it, the bogies being built in the old erecting shop.

Gradually whole sections of the factory became disused, including, as well as the foundries, the forge and much of the machine shops, boiler shop flanging section, and the machines required in boiler manufacture. Crafts handed down through generations died away, and many men had to find other employment since the new product required only fitters, welders, platers, sheet metal workers, pipe fitters and electricians on the shop floor. In spite of such drastic changes and reconstruction, production was maintained and the Company continued to make a profit throughout this period, something which none of its competitors at home did. The Drawing Office responded nobly under the challenge of this new work and there was a general feeling of optimism over Gorton Foundry. It was even suggested that work might have to be sub-contracted to Leiston and other associated companies.(8)

Delivery of the D7000 class commenced in May 1961, with the first engine being completed three months ahead of schedule; the last one was dispatched in 1964. Unfortunately there was trouble at first with the transmission equipment, but once that had been sorted out, they gave very good performance in service. Over the years, they proved to have the best availability of the Western Region diesel-hydraulics, and performed better than most of the diesel-electrics on the other Regions.(9) It was hoped that orders would be placed for up to four hundred more, and tenders were also submitted for some of the D800 class designed at Swindon, but the building of these engines was confined to Swindon and Crewe workshops.

The trouble with the transmission came at a vital period for the future success of the Beyer, Peacock diesel-hydraulic project, for until that was rectified, nobody would consider buying any engines of this design. Then the carpet was pulled out from under Beyer, Peacock's feet once again by British Railways, when the Railway Executive decreed that diesel-electrics were to be the future policy, and that medium-speed diesel engines of certain makers only were to be employed. Not only did this exclude the high-speed Maybach engine, but it also sounded the death-knell of the diesel-hydraulic, for railways overseas once more followed the lead given by England. Bristol-Siddeley stopped building the Maybach engines, and, while Hymek locomotives could have been supplied with other types of engine, it was obvious that there was no future for diesel-hydraulics and Beyer, Peacock (Hymek) Ltd.

Beyer, Peacock [Gorton] Limited

While the D7000 Class was being built, there were changes in the organisation of Beyer, Peacock & Co. Ltd. On 1 January 1960, the various subsidiaries became members of the Beyer, Peacock Group, with Beyer, Peacock & Co. Ltd. as the Holding Company, and in consequence the part at Gorton was renamed Beyer, Peacock (Gorton) Ltd. James Hadfield was its Chairman and Managing Director, and Leslie T. Dawes the Commercial Director. Otherwise the organisation at Gorton continued as before, with Michael Sunderland as Chief Engineer (Production), responsible for all manufacturing activity, assisted by Harold Lane as Works Manager, and David Patrick as Chief Engineer (Design), responsible for all technical activity, assisted by Stanley Cusick as Chief Draughtsman. Hadfield's many responsibilities, including being Managing Director of the Holding Company, obliged him to make the London Office in Locomotive House his headquarters.

[Below] "Hymeks" being constructed in the converted boiler shop.

The mechanical parts of ten 25kV electric locomotives, designed by Metropolitan-Vickers Electrical Co. Ltd. for British Railways, were manufactured under sub-contract in 1960.(10) This was one of the various designs purchased by British Railways for trials before deciding on the standard design to be adopted. Since further orders for diesel-hydraulic locomotives were not forthcoming, despite strenuous efforts, and the modest volume of work involved in diesel-electric shunters and other products was far from sufficient, tenders were submitted for other work, including main-line diesel-electric locomotives for British Railways, which were still obtaining a large number from private builders, under the 'Modernisation Plan', to supplement the ever-increasing output of their works. The first such order was for twenty-nine Type 1 Bo-Bo 900hp twin-engined diesel-electrics, identical with those designed and built by Clayton Equipment Ltd., Derby, but modified to take Crompton-Parkinson electrical equipment. Delivery commenced in March 1964 and was completed in April 1965.

[Above] 25 Kv ac electric locomotives under construction.

[Below] The "Clayton" diesel-electric locomotive.

[Above] The 25 Kv ac electric locomotive supplied to British Railways in association with Metropolitan-Vickers Ltd.

[Below] "Clayton" diesel-electric locomotives in the paintshop.

In 1962, a tender was submitted to the Nepal Government Railways for one or two Garratt locomotives, but the necessary credit authorisation could not be arranged, and no order followed. Spare parts, such as boilers for steam locomotives, continued to be built during these years, but this business gradually declined, and it too was hampered by the world slump, which affected the profitability of railways everywhere. Although tenders were submitted for diesel locomotives to many overseas railways, the few orders that were placed went elsewhere, to those countries which offered loans as well. Railways everywhere were switching to diesel traction, and 1962 saw the complete elimination of orders for new steam locomotives, but the economic situation and the need for credit financing determined when and how dieselisation took place. An independent private company like Beyer, Peacock did not have the resources to match Government sponsorship.(11)

Therefore the search continued to find alternative products which could be manufactured at Gorton. A venture into radial arm drilling machines during 1963-64 produced a small volume of work. Meanwhile in 1963, a licensing agreement was signed with the Westinghouse Corporation of America to manufacture its extensive range of industrial fans within the Beyer, Peacock Group. One of the group companies (Air Control Industries Ltd.) was already in this business, and the intention was to extend its range of fans and to gain a share of orders for large industrial fans, such as the ones used in electricity generating plants, etc. Unfortunately this project was born at a time when the Company policy was one of ruthless economy in all directions, and the technical staff was drastically reduced. In the works, where heavy expenditure had been incurred to facilitate building diesel locomotives, the production of fans received no similar consideration. The Central Electricity Generating Board was in no hurry to entrust the building of its fans to a new comer, having already two established suppliers. No orders were ever received from there, but a total of about fifty medium sized fans was built. In 1965, the Westinghouse agreement was terminated and another brave try had come to nought!

In spite of the tremendous effort and skill displayed by the technical and works staff in mastering each new product, the tide of the Company's commercial prosperity was running out. There was a considerable element of sentiment in the fight to restore Gorton Foundry to prosperity, since practically all the Directors and Executive Staff had spent many years of their working lives there, and such men do not give up easily. Unfortunately some of the other companies in the Group were also operating with heavy trading deficits at the same time, so no help could come from them.

In 1964, an order was won for fifty-four Type 2, 1,250hp Bo-Bo diesel-electric locomotives to British Railways drawings, with AEI power equipment, similar to those built at Derby. Intense competition from other rivals meant that this order was taken at a loss and it was hoped that time would be gained during which Gorton Foundry could be restored to prosperity. This order was not received soon enough to prevent a gap in production occurring in some departments, but work commenced in April 1964(12), and the first was delivered in July 1965. With around two-thirds of the value of these locomotives having to be sub-contracted to obtain the necessary power equipment, etc., the work load at Gorton was quite inadequate.

The desperate fight to restore the fortunes of Gorton Foundry ended in the summer of 1965, when financial interests from a new quarter took a strong hand in the affairs of the Group. Three new Directors joined the Board of the Holding Company—W.E.A. Robinson, J.C.S. Edwards and R.J. Hadfield, the latter, who was Managing Director of Richard Garrett Engineering Works, being the only one already connected. The long and distinguished business career of Harold Wilmot ended in August 1965, at the age of 70, with his retirement as Chairman from the Board. His son, Douglas, also resigned from the Board and left the Company. In September, W.E.A. Robinson took over as Chairman and at the end of the year, James Hadfield, then sixty-five, resigned from the Board and all his executive appointments.(13) The London Office was closed and Maurice Crane, Technical Sales Manager, left the Company, after 23 years service, to join The Hunslet Engine Co.

The new policy, in view of the prevailing heavy losses, was one of ruthless pruning of unprofitable enterprises, by closing down and selling. Immediately after the new Chairman took over, it was announced that Gorton Foundry would cease all production as soon as the thirty-sixth of the fifty-four Type 2 diesel-electric locomotives for British Railways had been completed, the remaining eighteen being built by Derby Works. The last locomotive was delivered early in 1966 and all manufacture ended soon after, when the last of the fans on order was completed.

So ended 112 years of locomotive building by this famous Manchester company whose contribution to locomotive engineering was second to none. There is a great sadness in the closure of a works with such historic traditions, but technological changes rendered many of its departments obsolete and unsuitable for other profitable activity. For those who had fought to the last to restore its prosperity, there was a sense of failure and regret for the many craftsmen deprived of employment. Gone for ever are the great days of steam when the distinctive works siren could be heard for miles around, when the passer-by could hear the busy chatter of smithy hammers, or the thump of the big forge hammer, which vibrated the ground around, or the musical notes of three-chime whistles on locomotives under test. The valuable site was sold, and most of the buildings were demolished, with the exception of the boiler shop block, which is now a Manchester Corporation maintenance depot.

The private locomotive industry in Great Britain always had problems through being denied any regular share of the requirements of the home railways, in contrast to the position of builders in the United States, or Germany for example. The advent of diesel traction attracted others to the industry, and the export field on which British builders had so largely relied was be-devilled by politics, credit facilities, etc., while at home British Railways spent millions on re-equipping their workshops to build their own diesel locomotives. The Hunslet Engine Company did make a successful transition to diesel locomotive manufacture, but it relied on small shunting engines. The North British Locomotive Company—the largest in the industry—set up its own plant to build diesel engines and hydraulic transmissions and ended up in liquidation. Vulcan Foundry survived by a close liason with the English Electric Co. In the end it lost its independence and became a division of that Company, but now no longer builds railway locomotives. Brush Electrical Engineering Co. built up a tremendous output during the British Railways modernisation plan, but by 1979 even it had abandoned locomotive production. Most of the other manufacturers of steam locomotives had already closed down and with the end of the British Railways modernisation plan in sight, Beyer, Peacock & Co. Ltd. closed Gorton Foundry, to enable the other members of the Group to continue to trade.

To add a postcript which shows the excellence of the Garratt design, just as Gorton Foundry was closing, the South African Railways decided to order eight more of the 2-6-2 + 2-6-2 heavy Garratts for the 2ft. 0in. gauge lines. Although diesel locomotives had been offered instead, the railway authorities were determined to have more steam engines, which they knew were reliable, rather than risk a new design. The boilers were built by Hunslet in Leeds, one of the few firms capable of this type of work at that time, while the rest of the engines were built by Hunslet Taylor & Co., its South African associates. Delivery of all eight was completed in 1968, and it is a credit to the original Beyer, Peacock design that it was in production for over forty years. It is a strange coincidence that the first, and what undoubtedly will be the last Garratts, were for the 2ft. 0in. gauge.

* * * * *

The Beyer, Peacock Group of Companies

The profits from the Beyer-Garratt locomotive were used to diversify the trading activities of Beyer, Peacock & Co. Ltd., by buying up other companies,(14) so that when the original Company was changed into a holding Company in 1960, the Group consisted of the following main constituents.

1 **Beyer, Peacock [Gorton] Ltd.**, Manchester
   (Railway Locomotives and heavy general engineering)
   Companies associated with Gorton were **Beyer, Peacock Equipment Ltd.** (maintenance machines for railway track, etc.) **Rail Traction Supplies Ltd.** (Marketing railway accessories.) **Federated Engineers Ltd.** (Marketing rubber accessories for railways.)

2 **Richard Garrett Engineering Works Ltd.**, Leiston (15)
   (Machine tools and packaging machinery)
   Companies associated with Leiston were **Thermic Ltd.**, Deal. (Originally manufacturers of thermic syphons for locomotives, but later of small machine tools.) **B.J.N. Engineering Co. Ltd.**, (makers of machine tools, especially planing machines).

3 **Denings of Chard Ltd.**
   (Agricultural machinery, iron castings)
   Associated with this Company were **Brecknell Willis & Co. Ltd.**, Chard, makers of electrical collector gear and pantographs etc. for railways, special machines and castings, **Fyna Industries Ltd.**, Chard, makers of hammer mills, and **Space Decks Ltd.**, Chard, which was a Company that held the licences for a patent type of steel structure for making flat roofs.

4 **Anti-attrition Metal Co.**, Maidenhead
   (Bearings and bearing metals)
   With the gradual rundown of Gorton, this Company was moved to Manchester in 1961-62 and closed down in 1966.(16)

5 **Air Control Installations Ltd.**, Ruislip
   (Fans, air conditioning, dust control)
   Associated with this Company was **Low Temperature Developments Ltd.**, Ruislip, manufacturers of industrial refrigeration plant and a patent holding company, **Mauri-Refrigeration Patents Ltd.**

There was in addition **Beyer, Peacock [Hymek] Ltd.** but this only existed to market diesel-hydraulic locomotives, and never manufactured anything.

The Struggle for Survival

Adverse trading conditions were affecting the profitability of other companies in the Group as well as Beyer, Peacock (Gorton) Ltd., so a policy of pruning and consolidation proceeded apace in 1966 and 1967 when viable product lines were re-allocated to larger subsidiaries from the smaller units prior to the latters' dissolution. Denings of Chard changed its name to 'Space Decks Limited' following the discontinuation of its agricultural machinery business, except for spares, so that it could concentrate on the assembly line manufacture of the 'Space Deck' structural steel roofing system. Simultaneously the patent owning company added the word (PATENTS) to its name to become Space Decks (Patents) Limited. Manufacture of large fans by Air Control Installations at Ruislip was discontinued and the surviving small (less than 9in. diameter) fan production was relocated in Group premises at Chard to enable the large Ruislip factory to be sold with vacant possession.

As a result, in early 1968 largely through the property sales, the Company found itself with large cash resources but still without any acceptable new activity in which they could be redeployed. A troublesome four-year old claim against the Company by Rhodesia Railways was withdrawn, each side bearing its own costs to date, and the way was clear for the Company to decide to repay in June 1968 the outstanding £300,000 of 5½ per cent. Preference stock units and four shillings out of the five shillings paid up on each Ordinary stock unit in issue. This absorbed £1,584,782, and left the Group composed of the following active constituent companies:-

100% owned,

Richard Garrett Engineering Works Ltd., Leiston, Suffolk.
Space Decks Ltd., (formerly Denings), Chard, Somerset.
Brecknell, Willis & Co. Ltd., Chard, Somerset.
Air Control Industries Ltd., Chard, Somerset.

52% owned,

Space Decks (Patents) Ltd., Chard, Somerset.

Associate Company, 36⅓ owned,

Locomotive Manufacturers Co. Ltd., property owning in London.

At this stage all involvement in the locomotive industry had ceased, even the supply of spares, which had been passed by agreement to the Hunslet Engineering Co. Ltd., but the original Beyer, Peacock & Co. Ltd. survived as the main holding company.

This history of the one of the leading members of the British locomotive manufacturing industry would not be complete without some brief details of events since 1968. The first in time was the disposal of Air Control Installations Ltd. to H.G. Kennedy, who was an employee of Beyer, Peacock for some twenty-five years, latterly as Company Secretary. He was succeeded in this position by R.L. Kirkcaldie, C.A., A.C.W.A. Then in 1970, the associate company, Locomotive Manufacturers Co. Ltd., realised its main asset, the office building and associated block of flats in Buckingham Gate, London, that had for so long been the headquarters of the industry and Beyer, Peacock itself, whose share of the proceeds was £475,000.

In the following year, Space Decks Ltd. secured a profitable contract for the construction of a very large supermarket in Kinshasa, Zaire (Congo), and started to fulfil some of the hopes that had been entertained for its future when the automated production line had been installed in 1967/8. This change of fortune, added to the steady level of profit from the Richard Garrett subsidiary, gave the Group performance a 'recovery stock' appearance with a market price low compared with its asset value, and therefore vulnerable to take over approaches. There were several preliminary enquiries for either part or all of the Group's undertakings, but nothing came of any of these until late in 1973 when Moore Holdings Ltd., a small Dublin conglomerate company with predominantly property development leanings, announced that it owned over 25 per cent. of the Company's issued capital and requested a seat on the Board for two of its nominees. W.E.A. Robinson, the Chairman who had already announced his impending retirement in March 1974 when he reached 65, resigned in October 1973 to enable the continuing Directors to carry out the negotiations with Moore Holdings and the Deputy Chairman, Col. J.A.T. Barstow, a non-executive Director of thirty years standing, accordingly was appointed to succeed him. At an Extraordinary General Meeting convened for the purpose, motions to appoint the Moore nominees were lost.

To expand the Group's management resources, the new Chairman appointed F.C.B. Bland as Group Managing Director in February 1974 and in May 1974 arranged for a 1 for 4 rights issue of ordinary stock to produce further finance of £375,000 for expansion and re-equipment. This proved to be a timely operation as the main property boom was collapsing and severe shortages of credit with deteriorating clash flows were widespread in industry and commerce. One concern acutely affected by liquidity problems was the Company's principal shareholder, Moore Holdings Ltd., which was put into receivership and forced to sell its stockholding which had been bought with borrowed money in the boom period and was now valued at well below half cost. Then followed a period of great uncertainty for Beyer, Peacock because the ultimate destination of this major stockholding was in doubt. Eventually it was taken up in 1975 by several City institutions — Investment Trusts and Unit Trusts — in lots of less than five per cent. each of the total issued capital.

The promise of stable ownership for such a large block of the Company's issued share capital was especially welcome as the Group order book was excellent and Space Decks in particular had secured some sizeable overseas contracts which augured well for its immediate prospects. Amongst these contracts was one for Dhahran Airport terminal building with National Chemical Industries Ltd. of Jeddah, Saudi Arabia, which subsequently tendered successfully for use of the 'Space Deck' system for a large proportion of the 1977 Saudi Arabian Government's school building programme. To save cost and valuable shipping space on the congested Middle East routes, the component units were to be shipped in piece part or knocked-down form for subsequent assembly in Jeddah by a joint venture organisation in partnership with National Chemical Industries Ltd. In the event, local assembly was carried out as planned, but the participants responsibilities varied considerably from the original concept.

Owing to the scale of existing Saudi Arabian orders and the potential future scope in the market, the idea of selling a 25 per cent. minority interest in Space Decks Ltd. to National Chemical Industries Ltd. had been mooted and was being actively investigated when, to the general surprise of the Beyer, Peacock Board, it was informed on 1 July 1976 that the National Chemical Industries Ltd. owned 27 per cent. of the holding company's issued ordinary capital; presumably the old Moore Holding block acquired from the City institutions. On 7 July 1976, it was announced that National Chemical Industries Ltd. held 36 per cent. of the Beyer, Peacock capital and was offering 25p per share for any Beyer, Peacock stock units not yet owned. The existing Board found itself unable to recommend to shareholders the acceptance of the terms offered on the grounds that they did not adequately reflect the underlying asset value of the shares (See Appendix I) so rejection was proposed.

Initial acceptances of the offer, however, raised the bidder's shareholding to 56 per cent. The closing date for acceptances was extended and the existing Board amended its advice by recommending acceptance rather than have members left as minority stockholders in a foreign controlled company. Final acceptances amounted to over 98 per cent. and the remaining 'lost' or 'dissenting' members' holdings were compulsorily acquired in August 1978 by means of a Scheme of Arrangement under Section 206 of the Companies Act 1948. Thus was the final vestige of public participation in the ownership of this famous enterprise finally extinguished and it passed into the hands of an organisation mainly interested in the construction industry.

Soon the last light engineering subsidiaries were sold off, for Richard Garrett Engineering Ltd. passed out of the Group in February 1979, only to be closed in November 1980, and Brecknell, Willis & Co. Ltd. left four months later. National Chemical Industries Ltd. had acquired the Bison Group Ltd. in June 1977 and in 1979 merged Space Decks Ltd. with its steelwork division. The shell of Beyer, Peacock & Co. Ltd. was made a subsidiary of the Bison Group and, after settlements of the various disposals and transfers, became a dormant company early in 1980, which really marked the end of the active days of this well known and highly respected name with long associations in the world of engineering.

[Below] The "Space Decks" roofing construction system enabled a large area to be covered by a light structure without supporting pillars.

NOTES

Notes to Chapter 1

1 For biographical details, see **Minutes of Proc. Inst. C.E.** Vol. XLVII (1877), pp. 290-297; **Modern English Biography,** by F. Boase, Vol. I (1892), col. 268; **The Engineer,** Vol. 41 (1876), p. 439; **Engineering,** Vol. 21 (1876), p. 505; **Beyer, Peacock Quarterly Review,** Vol. 1, No. 2, April 1927, pp. 13-24 (portrait)
2 B.P. Quart. Rev. Vol. 1, No. 2, p. 14
3 Z. Colburn, **Locomotive Engineering and the Mechanism of Railways** (1871), p. 39
4 **Sharp Stewart Collection,** Science Museum, London. Sharp Roberts Order Book, No. 1, 24 November 1835
5 W. Johnson, **The Imperial Cyclopaedia of Machinery** (1854), p. lxii
6 Colburn, op. cit., p. 41
7 D.K. Clark, **Railway Locomotives** (1860), p. 165 and Colburn, op. cit., p. 51
8 E.L. Ahrons, **The British Steam Railway Locomotive,** Vol. I, 1825-1925 (1927), p. 38
9 Colburn, op. cit., p. 50
10 ibid., p. 58
11 **Proc. Inst. Mech. E.,** 1848, p. 3
12 **Engineering,** Vol. 21, 16 June 1876, p. 505
13 Colburn, op. cit., p. 68 and Ahrons, op. cit., p. 81 and **The Development of British Locomotive Design Construction** (1914), p. 8
14 Ahrons **Brit. Loco.** p.38
15 **Sharp Stewart Col.,** Sharp Bros. Drawings, No. 224, 12 April 1849 and No. 246, October 1851; **The Vulcan Locomotive Works, 1830-1930** (1930), p. 60 and W.F. Pettigrew, **A Manual of Locomotive Engineering** (1909), p. 24
16 Ahrons, **Brit. Loco.** p.367
17 **Proc. Inst. Mech. E.,** No. 1847, p. 4 and **Sharp Stewart Col.,** List of Engines
18 **Journal Inst. Loco. Engineers,** Vol. VI, No. 4 New Series, April 1916, p. 145, R.H. Burnett's Presidential Address, also **The Engineer,** Vol. 41, 9 June 1876, p. 439 and **Engineering,** Vol. 21, 16 June 1876, p. 505
19 **A History of the North British Locomotive Co.,** (1953), p. 17
20 R.H. Parsons, **History of the Institution of Mechanical Engineers** (1947), p. 10 and L.T.C. Rolt, **The Mechanicals,** (1967), pp. 16-17
21 **Proc. Inst. Mech. E.,** November 1847, p. 2 and 1848, p. 3
22 **Sharp Stewart Col.,** Sharp Bros. Drawing No. 7324, 15 June 1852 and Sharp Stewart Drawing No. 7602, 18 October 1852 and **N.B. Loco. Co., op. cit., p. 19**
23 For biographical details, see **Minutes of Proc. Inst. C.E.,** Vol. XCVII (1889), pp. 404-7; W. Smith, **Old Yorkshire** (1890), II pp. 271-4 (portrait); **Figaro** 9 March 1889, p. 9 (portrait); F. Boase, **Modern English Biography,** Vol. II (1897), col. 1413; **The Engineer,** Vol. 67 (1889), p. 207; B.P. Quart. Rev. Vol. 1, No. 3, July 1927, pp. 9-18 (portrait)
24 R.N. Redman, **The Railway Foundry, Leeds** (1927), p. 5
25 **The Engineer,** Vol. 67, 8 March 1889, p. 207 and Ed. R.B. Wilson, **Sir Daniel Gooch,** (1927)
26 **The Engineer,** Vol. 80, 6 September 1895, p. 240, letter from I.W. Boulton, A.R. Bennett, **The Chronicles of Boulton's Siding** (1972), p. 41 and G. Dow, **Great Central,** Vol. 1 (1959), p. 34
27 **Beyer, Peacock Official Centenary History,** Chap. 1. This was never published but a copy survives in the B.P. archives. See also **Proc. Inst. Mech. E.,** January 1851, p. 22. R. Peacock, ''On the Workshops for the Locomotive, Carriage and Waggon Departments of the Manchester, Sheffield, and Lincolnshire Railway''
28 **The Engineer,** Vol. 67, 8 March 1889, p. 207
29 **Sharp Stewart Col.,** Sharp Roberts Order Book No. 2, 9 December 1841
30 **Railway Magazine,** September 1966, B. Reed, Builders for 111 Years, p. 497 also Ahrons, **Brit. Loco.,** p. 81; G.D. Dempsey D.K. Clare, **A Rudimentary Treatise on the Locomotive Engine.** (1879), p. 163; Ahrons, **Construction,** p. 44
31 Clark, op. cit., p. 280
32 ibid, pp. 133, 137 & 162
33 J.W. Lowe, **British Steam Locomotive Builders,** (1975), see appropriate names
34 **B.P. Quart. Rev.** Vol. 1, No. 2, April 1927, p. 24 also A. Birch, **The Economic History of the British Iron and Steel Industry** (1967), pp. 285-6
35 Beyer's Note Book, p. 87, 10 November 1854
36 **Aris' Birmingham Gazette,** Monday 6 November 1854
37 For biographical details, see **Minutes of Proc. Inst. C.E.** Vol. XCIII (1888), pp. 489-492; **Proc. Inst Mech. E.,** (1888), pp. 264-5; **The Times,** 24 March 1888, p. 14; **The Engineer,** Vol. 65 (1888), p. 283; G.G. Lerry, **Henry Robertson: Pioneer of Railways into Wales,** (1949); F. Boase, **Modern English Biography,** Vol. III (1901), Col. 208; B.P. Quart Rev. Vol. 1, No. 4, October 1927, pp.14-28 (portrait)
38 See N.W. Webster, **Joseph Locke: Railway Revolutionary** (1970), pp. 133-144, and G.G. Lerry, **Collieries of Denbighshire** (1968), pp. 22-3 and 92
39 I am indebted to Mr. G.S. Catterall for this information.
40 **Sharp Stewart Col.,** List of Engines
41 **Robertson's Papers,** National Library of Wales, Note Book March 1853
42 B.P. Col. Facsimile of letters from Mr. C.F. Beyer to Mr. H. Robertson 4 December 1854-12 June 1863. Letter 13 December 1854.
43 B.P. Col. Facsimile of letters, Beyer to Robertson, 4 December 1854. Also see J.G.H. Warren, **A Century of Locomotive Building by Robert Stephenson & Co. 1823-1923** (reprint 1970), p. 53. Robert Stephenson's began in 1823 with a capital of £4,000.

Notes to Chapter 2

1 B.P. Col., Beyer's Note Book No. 1, p. 54, 20 December 1853
2 **The Engineer,** Vol. 1, 20 June 1856, pp. 333-4
3 B.P. Col., Beyer's Note Book No. 1, p. 64, 13 May and p. 75, 14 June 1854
4 Robertson Papers, Meetings of Partners
5 ibid, Diary, 1855
6 B.P. Col., First Minute Book, p. 8, 10 February 1855
7 B.P. Col. Facsimile of letters, 13 December 1854
8 Robertson Papers, letter from Beyer, 10 October 1863
9 Robertson Papers, from Peacock, 31 October 1863 and from Beyer, 24 August 1865
10 Vulcan Loco, op. cit., p. 6 and J.F. Clarke, **Power on Land and Sea** (1979), p. 10 for R. & W. Hawthorn's links overseas in 1845
11 B.P. Col., Facsimile, 16 March 1857
12 B.P. Col., First Minute Book, p. 49, 22 July 1857
13 B.P. Col., Letter from Beyer to Robertson, 3 July 1857
14 N.B. Loco. Co., op. cit., pp. 26 & 34 and J.W. Lowe, op. cit., p. 140
15 B.P. Col., First Minute Book, p. 64, 18 February 1859 and p. 66, 21 January 1860
16 ibid, p. 67, 21 January 1861
17 Robertson Papers, Peacock to Robertson, 20 August 1864
18 ibid, Beyer to Robertson, 28 July 1865
19 B.P. Col., Facsimile, 18 January 1855
20 **Sharp Stewart Col.,** Drawing No. 153, 1 August 1846 and B.P. Quart. Rev., Vol. 2, No. 3, July 1928, p. 52
21 **Sharp Stewart Col.,** Drawing No. 242, 28 November 1850 and B.P. Quart. Rev., Vol. 2, No. 3, July 1928, p. 52
22 B.P. Quart. Rev., Vol. 2, No. 3, July 1928, p. 55, for obituary notice for Francis Holt, see **Transactions of the Federated Institution of Mining Engineers,** Vol. 5, 1892/3, p. 481
23 B.P. Col., W/1 Wages Book 1854-56
24 J.F. Clarke, op. cit., p. 14
25 B.P. Col., Centenary History, p. 56
26 J.G.H. Warren, op. cit., p.59
27 J. Thomas, **Springburn Story** (1964), p. 89. When Neilson moved his works to Springburn in 1861, he had the following equipment:
    6 planers
    5 slotters
    6 shapers
    2 screw-cutting machines
    1 nut mill
    19 lathes
    3 nut lathes
    3 steam hammers
    and J.F. Clarke, op, cit., p. 14
28 B.P. Col., CA/1
29 **The Engineer,** Vol. 1, 20 June 1856, p. 334
30 ibid

Notes to Chapter 3

1. B.P. Col., Memorandum of Partnership (see Chap. 1)
2. **Sharp Stewart Col.**, Sharp Roberts Order Book, No. 1, 18 April 1836
3. B.P. Col., First Minute Book, p. 28, 12 December 1855
4. ibid, p. 51, 22 July 1857
5. B.P. Col. Orders Received, 14 January 1860, from Berlin & Hamburg Railway
6. Robertson Papers, letters from Beyer, and B.P. Col., Facsimile, 12 June 1863
7. Robertson Papers, letter from Beyer, 28 July 1865, and B.P. Co., letter from C. Pihl to Beyer, 29 May 1868
8. B.P. Col., Facsimile, 22 February 1863
9. B.P. Col., First Minute Book, p. 50, 10 January 1857 and Orders Received, 31 December 1858, from Robertson to Beyer
10. B.P. Col., 8 February 1858
11. B.P. Col., Orders Received, 15 March 1856, from General Railway Station, Chester
12. B.P. Col., Orders Received, from Madras Railway, 29 December 1859
13. B.P. Centenary History, p. 46
14. B.P. Col., Orders Received, 17 July 1860, from Oppela & Tarnowitz Railway
15. See J. Smith, Ed., **The Great Human Exploit** (1973), p. 67 and J.W. Lowe, op. cit., p. 131
16. Ahrons Brit. Loco., pp. 43 & 113
17. ibid, p. 63 and J. Bourne, **A Catechism of the Steam Engine** (New Ed. 1876), p. 129; Clark, op. cit., p. 27 and Colburn, op. cit., p. 69
18. Ahrons, **Brit. Loco.**, p. 131; J. Bourne, **Recent Improvements in the Steam-Engine** (1880), pp. 177 & 181; Clarke, op. cit., p. 25*; Colburn, op. cit., pp. 92 & 264; Dempsey, op. cit., p. 95 and C. Highet, **Scottish Locomotive History** (1970), p. 52
19. B.P. Col., First Minute Book, p. 40, 10 January 1857
20. Ahrons, **Brit. Loco.**, p. 125, and **Construction** p. 161
21. B.P. Col., Orders Received, 2 April 1857, copy of a letter from P. Stirling to J. Beattie
22. B.P. Col., CW/3, order 401
23. B.P. Col., Orders Received, 9 May 1856, from B. Fothergill, L.S.W.R.
24. Ahrons, **Construction**, p. 10 and Clark, op. cit., pp. 214 & 238
25. Colburn, op. cit., p. 47 and E. Kitson Clark, **Kitsons of Leeds 1837-1937** (1937), p. 46
26. **The Engineer**, Vol. 1, 20 June 1856, p. 334
27. Ahrons, **Brit. Loco.**, p. 217 and Clark, op. cit., p. 14*
28. B.P. Col., Facsimile, from W. Bradshaw, 3 June 1863
29. ibid, from Robertson to Beyer, 21 January 1863
30. ibid, from Carl Beyer, 26 March 1857
31. B.P. Col., from G.H. Streiler, 16 May 1857
32. B.P. Col., Orders Received, 22 February 1859, from the Zaragoza & Alsasua Railway
33. ibid, B.P. & Co., to the Zaragoza & Alsasua Railway (no date)
34. ibid, from Shelton Colliery & Iron works, 1 January 1857
35. B.P. Col., Minute Book (1902), No. 1, p. 91, 23 June 1903; p. 165, 13 June 1905; Minute Book No. 2, 2 November 1921, para 11 and J.M. Dunn, **The Wrexham, Mold & Connah's Quay Railway** (1957), p. 24
36. B.P. Col., Letter from Beyer to Robertson, 8 September 1857
37. B.P. Col., Centenary History, p. 46 and Robertson Papers, Peacock to Robertson, 26 October 1864
38. J.F. Clarke, op. cit., p. 24
39. B.P. Col., First Minute Book, p. 36, 9 August 1856 and p. 43 21 February 1857
40. ibid, p. 56, 24 December 1857
41. ibid, p. 60, 19 May 1858, p. 63, 12 June 1858 and p. 65, 18 February 1859
42. ibid, p. 66, 21 January 1860
43. ibid, p. 69, 10 April 1863

Notes to Chapter 4

1. **The Engineer**, Vol. 9, 25 May 1860, p. 332, and Patent No. 2306, 11 October 1859
2. B.P. Col., Beyer's Note Book No. 1, p. 87, 10 November and 13 November 1854
3. B.P. Col., Orders Received, 14 August 1854, Manchester, Sheffield & Lincolnshire Railway
4. ibid, 7 October 1854, Shrewsbury & Birmingham Railway and 20 March 1855, from B. Fothergill, Machinist & Consulting Engineer
5. ibid, 12 February 1856, from the Swedish Government Railway
6. ibid, 13 May 1858, from the Empress Elizabeth Railway and 5 July 1860, from the Zaragoza & Alsasua Railway
7. ibid, 27 September 1854, from Bristol & Exeter Railway
8. ibid, 30 September 1854, from the Great Western Railway, and Beyer's Note Book No. 1, p. 85, 29 September 1854
9. B.P. Col., Orders Received, 30 September 1854, from the Great Western Railway

10. B.P. Col., Facsimile, 13 June 1855
11. B.P. Col., First Minute Book, 21 July 1855, p. 20
12. ibid, 31 August 1855, p. 31
13. B.P. Col., Orders Received, 26 January 1854, from East Indian Railway
14. ibid, 31 January 1854, from B.P. & Co., to East Indian Railway
15. I am indebted to Mr. H.C. Hughes for the following information, "James Rendel, Consulting Engineer of the East Indian Railway, advised the purchase of the following:

    35 engines from E.B. Wilson,
    10 engines from R. & W. Hawthorn,
    15 engines from Slaughter,
    15 engines from Tayleur,
    25 passenger engines from Tayleur,
    10 passenger engines from Beyer, Peacock

    The ten engines were put into service as Nos. 12-19 and 23-24 during 1856-58.''
16. Ahrons, **Brit. Loco.**, p. 124
17. **The Engineer**, Vol. 1, 20 June 1856, p. 334
18. **Record of the International Exhibition** (1862), p. 295 and **The Engineer**, Vol. 13, 2 May 1862, p. 267
19. **Record of the International Exhibition** (1862), p. 271
20. **The Engineer**, Vol. 14, 3 October 1862, p. 206, from the "Illustrated News"
21. Dempsey, op. cit., p. 152 and Colburn, op. cit., pp. 68 f and 126 f
22. **Journal of the Institution of Locomotive Engineers**, Vol. VI, No. 4 (New Series), April 1916, R.H. Burnett, "Vice President's Address", p. 146
23. Robertson Papers, Letters from Beyer, 9, 19 & 31 July 1863
24. ibid, Letter from Beyer, 10 August 1863
25. ibid, Letter from Beyer, 18 September 1863 and B.P. Col., Progressive Numbers Book, Vol. 1
26. Robertson Papers, copy of letter from Peacock to Beyer, 2 October 1863
27. B. Reed, **Locomotives in Profile**, Vol. 1, (1971), p. 221 f
28. Ahrons, **Construction**, p. 23, Clark, op. cit., p. 61* and Colburn, op. cit., p. 99
29. B.P. Col., Facsimile, 21 January 1863
30. B.P. Col., Centenary History, p. 44
31. Vulcan Loco., op. cit., p. 64
32. Robertson Papers, Beyer to Robertson, 10 August 1863
33. ibid, Beyer to Robertson, 2 October 1863
34. ibid, Beyer, to Robertson, 6 October 1863
35. The quotations about the Norwegian Government Railway locomotive Order No. 2000 are taken from a bundle of correspondence in the B.P. Collection between Beyer and C. Pihl, the Norwegian Railway Engineer.
36. B.P. Col., from C. Pihl, 29 May 1868
37. **Engineering**, Vol. 2, 21 December 1866, p. 471
38. ibid, Vol. 10, 11 November 1870, p. 348
39. **Jour. Inst. Loco. Engrs.**, Vol. VI, No. 4 (New Series), April 1916, R.H. Burnett, "Vice President's Address," p. 147

Notes to Chapter 5

1. Robertson Papers, Partnership Meeting, 17 February 1869
2. **Engineering**, Vol. 21, 16 June 1876, p. 505
3. **The Engineer**, Vol. 17, 8 January 1864, p. 18
4. D.S.L. Cardwell (Ed.), **Artisan to Graduate** (1972), p. 11
5. Robertson Papers, Letter from Beyer, 27 November 1865
6. B.P. Quart. Rev., Vol. 1, No. 2, April 1927, p. 20 and for biographical notes, see Chap. 1, Note 1
7. Robertson Papers, Valuations of 1876
8. Ahrons, **Brit. Loco.**, pp. 43 & 163
9. J.G. Winton, **Modern Steam Practice & Engineering** (1885), p. 712
10. ibid, p. 732
11. D.K. Clark, **A Treatise on Steam Engines and Boilers** (1890), Vol. 1, p. 656
12. Ahrons, **Brit. Loco.**, p. 206 and D.K. Clark, **The Railway Locomotive** (1860), pp. 7* & 14*
13. O.S. Nock, **Historic Railway Disasters** (1966), p. 52 f; Pettigrew, op. cit., p. 257 f and Winton, op. cit., p.689
14. **The Engineer**, Vol. 73, 5 February 1892, p. 106
15. Ahrons, **Brit. Loco.**, p. 237 and A.E. Durrant, **Australian Steam** (1978), p. 57
16. H. Fayle, **Narrow Gauge Railways of Ireland** (1946), pp. 16 & 19
17. Ahrons, **Brit. Loco.**, pp. 237-8; **Construction**, p. 103 f and B.P. Col., Beyer's Note Book No. 2, pp. 202-4
18. Ahrons, **Brit. Loco.**, p. 237; B.P. Quart. Rev., Vol. 2, No. 3, July 1928, pp. 13-20; Vol. 2, No. 4, October 1928, pp. 3-21 and **The Engineer**, Vol. 51, 4 March 1881
19. B.P. Col., Various Cost of Work Books
20. B.P. Col., Cost Work Book No. 9
21. B.P. Col., Various Cost of Work Books
22. Robertson Papers, Notes in Annual Accounts, 12 February 1869

Notes to Chapter 6

1 B.P. Col., Centenary History, p. 93
2 B.P. Col., BC/1, Memorandum and Articles of Association of Beyer, Peacock and Company Limited, incorporated 26 April 1883
3 Robertson Papers, "List of Shares Allocated", 18 August 1883
4 For biographical notes, see Chap. 1, note 37
5 For biographical notes, see Chap. 1, note 23
6 B.P. Quart. Rev. Vol. 1, No. 3, July 1927, p. 18
7 For biographical details, see B.P. Quart. Rev., Vol. 2, No. 2, April 1928, pp. 20-38 and **Proc. I. Mech. E.** (1892), p. 406
8 Ahrons, **Brit. Loco.**, p.224 and D.K. Clark, **The Steam Engine** (1890), Vol. 2, p. 31
9 Ahrons, **Brit. Loco.**, p. 283 and **Railway Magazine**, September 1966, p. 497 and October 1966, p. 568; B. Reed, "Builders for 111 Years"
10 For biographical details, see B.P. Quart. Rev., Vol. 2, No. 1, January 1928, pp. 16-29, Centenary History, pp. 95-100 and Obituary Notice in B.P. Quart. Rev., Vol. 2, No. 2, April 1927, p. 42
11 Robertson Papers, Paper 12 May 1885
12 Patent No. 696, 1887 and No. 18,157, 1889
13 The details of the foundation of the Locomotive Manufacturers' Association are taken from a file of notes in the B.P. Archives which were copies from the original L.M.A. Minute Book. The name Avonside Wilson is probably a mis-print for Avonside Engine Co. and Nasmyth Wilson & Co.
14 Up to 1896, the figures are taken from the First Minute Book of the L.M.A. and the rest from J. Thomas, **Springburn Story** (1964), p. 255
15 B.P. Col., Centenary History, pp. 102-13 for this and subsequent quotations
16 Kitson Clark, op. cit., p. 46. The last ones were made by Kitsons in 1889.
17 B.P. Quart. Rev., Vol. 5, No. 1 January 1931, pp. 49-62
18 **The Engineer**, Vol. 88, 22 September 1899, p. 303 and 10 November 1899, p. 470
19 B.P. Quart. Rev., Vol. 2, No. 1, January 1928, p. 24. Also there are many calculations in the designers books in the B.P. Archives.
20 **Illustrated London News**, 8 November 1890, p. 579, Public traffic began on Thursday, 18 December 1890 (**The Railway Times**, 20 December 1890).
21 Thomas, op. cit., pp. 205-6
22 Lowe, op. cit., p. 8
23 B.P. Col., P/1, 31 May & 25 October 1894 to W.J. Adams, Sydney

Notes to Chapter 7

1 **The Engineer**, Vol. 61, 19 February 1886, pp. 143 & 150
2 Ahrons, **Brit. Loco.**, p.283 and Durrant, **Aust Steam**, p. 26
3 ibid, p. 305 and Lowe, op. cit., p. 60
4 B.P. Col., General Arrangement Drawing No. 6692
5 **The Engineer**, Vol. 75, 10 February 1893, p. 128 and Vol. 82, 3 July 1896, p. 15 and **Engineering**, Vol. 62, 6 November 1896, p. 579
6 Ahrons, **Brit. Loco.**, p. 306, and **The Engineer**, Vol. 89, 23 February 1900, p. 195
7 For discussions on compound locomotive designs, see Ahrons, Brit. Loco., pp.243-262; D.K. Clark, **Steam Engine**, Vol. 2, pp.603-625; **Trans. Newcomen Soc.**, Vol. XLIII, 1970-71; J.T. Van Riemsdijk, "The Compound Locomotive, Part 1, 1876-1901"; pp. 1-17 and Winton, op. cit., pp. 693-8
8 O.S. Nock, **The Premier Line** (1952), p. 83
9 Highet, op. cit., p. 143. The Highland Railway introduced the first 4-6-0 tender engines to the British Isles in 1894.
10 Redman, op. cit., p. 15
11 Ahrons, **Brit. Loco.** pp.289 & 306 and **Construction** p.73
12 Fayle, op. cit., p. 19 and P.G. Whitehouse **Narrow Gauge Album** (1957), pp. 80-2
13 Ahrons, **Brit. Loco.** p.293 and Durrant **Aust Steam**, p. 22
14 Kitson Clark, op. cit., p. 81. Kitsons started to build tram engines in 1876 and J.F. Clarke, op. cit., p.25, Hawthorn's started in 1880
15 D.K. Clark, **Steam Engine**, Vol. 2, p. 641 f
16 B.P. Col., various Cost of Work Books
17 J.I.C. Boyd, **Narrow Gauge Rails in Mid-Wales** (1952), pp. 52-60. This line was closed in 1935.
18 B.P. Quart. Rev., Vol. 4, No. 2, April 1930, pp. 44-48 and Patent No. 9,472, 1886
19 **Engineering**, Vol. 57, 13 April 1894, p. 477
20 B.P. Quart. Rev., Vol. 5, No. 2, April 1931, pp. 9-21
21 ibid, Vol. 4, No. 4, October 1930, pp. 29-30
22 ibid, Vol. 4, No. 4, October 1930, pp. 18-20
23 Ahrons, **Brit. Loco.** p. 313; Kitson Clark, op. cit., p. 95; L. Wiener, **Articulated Locomotives** (1930), pp. 506 & 515 and Patent No. 15, 338, 1888 and B.P. Col. G.A. 7123

Notes to Chapter 9

1 Memorandum and Articles of Association of Beyer, Peacock & Co. (1902) Limited, pp. 7 & 23-4
2 **Financial Times**, Friday, 18 April 1902, see leader entitled "Peacock on Toast".
3 B.P. Col., Centenary History, p.105
4 B.P. Board Minutes, No. 1, 1 and 27 May 1902 and 6 June 1902
5 ibid, 6 and 20 June 1902
6 B.P. Company Minutes, No. 1, 31 July 1902
7 See North British Locomotive Co., (1953)
8 Vulcan Loco. Works, op. cit., p. 18 and Warren, op. cit., p. 417
9 L.T.C. Rolt, **A Hunslet Hundred** (1964), p. 70 and B.P. Board Minutes, No. 1, various meetings in 1909
10 O.S. Nock, **British Steam Railways** (1961), p. 189
11 B.P. Col., Report "Re the Adoption of Electric Traction by Messrs. Beyer, Peacock & Co. Ltd.," 12 August 1902
12 B.P. Board Minutes, No. 1, 1 April 1903
13 ibid, 23 June 1903 and reports by R.R. Lister, 28 May and 18 June 1903
14 ibid, 3 November 1903 and report by R.R. Lister 24 October 1903 and **Engineering**, Vol. 81, 9 February 1906, p. 195
15 **The Engineer**, Vol. 101, 2 March 1906, p. 216 f and R.H. Clark, **The Development of the English Steam Wagon** (1963), p. 83 f
16 B.P. Board Minutes No. 1, 3 February, 18 April 1904, and Rolt **Hunslet Hundred**, p. 65
17 B.P. Board Minutes No. 1, November 1905, 2 February 1911, and No. 2, 23 December 1916
18 ibid, No. 1, 30 May and 1 July 1910
19 ibid, No. 1, 2 October 1913
20 ibid, No. 1, 17 July 1907 and 22 May 1912
21 B.P. Quart Rev., Vol. 2, No. 4, October 1928, pp. 23-33
22 Ahrons, **Brit. Loco.**, pp. 322 & 352; **Construction**, p. 186 f; Highet, op. cit., p. 205; E. Mason, **The Lancashire & Yorkshire Railway** (1954), pp. 95-6 and Nock, **Brit. St. Rly.**, p 198
23 **The Engineer**, Vol. 114, 8 November 1912, p. 498 and Ahrons, **Construction**, p. 190, for N. Ireland
24 D.F. Holland, **Steam Locomotives of the South African Railways**, Vol. 2 (1972), p. 59
25 Ahrons, **Brit. Loco.**, p. 332 and **The Engineer**, Vol. 97, 10 June 1904, p. 593
26 Ahrons, **Brit. Loco.**, p. 338 and **Construction**, p. 38; and G. Dow, **Great Central**, Vol. II (2 imp. 1971), p. 137
27 B.P. Col., DM/3, H. Guthrie, Note Book Vol. 3, p. 61
28 Report on visit to Welshpool & Llanfair Light Railway, January 1903 and Boyd, op. cit., pp. 123-5
29 Ahrons, **Brit. Loco.**, p. 351 and **The Engineer**, vol. 105, 10 January 1908, p. 40
30 **The Engineer**, Vol. 107, 11 June 1909, p. 601 and **Engineering** Vol. 92, 7 July 1911, p. 22
31 ibid, Vol. 110, 15 July 1910, p. 70
32 D. Rock Carling, **4-8-0 Tender Locomotives** (1971), p. 59
33 B.P. Company Minutes No. 1, 13 May 1920

Notes to chapter 10

1 Kitson, op. cit., p. 101, Patent No. 17,165, 11 June 1908, and Scheme 71411
2 Garratt Archives, copy of letter to S.J. Sarjant, Great Indian Peninsular Railway, 26 May 1909
3 Patent No. 13,937, 14 November 1885
4 Patent No. 8,682, 25 April 1899
5 The account of H.W. Garratt's life is based on papers in the Garratt archives belonging to his daughter, Mrs. M. Mumford
6 Ahrons, **Brit. Loco.**, p. 24, J. Bourne, **Recent Improvements to the Steam Engine** (1880), p. 196, Colburn, op. cit., p. 85, Wiener, op. cit., p. 124
7 See A.E. Durrant, **The Mallet Locomotive** (1974)
8 Wiener, op. cit., p. 124 & 174
9 See R.A.S. Abbott, **The Fairlie Locomotive** (1970); **Trans. Newcomen Soc.**, P.C. Dewhurst, "The Fairlie Locomotive", Pt. 1, Vol. XXXIV, 1961-62, p. 105 f; Pt. 2, Vol. XXXIX, 1966-67, p. 1 f and Vulcan Loco. op. cit., p. 67
10 Kitson, op. cit., p. 96
11 Patent No. 17,165, 11 June 1908
12 Wiener, op. cit., p. 264
13 B.P. Board Minutes No. 1, 5 October 1908
14 ibid, 19 April 1909
15 ibid, 4 November 1909
16 B.P. Col., Letter from W.J. Newbiggin, W. Adams & Co. Ltd., 12 December 1910
17 B.P. Col., Letter from W.J. Newbiggin, Melbourne, 22 August 1912
18 **Engineering**, Vol. 88, 10 December 1909, p. 802
19 B.P. Board Minutes No. 1, 6 and 27 January 1910
20 B.P. Col., Report by F.G. Royal Dawson, Calcutta, 22 May 1911, and **The Engineer**, 10 March 1911, p. 240
21 B.P. Col., DM/12, F. Hayes Note Book, p. 104
22 **The Narrow Gauge**, No. 79, 1978, M. Swift, "The Darjeeling-Himalayan Railway Garratt", p. 12

23 B.P. Col., Report by W. Wakefield, Manchester, 6 November 1922
24 B.P. Company Minutes No. 1, 1 March 1911
25 **The Railway Magazine,** November 1966, pp. 24-6
26 B.P. Col., Letter from Western Australian Government, 12 September 1912; see **Railway Gazette,** 8 December 1911
27 Durrant, **Australian Steam,** p. 104, and **Engineering,** Vol. 94, 13 September 1912, p. 355, and Wiener, op. cit., p. 222
28 B.P. Col., Letter from W.J. Adams & Co., 16 December 1912
29 Jour. Inst. Loco. Eng., July-August 1916, H.W: Dearberg, ''The Garratt Locomotive''
30 B.P. Col., Letter from P. Grant & Co., 15 December 1912, and Wiener, op. cit., p. 200
31 B.P. Col., Letter from P. Grant & Co., 21 December 1915
32 B.P. Order No. 1184
33 B.P. Col., Letter from P. Grant & Co., 21 December 1915
34 B.P. Col., Letter from P. Grant & Co., 29 March 1916

Notes to Chapter 11

1 B.P. Col., Order Book Entry for No. 01060
2 B.P. Col., Letter from W. Wakefield, 6 November 1922
3 S.M. Moir, **Twenty Four Inches Apart** (1963), p. 82
4 Holland, op. cit., Vol. 2, p. 31 and A.E. Durrant, **The Mallet Locomotive** (1974), p. 68
5 B.P. Col., Letter from W. Wakefield, 6 November 1922
6 ibid, 24 May 1921
7 ibid, 28 June 1921
8 ibid, 13 May 1922 and A.E. Durrant, **The Garratt Locomotive** (1969), p. 87
9 Durrant, **Garratt Loco.,** p. 87 and Notes in B.P. Col.,
10 O.S. Nock, **The British Steam Railway Locomotive** (1966), p. 75
11 Wiener, op. cit., p. 168
12 B.P. Col., Letter from W. Wakefield, 12 June 1921
13 ibid, 6 November 1922
14 B.P. Col., Extracts from S.A.R. Reports
15 **Beyer Garratt Articulated Locomotives,** (1947), p. 62
16 Durrant, **Garratt Loco.,** p. 89 and Holland, op. cit., Vol. 2, p. 49
17 **B.G. Art. Locos.,** p. 60
18 B.P. Col., Notes of the Continental Business Tour, 11 May to 4 June 1921
19 B.P. Board Minutes No. 2, 6 December 1922
20 Cyril Williams wrote many accounts of his travels in the **Beyer, Peacock Quarterly Review**

Notes to Chapter 12

1 B.P. Board Minutes, 3 January 1923 and 17 January 1924
2 ibid, 16 January 1919, 29 July and 5 October 1921 and B.P. Company Minutes, 22 March 1922
3 B.P. Board Minutes, 8 February 1923
4 ibid, 23 October 1927
5 ibid, 11 April 1919
6 B.P. Quart. Rev., Vol. 1, No. 2, April 1927, p. 5
7 B.P. Company Minutes, 16 March 1923
8 B.P. Col., **Notes of the Continental Business Tour 1921** by E.F. Lange, p. 2
9 **The Engineer,** Vol. 155, 27 January 1933, p. 98 and B. Reed, **A Source Book of Locomotives** (1970), p. 85
10 Nock, **Brit. St. Rly. Loco.,** p. 48
11 ibid, p. 132
12 Rolt, **Hunslet Hundred,** p. 149
13 B. Fawcett, **Railways of the Andes** (1965)
14 Nock, **Brit. St. Rly. Loco.,** p. 97, and **The Locomotives of Sir Nigel Gresley** (1946), p. 96
15 B.P. Board Minutes, 6 December 1921
16 ibid, 6 March 1924
17 ibid, 2 October 1923 and 2 January 1924
18 ibid, 22 June 1926; B.P. Quart. Rev., Vol. 1, No. 4, October 1927, pp. 4-13; **The Engineer,** Vol. 147, 19 April 1929, p. 424; **Engineering,** Vol. 124, pp. 16 & 23, December 1927, and Nock, **Brit., St. Rly. Loco.,** p. 111
19 I am indebted for this information to B. Hinchliffe, for lending me his unpublished manuscript on ''The Beyer-Ljunström Locomotive'' and L.T. Davenport for information on the test to be found in a report ''Engine Tests on Midland Division, Leeds & London, Ljungström Turbine Engine'', March and April 1928.
20 B.P. Board Minutes, 11 January, 22 February 1927 and 12 June 1928
21 ibid, 12 November 1940
22 ibid, 1 January 1919, and B.P. Company Minutes, 13 May 1920
23 B.P. Board Minutes, 26 January 1926
24 B.P. Quart. Rev., Vol. 3, No. 3, July 1929, pp. 5-7
25 ibid, Vol. 6, No. 2, July 1932, p. 4
26 See R.A. Whitehead, **Garretts of Leiston** (1964), and **Garrett 200** (1978), for histories of this Company
27 B.P. Board Minutes, 28 July and 5 December 1933
28 B.P. Col., BBS/1, Board Statements

Notes to Chapter 13

1 B.P. Board Minutes, 1 August 1923
2 **The Locomotive,** 15 March 1924
3 Nock. **Brit. St. Rly. Loco.,** p. 80 and Wiener op. cit., p. 214

4 **Beyer-Garratt Articulated Locomotives** (1947), p. 42
5 B.P. Board Minutes, 4 December 1923, 7 July 1924 & 22 September 1925
6 Wiener, op. cit., pp. 158 & 161
7 ibid, pp. 162-5 and B.P. Col., **Golwé Articulated Locomotives,** Forges, Usines et Founderies, Haine-St.-Pierre, September 1927
8 Durrant, **Garratt Loco.,** and Wiener, op. cit., p. 209
9 B.P. Board Minutes, 5 May 1924
10 **The Engineer,** Vol. 139, 26 June 1925; **Engineering,** Vol. 119, 26 June 1925, p. 792 and Vol. 120, 3 July 1925, p. 12; G. Glover, **British Locomotive Design 1825-1960** (1967), p. 97, and O.S. Nock, **The Locomotives of Sir Nigel Gresley** (1946), p. 58
11 Two schemes for Super-Garratts were prepared for the South African Railways, No. 98,187 in 1925 and 104,841 in 1928. Both were 2-6-6-2 + 2-6-6-2, the earlier with length 94ft. 2in., 70,630lb. Tractive Effort, water capacity 6,000 gallons, maximum axle-load 12 tons 10cwt, weight empty 146 tons. See also B.P. Quart. Rev., Vol. 2, No. 3, July 1928, p. 10
12 **B.G. Art. Locos.,** p. 9
13 B.P. Board Minutes, 21 April 1925 and Wiener, op. cit., p. 217
14 **B.G. Art. Locos.,** p. 116
15 B.P. Quart. Rev., Vol. 5, No. 1 January 1931, p. 38
16 **Railway Magazine,** December 1966, p. 695
17 **B.G. Art. Locos.,** p. 146
18 B.P. Company Minutes, 1 March 1912

Notes to Chapter 14

1 The Beyer-Garrats covered in this chapter are all mentioned in Beyer, Peacock's own book, **Beyer-Garratt Articulated Locomotives** and in A.E. Durrant's **The Garratt Locomotive,** so general references from these two sources have not been quoted.
2 **The Locomotive,** 15 January 1929 and B.P. Quart. Rev., Vol. 3, No. 2, April 1919, p. 28
3 B.P. Board Minutes, 12 June 1928, Patent No. 258,305 and Wiener, op. cit., p. 226
4 E.J. McClare, **The N.Z.R. Garratt Story** (1978)
5 **The Engineer,** Vol. 151, 24 April 1931, p. 453
6 B.P. Quart. Rev., Vol. 5, No. 1, January 1931, p. 3 and Nock, **Brit. St. Rly. Loco.** p. 80
7 B.P. Quart. Rev., Vol. 4, No. 2, April 1930, p. 31
8 ibid, Vol. 4, No. 4, October 1930, p. 42
9 Fawcett, op. cit., pp. 58 & 158 and B.P. Board Minutes, 12 July 1955
10 B.P. Quart. Rev. Vol. 5, No. 2, April 1931, pp. 34 & 42
11 **The Engineer,** Vol. 148, 2 August 1929, p. 128 and Wiener, op. cit., p. 622
12 B.P. Quart. Rev., Vol. 4, No. 1, January 1930, p. 3
13 ibid, Vol. 4, No. 4, October 1930, p. 42
14 **Railway Gazette,** 9 December 1938 and Nock, **Brit. St. Rly. Locos.,** p. 84
15 **Railway Gazette,** 5 January 1940
16 ibid, 7 February 1936 and **B.G. Art. Locos.,** p. 99
17 B.P. Quart. Rev. Vol. 5, No. 1, January 1931, p. 27 and Vol. 6, No. 1, January 1932, p. 27
18 ibid, Vol. 6, No. 2, January 1932, **The Engineer,** Vol. 154, 11 November 1932, p. 480 and Vol. 163, 9 April 1937, p.426 and **Railway Gazette,** 27 March 1936
19 B.P. Board Minutes, 16 July 1935 and 16 June 1936
20 **Railway Gazette,** 21 July 1939
21 **Engineering,** Vol. 151, 30 May 1941, p. 433 and Nock, **Brit. St. Rly. Locos.,** p. 80
22 **B.G: Art. Locos.,** p. 24
23 ibid: see also R. Ramaer, **Steam Locomotives of the East African Railways** (1974), p. 50

Notes to Chapter 15

Notes

In 1945, Beyer, Peacock & Co. Ltd. published a book **The Second World War** about the contributions they and their associated companies had made to the war effort. This book has formed the basis for the first part of this chapter.

1 B.P. Board Minutes, 2 February 1937
2 ibid, 24 March 1936
3 O.S. Nock, **William Stanier** (1964), pp. 104-5
4 B.P. Board Minutes, 21 October 1941, and 19 May 1942
5 **The Railway Gazette,** 9 August 1940 and **Engineering,** Vol. 151, 30 May 1941, p. 433
6 B.P. Board Minutes, 15 July 1942
7 ibid, 9 March 1943
8 **Beyer-Garratt Articulated Locomotives,** p. 48
9 **The Engineer,** Vol. 175, 11 June 1943, p. 463
10 S. Jackson Obituary, **Proc. Inst. Mech. E.,** Vol. 151, 1944, p. 215
11 **Railway Gazette,** 29 June 1945
12 ibid, 8 December 1944
13 **Engineering,** Vol. 160, 2 November 1945, p. 350
14 **Railway Gazette,** 22 March 1946, **The Engineer,** Vol. 181, 1 March 1946, **Modern Transport,** 23 February & 2 March 1946 and **The Locomotive,** 15 April 1946
15 A.E. Durrant, **Australian Steam** (1978), pp. 73-79

Notes to Chapter 17

1. B.P. Board Minutes, 9 September 1947 & 6 July 1948
2. B.P. Board Minutes, 18 October, 6 December 1949, 4 April, 13 June, 12 September 1950, 18 April 1951 and 18 February 1958
3. Nock, **Brit. St. Rly. Loco.**, p. 250 and Durrant, **Aust. Steam**, p. 98
4. **Railway Gazette**, 23 June 1950, Nock, **Brit. St. Rly. Loco.**, p. 251
5. Durrant, **Aust. Steam**, p. 70
6. Ramaer, op. cit., pp. 50 & 66
7. Durrant, **Garratt Loco.**, p. 129, Nock, **Brit. St. Rly. Loco.**, p. 272 and Ramaer, op. cit., p. 73
8. Durrant, **Aust. Steam**, p. 37 f., **Railway Gazette**, 4 July 1952 and **The Railway Magazine,** October 1975, p. 493 ''Garratts Last Fling''
9. B.P. Board Minutes, 17 January 1950, 21 February and 17 October 1951
10. ibid, 17 September 1952. Order 11172 was cancelled. The five engines for Order 11174 were completed before Order 11173 and tested with some parts missing. They were then dismantled and some parts were used to complete the five engines of Order 11173. Order 11173 was despatched as complete engines and the remaining parts of Order 11174 sent as components. See also Durrant, **Aust Steam**, p. 39.
11. C.C. Singleton & D. Burke, **Railways of Australia** (1963), p. 54
12. Rhodesian Railways Orders 11137, 11139, 11144, 11148 and 11149
13. **Railway Gazette**, 10 April 1953
14. ibid, 5 March 1954
15. ibid, 28 June 1955 and Nock, **Brit. St. Rly. Loco.**, p. 256
16. **Engineering,** Vol. 187, 9 January 1959, p. 52
17. B.P. Company Minutes, 29 April 1957 and Nock, **Brit. St. Rly. Loco.**, p. 258
18. Board Minutes, 26 November 1958 and Moir, op. cit., p. 89
19. B.P. Col., Board Statements 1947 and B.P. Group Reports, 1956
20. B.P. Board Minutes, 16 November 1954
21. ibid, 18 June 1954 and 25 January 1955
22. B.P. Company Minutes, 26 April 1954
23. B.P. Board Minutes, 9 September 1947 for Haine-St.-Pierre and 17 January 1951 for Henschel & Sohn
24. B.P. Group Report, 1955, section 111
25. Rolt, **Hunslet Hundred**, p. 146
26. These details about potential orders are taken from the appropriate B.P. Group Reports.

Notes to Chapter 18

1. B.P. Schemes Book, Vol. 2, 12 January 1931, No. 111463 and 1 July 1931, No. 111907-8
2. B.P. Board Minutes, 16 January & 16 February 1946
3. ibid, 30 October 1956
4. ibid, 4 September & 30 October 1956. See also G. Toms **Brush Diesel Locomotives, 1940-78** (1978)
5. B.P. Board Minutes, 19 March 1957
6. ibid, 1 October 1957 & 18 February 1958. See also **Engineering** Vol. 185, 30 May 1958, p. 681
7. B.P. Board Minutes, 30 September 1958
8. ibid, 10 June 1958
9. B. Reed, **Diesel Hydraulic Locomotives of the Western Region** (1974), p. 105
10. B.P. Board Minutes, 28 October 1958
11. B.P. Group Report, 1962, p. 215.5 & 216.1
12. ibid, 1964, p. 214.5
13. B.P. Company Reports 27 June 1966
14. **Engineering,** Vol 186, 12 September 1958, p. 335
15. See R.A. Whitehead, **Garrett 200** (1978), p. 239 f for an account of the later history of this firm.
16. B.P. Group Report, 1961, p. 513.7
17. R.A. Whitehead, **Garrett 200** (1978), pp. 225 & 230

Loading a boiler unit of a New South Wales Government Railways AD 60 Class Beyer-Garratt.

Appendix I

Products and Profits

Year	Capital Total	Assets Buildings	Machinery Additions	Engines Built No.	Engines Built Total	Deliveries of Completed Work	Cost of Work Completed	Net Profits	Dividends	Notes
	£	£	£			£	£	£	%	
Products and Profits for the first Partnership 1854-1868										
1854	29,000	NA	NA	None	None	NA	NA	None	NA	1
1855	40,000	NA	NA	20	20	NA	NA	2,094	NA	2
1856	NA	10,922	NA	25	45	NA	NA	13,121	NA	2
1857	NA	13,056	NA	25	70	NA	NA	17,854	NA	
1858	NA	15,024	NA	27	97	NA	NA	22,075	NA	
1859	NA	15,606	NA	33	130	NA	NA	21,770	NA	
1860	NA	23,560	NA	51	181	NA	NA	24,002	NA	
1861	NA	29,048	NA	65	246	NA	NA	34,567	NA	
1862	NA	30,946	NA	84	330	NA	NA	27,346	NA	
1863	NA	31,298	NA	66	396	NA	NA	88,461	NA	
1864	NA	38,861	NA	86	482	NA	NA	75,376	NA	
1865	NA	46,476	NA	114	596	NA	NA	80,396	NA	
1866	NA	48,019	NA	111	707	NA	NA	80,965	NA	
1867	193,335	48,022	NA	80	787	252,018	106,101	61,529	NA	3,4
1868	194,520	48,022	NA	57	844	163,061	127,993	38,622	NA	
								578,184		
Products and Profits for the second Partnership 1869-1882										
1869	197,177	NA	NA	67	911	238,253	190,116	53,022	NA	5
1870	198,312	NA	NA	90	1001	285,743	235,609	50,732	NA	
1871	202,521	NA	NA	103	1104	238,247	NA	60,991	NA	
1872	203,241	NA	NA	102	1206	322,322	266,910	63,338	NA	
1873	208,120	NA	NA	112	1318	396,765	315,895	82,381	NA	6
1874	213,384	NA	NA	123	1441	363,234	NA	75,022	NA	7
1875	NA	NA	NA	95	1536	272,469	NA	54,738	NA	
1876	218,157	NA	NA	95	1631	247,785	211,706	43,323	NA	8
1877	218,997	NA	NA	101	1732	284,890	235,417	48,908	NA	
1878	219,888	NA	NA	102	1834	270,404	222,628	40,631	NA	
1879	226,263	NA	NA	63	1897	149,880	135,966	12,090	NA	
1880	231,695	NA	NA	91	1988	226,643	193,382	28,016	NA	
1881	236,575	NA	NA	107	2095	210,943	186,266	24,893	NA	
1882	251,230	NA	NA	131	2226	370,492	320,750	42,232	NA	
								680,317		
Products and Profits for the Private Limited Company 1883-1902										
		Machinery								
1883	274,652	147,633	13,123	144	2368	337,490	287,874	49,616	10	9
1884	287,956	143,374	3,298	149	2508	369,258	305,017	64,241	10	
1885	291,214	138,972	2,295	116	2669	424,445	346,155	78,290	10	
1886	298,773	137,793	5,915	132	2801	270,760	236,099	34,660	7½	
1887	305,359	137,076	6,312	60	2861	137,421	NA	1,013	[5]	10
1888	NA	130,837	741	111	2972	NA	NA	24,732	[5 or 7½]	11
1889	NA	124,705	525	142	3114	NA	NA	26,245	[10]	
1890	NA	121,657	3,258	143	3257	NA	NA	73,856	[10]	
1891	NA	NA	NA	144	3401	NA	NA	NA	[10]	
1892	NA	115,746	1,813	101	3502	NA	NA	NA	[10]	
1893	NA	112,788	2,829	52	3554	NA	NA	20,776	[5]	
1894	NA	108,030	881	74	3628	NA	NA	771	[5]	
1895	NA	102,929	301	57	3685	220,479	197,968	19,344	[5]	12
1896	NA	99,032	1,249	120	3805	343,706	293.739	20,390	[5]	
1897	NA	96,419	2,338	90	3895	164,478	142,616	74,736	[10]	
1898	NA	98,211	6,613	102	3997	369,468	309,535	39,423	[10]	
1899	385,698	105,480	12,179	98	4095	378,605	340,772	64,489	[10]	
1900	403,308	118,646	18,440	109	4204	454,203	394,330	37,875	7½	
1901	NA	127,500	14,787	109	4313	507,651	419,943	94,356	[10]	
1902	NA	131,774	10,648	105	4418	525,420	433,470	101,635	[10]	

Notes

1 The figure for the total Capital Assets is for October 1855. The profit figures until 1868 are taken from "A Summary of Half Yearly Trade Profits for Fourteen Years, ending December 31st. 1868" in the Robertson Papers.

2 The figures for the Capital Assets, Buildings, for 1856 and 1857 are for the month of June in both cases.

3 The Cost of Completed Work in 1867 is for the last six months only.

4 The figure for profits in 1867 includes £3,000 paid to Owens College.

5 The figures for net profits between 1869 and 1872 are taken from the Robertson Papers, "Statement of the Annual Amount of the last Ten Years Deliveries, etc".

6 The figures for net profits until 1882 are after "Payment of Commissions and Interest" and are taken from the Robertson Papers, "Profits on Ten Years ending 31st. December 1882."

7 The figure for the Capital Assets, Total, in 1874 is for June.

8 The figure for the Capital Assets, Total, in 1876 includes liabilities to C.F. Beyer's executors of £68,222.

9 The machinery figures in the Capital Assets includes depreciation allowances but the total figures do not appear until 1887.

10 Dividend figures in brackets [] are conjectural and are based on comments in the Centenary History.

11 The figures for net profits quoted from 1888 onwards are the gross figures computed for Income Tax Returns.

12 The figures for deliveries of competed work and cost of completed work from 1895 onwards are taken to the end of June following the Company's accountancy year.

Products and Profits for the Public Limited Company 1902-1977

Year	Fixed Assets Net Book Value	Total Net Assets	Cost of Completed Work	Balance for Year	Engines Built No.	Garratts	Total	Ordinary Share Capital	Shareholders Funds	Dividends Ordinary Shares	Loan Capital
	£,000	£,000	£,000	£,000				£,000	£,000	%	£,000
1902	429	687	NA	59	105	none	4,418	499	379	10	308
1903	443	684	NA	24	93	none	4,511	500	377	5	307
1904	444	661	NA	[16]	110	none	4,621	500	355	none	306
1905	444	673	NA	21	119	none	4,740	500	367	none	306
1906	436	681	NA	53	142	none	4,882	500	375	10	306
1907	439	713	NA	62	147	none	5,029	500	407	7 ½	306
1908	428	738	NA	57	152	none	5,181	500	455	7 ½	306
1909	419	756	NA	50	131	2	5,312	500	450	7 ½	306
1910	432	743	NA	14	116	1	5,428	500	437	5	306
1911	430	727	NA	11	108	6	5,536	500	427	5	306
1912	400	727	NA	17	100 [1]	7	5,636	500	421	5	306
1913	396	764	NA	69	110 [2]	9	5,746	500	458	7 ½	306
1914	394	812	NA	83	99	3	5,845	500	506	10	306
1915	391	817	NA	34	56	3	5,901	500	511	7 ½	306
1916 [3]	NA	NA	NA	NA	28	none	5,929	NA	NA	none	NA
1917	NA	NA	NA	NA	1	none	5,930	NA	NA	none	NA
1918	NA	NA	NA	NA	8	none [4]	5,938	NA	NA	none	NA
1919	354	971	NA	301	16	3	5,954	500	675	40	306
1920	441	930	NA	[125]	43	2	5,997	600	624	none	306
1921	453	969	NA	71	85	none	6,082	600	663	5	306
1922	435	860	NA	16	44	none	6,126	600	692	5	168
1923	408	752	NA	[87]	34	2	6,160	600	589	none	163
1924	427	687	NA	[43]	42	20	6,202	600	524	none	163
1925	483	661	NA	10	71	35	6,273	600	501	none	160
1926	499	635	NA	11	59	16	6,332	600	480	none	155
1927	503	658	NA	35	75	63	6,407	600	508	2 ½	150
1928	520	661	NA	39	101	28	6,508	600	517	5	144
1929	539	662	NA	26	75	50	6,583	600	524	3	138
1930	526	704	NA	147	96	93	6,679	600	578	8	126
1931	515	627	NA	[67]	41	5	6,720	600	501	none	126
1932	517	552	NA	[47]	12	6	6,732	600	433	none	119
1933	517	506	NA	[46]	32	none	6,764	600	387	none	119
1934	517	486	52	[20]	6	1	6,770	600	367	none	119
1935	517	469	101	[27]	9	6	6,779	600	350	none	119
1936	517	501	282	[3]	34	10	6,813	600	347	none	154
1937	511	526	456	25	50	24	6,863	600	372	none	154
1938	498	582	683	51	35	28	6,898	600	423	none	159
1939	489	614	665	52	37	23	6,935	600	475	none	139
1940	489	639	745	54	25	10	6,960	600	505	none	135
1941	491	586	895	[24]	31	none	6,991	600	455	none	131
1942	495	589	1,079	38	13	none	7,004	600	460	none	129
1943	480	576	1,259	41	47	35	7,051	600	468	none	108
1944	464	591	1,359	24	46	30	7,097	600	485	none [5]	106
1945	670	868	1,228	106	34	28	7,131	600	762	none	106
1946	683	1,161	1,389	56	45	28	7,176	900	1,161	5	NA
1947	883	1,433	1,385	150	49	41	7,225	900	1,323	6	NA
1948	905	1,528	1,495	132	33	10	7,258	900	1,426	6	NA
1949	937	1,687	1,769	146	49	44	7,307	900	1,543	6	NA
1950	939	1,873	2,466	195	52	30	7,359	900	1,696	10	NA
1951	1,033	2,182	2,639	261	88	27	7,447	933	1,965	10	NA
1952	1,072	2,314	3,941	172	50	43	NA	933	2,087	12 [6]	NA
1953	1,066	3,224	4,589	238	72	58	NA	1,500	2,978	16	NA
1954	1,064	3,374	3,494	264	52	44	NA	1,500	3,123	16	NA
1955	1,049	3,533	3,592	307	56	34	NA	1,500	3,306	16	NA
1956	1,149	3,620	4,217	236	67	65	7,766	1,500	3,422	16	NA
1957	1,592	4,318	4,834	296	66	63	7,832	1,675	4,026	16	NA
1958	1,855	4,635	2,578	149	26	26	7,868	1,906	4,372	3	NA
1959	1,837	4,369	NA	[2]	none	none	NA	1,906	4,161	21	NA
1960	1,930	4,464	NA	179	none	none	NA	1,906	4,205	12	NA
1961	1,909	4,421	NA	102	none	none	NA	1,906	4,188	12	NA
1962	1,757	4,333	NA	137	none	none	NA	1,906	4,233	7 ½	NA
1963	1,719	4,270	NA	0	none	none	NA	1,906	4,170	5	NA
1964	1,687	4,119	NA	[90]	none	none	NA	1,906	4,019	5	NA
1965	1,375	3,180	NA	[931]	none	none	NA	1,906	3,080	none	NA
1966	733	3,483	NA	346	none	none	8,087	1,906	3,443	none	NA
1967	806	3,583	NA	238	none	none	none	1,906	3,536	8	NA
1968	841	1,992	NA	23	none	none	none	321	1,921	13	NA
1969	1,122	2,102	NA	187	none	none	none	321	1,996	35	NA
1970	1,082	2,325	NA	350	none	none	none	321	2,212	40	NA
1971	1,106	2,436	NA	230	none	none	none	321	2,302	40	NA
1972 [7] 1973	1,041	2,481	NA	210	none	none	none	321	2,368	42	NA
1974	1,014	2,296	NA	[69]	none	none	none	321	2,207	42	NA
1975 [8]	1,036	2,870	NA	39	none	none	none	401	2,621	5	NA
1976	1,024	2,900	NA	67	none	none	none	401	2,578	42	NA
1976	996	3,256	NA	16	none	none	none	401	2,745	none	NA
1977	1,605	3,745	NA	800	none	none	none	401	3,554	none	NA

Notes

1 The total for this year includes 6 Meyers.
2 132 locomotives were completed and packed but 30 were delayed in shipment.
3 No accounts were issued during the War.
4 The number of Garratts built per annum has been estimated from the dates of orders given in the Progressive Numbers Books, but the number of Engines is taken from the official figures in Board Statements and draughtsmens figures.
5 The figures after 1944 are for the whole consolidated group. Figures for Gorton Foundry only have not survived.
6 The official figures for numbers of engines built terminate in 1952 and those given afterwards are estimates although the figure 7,868 for the total of all engines built up to the last steam one is correct.
7 The accountancy period covered 15 months to 31 March 1974.
8 This accountancy period covered 9 months to 31 December 1976.

Appendix II

Men Employed and Wage Rates 1854-1855

Category	1854		1855					Wage Rates on 10 Aug
	24 Jun	1 Sep	29 Sep	29 Dec	30 Mar	29 Jun	10 Aug	
Accountant	-	1	1	1	1	1	1	50/-
Clerk	-	-	-	2	2	3	3	27-35/-
Office Boy	-	-	-	-	-	-	1	3/-
Draughtsman	1	1	2	3	4	5	6	25-60/-
Foreman	-	2	2	4	7	7	7	40-100/-
Asst.Foreman	-	-	-	1	1	-	-	
Pattern Maker	1	4	4	8	6	7	7	28-32/-
Joiner	-	2	7	9	8	7	7	21-27/-
Joiners Labourer	-	-	-	-	1	1	1	16/-
Millwright	-	-	-	-	-	1	1	34/-
Fitter	-	3	5	14	47	38	45	26-34/-
Fitters Apprentice	-	1	1	5	9	10	12	4-13/-
Fitters Labourer	-	-	-	-	5	10	11	15-18/-
Turner	-	-	6	12	22	21	22	30-36/-
Turners Apprentice	-	-	-	2	2	3	7	13/-
Turners Labourer	-	-	-	4	5	5	5	15-18/-
Key Groover	-	-	-	-	1	1	1	19/-
Erector	-	-	-	1	10	28	38	28-34/-
Erectors Apprentice	-	-	-	-	2	1	-	
Erectors Labourer	-	-	-	-	-	10	14	15/-
Driller	-	-	1	5	7	8	8	16-20/-
Boy Driller	-	-	-	-	-	-	3	5/6
Planer	-	-	1	4	10	12	10	18-26/-
Shaper	-	-	1	4	3	3	5	16-19/-
Boy Shaper	-	-	-	-	2	1	1	9/-
Screwer	-	-	-	1	1	1	1	14/-
Centerer	-	-	-	-	1	1	1	20/-
Smith	-	1	8	20	23	24	24	28-40/-
Smiths Apprentice	-	-	-	1	1	-	-	
Smiths Labourer	-	-	-	2	2	2	2	18/-
Striker	-	1	12	36	53	50	45	18-24/-
Boy Striker	-	-	-	-	3	4	6	6-8/-
Rivet Maker	-	-	1	-	-	1	2	18-24/-
Spring Maker	-	-	-	-	-	1	1	32/-
Holder Up	-	-	1	1	4	8	10	3-27/-
Hardner	-	-	-	-	1	1	1	18/-
Bolt Maker	-	-	-	-	-	1	1	30/-
Hand Driller	-	-	-	-	7	7	6	15/-
Rivetter	-	-	3	2	2	8	7	18-32/-
Rivet Boy	-	-	4	3	3	6	6	6/-
Boiler Maker	-	-	3	3	4	5	6	30-38/-
Boiler Makers Labourer	-	-	-	-	1	1	-	
Helper	-	-	1	3	8	8	7	10-20/-
Engineman	-	-	1	1	1	1	1	26/-
Enginemans Boy	-	-	1	1	-	-	-	
Hammerman	-	1	3	3	3	3	2	12-22/-
Moulder	-	-	-	6	8	-	-	
Brass Moulder	-	-	-	-	-	1	1	34/-
Iron Moulder	-	-	-	-	-	5	5	32-36/-
Blast Tenter	-	-	-	1	1	1	1	28/-
Coreman	-	-	-	1	1	1	1	28/-
Coremakers Boy	-	-	-	1	1	1	1	4/-
Sand Preparer	-	-	-	1	1	1	-	
Foundry Labourer	-	-	-	-	3	3	4	16-18/-
Fetler	-	-	-	-	1	4	4	15-19/-
Rubber Off	-	-	-	-	-	-	1	3/-
Grinder	-	-	-	-	-	1	1	28/-
Boy Grinder	-	-	-	-	-	-	1	6/-
Painter	-	-	-	-	-	1	2	24-28/-
Gas Fitter	-	-	-	-	-	-	1	27/-
Night Watchman	1	-	-	-	-	-	-	
Store Dealer	-	-	-	1	-	-	-	
Slotter	-	-	-	-	1	-	-	
Spoker	-	-	-	-	1	-	-	
Carters	-	-	-	-	2	-	-	

Appendix III

Tank Engines based on the 0-4-0 design for Chester Station
The first two orders were for 0-4-0 type but all the subsequent ones were 0-4-2.

Date	Order	Purchaser	Cost £	Sold for £	Profit
1856	99	Chester Station	1,406	1,790	17%
		Cannock Chase Coly.	1,406	1,500	17
1856	128	Fleetwood & W. Riding	1,268	1,600	28 1/8
		Shelton Coly.	1,268	1,650	28 1/8
1856	140	Dowlais Iron	1,388	1,650	19
		G. Thompson	1,388	1,650	19
1857	169	GWR	1,217	1,700	39 ¾
1857	184	New Brit. Iron Co.	1,270	1,700	33 ¾
1858	292	Swedish Gov.	1,439	1,900	32
1861	460	Ld. Bute, Cardiff	1,309	1,775	35 ½
		Knighton Rly.	1,282	1,775	38 ¼
		Cannock Chase Coly.	1,283	1,775	38 ¼
1861	543	Grassmore Coly.	1,291	1,700	31 5/8
		Swedish Gov.	1,342	1,900	41 ½
1863	737	Shelton Coly.	1,234	1,650	33 5/8
1864	820	Cannock Chase Coly.	1,218	1,775	45 ½
1865	977	Swedish Gov.	1,237	1,900	53 ½
1867	2057	Berlin & Hamburg	1,340	1,900	41 ¾
1867	2113	Cannock Chase Coly.	1,162	1,775	52 ½
1871	2372	Greenfield & Co.	1,170	1,462	25
1871	2732	W. Cannock Coly.	1,121	1,600	42 ½
1871	2797	Greenfield & Co.	1,130	1,462	32 ½
1872	2908	Swedish Gov.	1,300	1,900	46 1/8
1872	2921	Cannock Chase Coly.	1,226	1,800	46 ¾
1873	2972	Greenfield & Co.	1,396	1,850	32 ½
1873	3031	Shelton Coly.	1,300	1,800	38 3/8
1877	3573	Swedish Gov.	1,444	1,600	8 ½
1879	3801	Swedish Gov.	1,123	1,400	24 5/8
1879	3802	Newcastle Coal	1,164	1,600	37 3/8
1879	3860	Coppice Coly, J. Owen	1,004	1,100	9 ½

The last but one 0-4-2 saddle tank engine based on the 0-4-0 design for Chester Station was bought by the Newcastle Coal Company [3802].

Appendix IV

Turnover and Employees 1928-1964

Year	Work Completed £	Output in tons	Average no. of employees	No. of Locomotives	Tonnage	Value £
1928	NA	NA	2,395	NA	NA	NA
1929	NA	NA	2,185	NA	NA	NA
1930	NA	NA	2,514	NA	NA	NA
1931	NA	NA	959	NA	NA	NA
1932	NA	NA	314	NA	NA	NA
1933	NA	NA	430	NA	NA	NA
1934	51,975	615	163	6	47	38,440
1935	101,358	1,102	236	10	850	80,765
1936	282,237	3,642	764	34	3,084	247,264
1937	455,594	4,957	1,077	53	3,877	368,404
1938	682,576	6,037	1,303	37	4,728	507,098
1939	664,750	5,550	1,425	32	3,012	353,994
1940	742,746	8,805	1,590	30	3,258	415,975
1941	890,022	10,651	1,803	26	2,483	335,000
1942	1,079,241	11,111	1,807	19	1,104	240,549
1943	1,259,479	9,223	1,907	45	4,260	764,023
1944	1,358,575	10,332	2,043	44	5,566	1,033,207
1945	1,227,738	8,553	1,811	38	4,434	911,440
1946	1,388,794	7,016	1,831	42	5,249	1,115,576
1947	1,384,902	6,214	1,783	40	4,414	1,039,340
1948	1,494,985	6,968	1,812	46	5,409	1,243,707
1949	1,769,307	6,582	1,944	44	5,527	1,481,601
1950	2,044,585	8,850	1,934	68	7,724	2,201,808
1951	2,020,249	9,733	1,834	86	8,132	2,187,618
1952	2,787,780	10,472	1,919	56	8,861	2,589,494
1953	2,677,588	10,543	1,988	84	8,577	3,048,486
1954	2,677,809	8,640	2,047	NA	NA	NA
1955	2,971,197	9,180	1,911	NA	NA	NA
1956	3,123,025	10,376	1,794	NA	NA	NA
1957	3,250,910	9,014	1,892	NA	NA	NA
1958	2,385,553	6,866	1,275	NA	NA	NA
1959	1,463,911	3,758	654	NA	NA	NA
1960	2,046,780	5,135	738	NA	NA	NA
1961	1,610,228	3,046	805	NA	NA	NA
1962	2,806,684	4,876	973	NA	NA	NA
1963	1,904,519	3,230	728	NA	NA	NA
1964	1,572,175	2,280	556	NA	NA	NA

Appendix V

Production Figures showing value of sub-contract work 1950-1959

Year	Production Sales £	Sub-contracting £	B.P. Production Sales £
1950	2,465,980 *	421,395	2,044,585
1951	2,639,149 *	618,900	2,020,249
1952	3,940,782 *	1,153,002	2,787,780
1953	4,588,608	1,911,020	2,677,588
1954	3,494,462	816,653	2,677,809
1955	3,592,481	621,284	2,971,197
1956	4,217,255	1,094,230	3,123,025
1957	4,483,976	1,233,066	3,250,910
1958	2,757,836	372,283	2,385,553
1959	1,474,252	10,341	1,463,911

* Work completed figures, not production sales.

Appendix VI

Garratt Locomotives built under Sub-Contract or Licensees

Beyer, Peacock and H.W. Garratt shared the costs of taking out patent rights for his locomotive in countries overseas so together they arranged with other locomotive builders to construct this new articulated type. The first to be granted a licence was the Baldwin Locomotive Works of America in December 1910. In 1911, agreements were reached with Messrs Henschel & Sohn of Cassel in Germany and Messrs La Société Anonyme de St. Léonard of Liége, Belgium, who were the first to construct any Garratts.(1)

Between 1911 and 1927, the **Société Anonyme St. Léonard** built some 27 locomotives, mainly for African territories. It started with two in 1911 for the C. de F. Vicinaux du Mayumbe in the Belgian Congo for the 600mm-gauge.(2) These were 0-4-0 + 0-4-0 type and had the distinction of being the smallest Garratts ever built, weighing 23.15 tons and developing 9,000lb. Tractive Effort. They replaced some twin locomotives and were designed to burn either coal or wood. A larger version for the 750mm-gauge was built for the Zaccar Mines in North Africa. It was completed in 1912 and was the third smallest Garratt, weighing 27.5 tons and developing 12,800lb. Tractive Effort. The second smallest were those built by Beyer, Peacock for the Arakan Flotilla Co (see Chap. 10). In 1911, one engine was built for the C. de F. du Congo, a 0-6-0 + 0-6-0 for the 750mm-gauge with a special boiler having an experimental oil-burning system. The fuel oil was carried in a cylindrical tank on the front bogie and it was hoped that, by making flames travel along an extra set of large tubes under the boiler, better evaporation would be obtained. H.W. Garratt went to Belgium and photographed the trials of this locomotive. The boiler was not a success and was abandonned for twelve more engines in 1919, nine in 1924 and another nine in 1925 to slightly altered designs.(3) In 1922, it built four metre-gauge 2-6-0 + 0-6-2 type for the F.C. Catalanes in Spain and four more to a repeat order in 1925. These locomotives were distinctive in having cylindrical tanks on the front power unit. Then in 1926 came another two metre-gauge 2-6-0 + 0-6-2 type for the Madagascar Railway and it finished with a couple of its first 0-4-0 + 0-4-0 supplied to the Porto Feliz. Sugar Co. in 1927.

[Top] The Société Anonyme de Saint Léonard supplied the smallest Garratts ever built to the Chemin de Fer Vicinaux du Mayumbe in 1911.   [Garratt archives]

[Upper Middle] The 0-6-0 + 0-6-0 Garratt with special oil-fired boiler unit built by the Société Anonyme de Saint Léonard in 1911 for the Chemin de Fer du Congo, photographed by H.W. Garratt undergoing trials in Belgium.   [Garratt archives]

[Lower middle] The metre gauge 2-6-0 + 0-6-2 Garratt built in 1922 for the F.C. Catalanes by the Société Anonyme de Saint Léonard.

[Foot] Probably the only Garratts ever fitted with conical chimneys were two metre gauge 2-6-0 + 0-6-2s for the Madagascar Railway built in 1926 by the Société Anonyme de Saint Léonard.

[Above] The 2-6-2 + 2-6-2 light-weight Garratt built by the Société Franco-Belge of La Croyère for the South African Railways 2ft. gauge.

Three other Belgian companies built Beyer-Garratt locomotives under licence at various times as follows:-

The **Société Franco-Belge de Materiel de Chemins de Fer** of La Croyère (not to be confused with the French company of somewhat similar name), built two very small 2-6-2 + 2-6-2 engines in 1927 for a section of the 2ft.-gauge South African Railways with a maximum axle-load of 3.7 tons, weight 33.75 tons, 11,780lb. Tractive Effort.(4) A third followed in 1931.

John Cockerill & Co. of Seraing built four of the South African Railways 2ft.-gauge 2-6-2 + 2-6-2 class NG/G 16 in 1937, weight 60.55 tons, 21,360lb. Tractive Effort.

The third company was **Forges Usines et Fonderies du Haine Saint-Pierre**, who built two more of the 750-gauge 0-4-0 + 0-4-0 Garratts for the Mines du Zaccar in 1936 and 1937. Presumably thinking this would be a profitable line of business, in 1938, it negotiated a licence agreement with Beyer, Peacock to build Garratts.(5) Like other agreements reached at this time, for example with the American Locomotive Company, nothing was built and again no orders resulted from further discussions in 1947.(6) Then in 1952 it built twelve 4-8-2 + 2-8-4 for the Mozambique Railways, their first new Garratts. The design closely followed that of the wartime EC 4 class Heavy Garratt built by Beyer, Peacock for the East African Railways, but altered to 3ft. 6in. gauge and with 'Alliance' couplers.

Another licensee was the **Compania Euskaldũa** in Bilbao, Spain, which built six 4-6-2 + 2-6-4 in 1931 for the 5ft. 6in.-gauge F.C. Central de Aragon.(7) Beyer, Peacock supplied a set of reference drawings for the passenger Garratt built for the San Paulo Railway in 1927 (see Chap. 13) together with the project design so there was considerable similarity in detail between these locomotives. Weighing 180.5 tons and developing 46,350lb. Tractive Effort with 5ft. 8 7/8in. diameter coupled wheels, the largest at that date on any Garratt, they were designed as powerful passenger engines to operate over mountain sections including one of the 9½ miles of continuous 1 in 46.5 gradient with many curves, and elsewhere to run at speeds of up to 62mph. Their equipment included 'A.C.F.I.' feed water heaters, 'Wagner' water purifiers, 'Nicholson' thermic syphons, 'Le Chatelier' counter-pressure brake in addition to steam and hand brakes, Beyer, Peacock patent movable front tank to facilitate tube removal and also the latest Beyer, Peacock patent adjustable pivot centres. In 1949, the F.C. Central de Aragon approached Beyer, Peacock to supply it with drawings to enable it to bring these locomotives up to date with the most modern practice.(8)

Eskaldũa also built a metre-gauge 2-6-2 + 2-6-2 in 1930 for the Compania Minera de Sierra Menera. The two engines for this order were very similar to the one built by Beyer, Peacock for the Dundee Colliery, South Africa, in 1927 (see Chap. 12). These locomotives incorporated the latest features such as the patent pivot centres and movable front tanks designed by Beyer, Peacock. Mallets were already at work on the Compania de Sierra Menera's lines and the two types of locomotives articulated and semi-articulated, worked together for many years.

[Below] The handsome 4-6-2 + 2-6-4 express passenger Garratts built by the Compania Euskalduna of Bilbao for the Central of Aragon Railway in 1929.

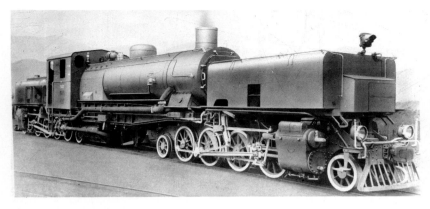

[Left] The only Garratts ever built in Italy were ordered by the Ethiopian Railway and constructed by Ansaldo in 1939.

In 1937, **Messrs Ansaldo** of Italy sought a licence to build six 2-8-2 + 2-8-2 Beyer-Garratts for the C. de F. Franco Ethiopien. Beyer, Peacock agreed to supply three drawings in exchange for a royalty of £3 per ton on the actual empty weight of the locomotives, payment being 50 per cent. immediately and the balance within twelve months of the date of the first payment. £570 was received in March 1938 and three of the locomotives were delivered to Ethiopia in 1939. The other three were diverted to Libya but one was presumably sunk at sea and the other two so badly damaged by bombing that they were scrapped in 1945.(9) These were the only Garratts built in Italy.

The most important manufacturing licensee was **Société Franco-Belge** at Raismes in Northern France who built the following:-

P.L.M. Algeria 1050mm-gauge 4-8-2 + 2-8-4, weight 142 (class YAT) 47,400lb. Tractive Effort, 4 built in 1931. These were almost identical to the EC 2 class built by Beyer, Peacock for the Kenya & Uganda Railway in 1930. They hauled a mean load three times that of the other locomotives and saved fuel per ton hauled. Their introduction reduced train mileage and enabled the traffic to be handled with 30 per cent. less personnel.

P.L.M. Algeria 4ft. 8½in.-gauge, 4-6-2- + 2-6-4, 1 built (class AT) in 1932, weight 197.7 tons, 53,600lb Tractive Effort.

This was a prototype main line passenger locomotive with coupled wheels 5ft. 10 7/8in. diameter, designed for speeds over 70mph. The complete set of manufacturing drawings was prepared by Beyer, Peacock, all in the metric system and incorporating all current patented features including the rotary bunker (see Chap. 14).(10)

Algerian State Railways 4ft.8½in.-gauge, 4-6-2 + 2-6-4,
(class BT) weight 212.6 tons, 65,900lb. Tractive Effort.
12 built in 1936. 6 built in 1939.
4 built in 1937. 7 built in 1940.

[Below] The experimental 4-6-2 + 2-6-4 high-speed Garratt built by the Société Franco-Belge for the Paris, Lyons & Mediterranean Railway [Reseau Algerien] in 1932 and capable of speeds over70 mph.

The success of the AT class led to the above series of orders for the BT class, the P.L.M. having been amalgamated with the Algerian State Railways in the meantime. The dimensions of cylinders and coupled wheels were the same as on the AT class but the tractive effort was substantially increased by raising the boiler pressure from 227.5 to 284 psi, while the maximum axle-load was increased from 17.7 to 18.2 tons. The royalty which the Société Franco-Belge had to pay Beyer, Peacock for the first nine locomotives was £1,500 upon receipt of the order and in addition £1 10 0 per ton on the actual empty weight of the locomotives when completed.(11)

The detail design of these spectacular locomotives was left entirely in the hands of the Société Franco-Belge and the railway authorities. The most striking features were the streamlining and the use of 'Cossart' vertical piston-type valves and gear instead of Walschaert's which was claimed to give freer running at high speed with very early cut-off. The reverse gear was operated by an electric motor mounted on the side of the boiler frame with current supplied by an additional turbo-generator, and with provision for operation by compressed air in emergencies—altogether a rather complicated arrangment! The bunker was totally enclosed within the impressive semistreamlined shape and fitted with a steam-operated coal pusher instead of the rotary bunker, probably because firing with briquettes was adopted. The smokebox had double chimneys arranged transversely with twin 'Kylchap' blast pipes.

These locomotives gave a great performance in service, but were severely run down during the War when spares could not be obtained from France and by 1951 they were all withdrawn and replaced by diesels. On trials, one of the BT class attained 82mph and scheduled speeds up to 75mph were regular. Between Algiers and Oran, a distance of 262 miles, any train previously with more than a 256 ton load needed to be double-headed and took nine hours. In 1933, the prototype Garratt hauled 433 tons in a running time of 6 hours 57 minutes. On normal working, these Beyer-Garratts must have maintained the fastest schedules of any articulated locomotives and the speed

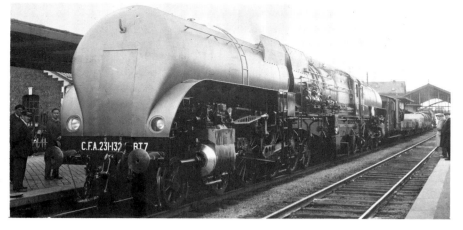

[Left] The streamlined 'Pacific' Garratt built by the Société Franco-Belge in 1936 for the Algerian State Railways which may well have held the world speed record for articulated locomotives at 82 miles per hour.

[Below] An impressive engine for the metre-gauge Ivory Coast Railway built by the Société Franco-Belge in 1938.

[Foot] In 1953, the Société Franco-Belge built ten 4-8-2 + 2-8-4s based on the Standard Light Garratt [Order 11163] for the South Australian Railways.

of 82mph is again a world record for such machines. (12)

Ivory Coast Metre-gauge 4-8-2 + 2-8-4, weight 148 tons, 44,750lb. Tractive Effort.

> 10 built in 1938.
> 10 built in 1939.
> 7 built in 1941.

These 27 locomotives for service in French territory in West Africa were wood burners and unusual in appearance, having U-shaped tanks, smoke deflectors and partial casings. It is doubtful whether these served any useful purpose as a peak speed of 62mph with good stability was reached, but service speeds were much less than this. They were a development of the Algerian metre-gauge Beyer-Garratts and had double chimneys and blast pipes similar to the BT class.

An inquiry about Garratts for Yugoslavia in 1938 came to nothing(13) and no more Garratts were built by the Société Franco-Belge until 1951, and in only one case was it greatly involved in the design work. Because Gorton was full to capacity, between 1951 and 1954 it built a total of fifty-two, all under contract from Beyer, Peacock as follows:-

Queensland Government Railways, 3ft. 6in.-gauge, 4-8-2 + 2-8-4, twenty built in 1951 which were identical with the ten built by Beyer, Peacock in 1950. Ten 4-6-4 + 4-6-4 were built for the **Rhodesia Railways** in 1952 which were identical with the thirty 15A class built by Beyer, Peacock in 1949-50. These were followed by ten 4-8-2 + 2-8-4 built in 1953 for the **South Australian Railways.** This was the fourth of a series of five designs all based on the wartime 'Standard Light Garratt', redesigned for 3ft. 6in.-gauge. Further, they had to be converted first to 5ft. 3in. and eventually to 4ft. 8½in.-gauges plus provision for changes in type and location of drawgear, all with a minimum of alteration. Other changes were driving controls on the left hand side and the air brake equipment was the Australian Westinghouse type. Also they were to be built as oil-burners but with provision for easy conversion to coal-burning with a mechanical stoker. Altogether it was like designing the locomotive twice over. This was a most successful design, and was the last type of steam locomotive to work in South Australia until 1969.

Société Franco-Belge prepared all the drawings under supervision by Beyer, Peacock. For the gauge conversion, the first step from 3ft. 6in to 5ft. 3in. inevitably involved moving the wheels and frames out and fitting new axles, frame stays, etc. For the second step from 5ft. 3in. to 4ft. 8½in.-gauge, the wheel centres were designed to

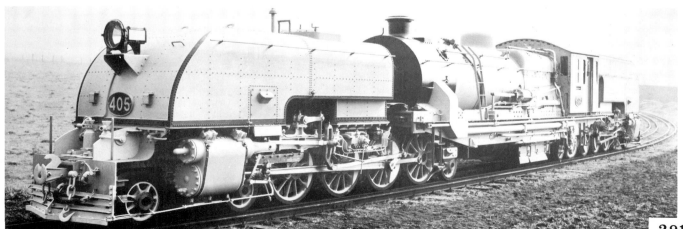

achieve this by pressing them off the axles, switching them to the opposite sides and fitting new tyres. The brake hangers were designed for a similar interchange. These were well equipped locomotives, with roller bearings on all axles. A detail of interest was the multiple-bearing cross-head and slide bar—the only Garratts with this feature. These conversion arrangements were never carried out due to a change to diesel locomotives only about thirteen years later.

The last Beyer-Garratts built by the Société Franco-Belge were twelve 4-8-2 + 2-8-4 metre-gauge class 60 for the **East African Railways**. These were the fifth and last design based on the wartime 'Standard Light Garratt' and were part of an order for twenty-nine placed with Beyer, Peacock who built the rest at Gorton (see Chap. 17).

One more licensing agreement, and a very important one, was with **Henschel & Sohn of Cassel** in Germany. They had built six 2-8-2 + 2-8-2 in 1929 for the Royal State Railways of Siam which were followed by a further two identical in 1936. But in 1936, Beyer, Peacock had reached agreement with the German Locomotive Manufacturers Association whereby German manufacturers undertook not to quote for Garratt locomotives without Beyer, Peacock's authority.(14) This agreement was not honoured by **Krupps** in 1952 when they quoted for and built six 4-8-2 + 2-8-4 for the Luanda Railway.

It was Henschels who subcontracted to build the Beyer-Garratts for the **Great Western Railway of Brazil** which had been ordered in 1939, but which Beyer, Peacock had been unable to build through the outbreak of the Second World War (see Chap. 15). The order was increased from two to six locomotives of 4-8-2 + 2-8-4 metre-gauge type which were yet another of the five designs based on the wartime 'Standard Light Garratt'. They were oil-burners like those Beyer, Peacock supplied to the Luanda Railway, on which their design was based, and were delivered in 1952.

Henschels collaborated with Beyer, Peacock in building a total of 120 of the **South African Railways GMAM** class of which 25 were built in Germany in 1952 and another 30 in 1954 (see Chap. 17) to drawings prepared by Henschels. Beyer, Peacock was particularly anxious to see that the next order from South Africa for the GO class was not taken by an outside firm except under its control.(15) This class was designed and built by Henschels again in collaboration with Beyer, Peacock, and closely followed the GMAM class in detail design and equipment, but the maximum axle-load was reduced to 13.7 tons by carrying less supplies and fitting a smaller boiler. The cylinders were 18½ in. diameter instead of 20½ in. Like the GMAM class, they had the latest self-adjusting pivot centres, Hadfield power reverse gear, the latter together with mechanical stokers being manufactured by Beyer, Peacock.

For the **Moçamedes Railway** in Angola, Henschels built six 4-8-2 + 2-8-4 in 1955 which were based on the Benguela Railway 10C class supplied by Beyer, Peacock in 1952 and their power characteristics were identical to that class. They had many detail arrangements of German practice and were oil-burners. Equipment included Henschel exhaust steam feed water heaters, Beyer, Peacock patent self-adjusting pivot centres and Hadfield power reverse gear. The last Beyer-Garratts built by Henschel & Sohn followed this general design but were more powerful and were coal-fired by mechanical stokers. Five were delivered in 1956 to the **Mozambique Railway**. Other differences were that they had cast steel beds similar to the South African Railways GMAM and GO classes and had roller bearings on all axles.

Haine St. Pierre in Belgium built twelve 4-8-2 + 2-8-4 coal-burners for the Mozambique Railways in 1952 and another similar batch of 12 but oil-burners for the Bas Congo au Katanga Railway in 1956. The ones for the South African Railways built by the North British Locomotive Co. have been described already.

In 1956, Beyer, Peacock received a letter from the Wiener-Lokomotivfabrik A/G of Vienna intimating that they intended to quote for Garratt locomotives and asking what patents Beyer, Peacock held. Beyer, Peacock replied that it presumed that Wiener-Lokomotivfabrik was asking for a provisional licence agreement which it was quite willing to grant and proposed that discussions be held in London or Vienna.(16) Nothing came of these suggestions and this seems to have been the last time that Beyer, Peacock was involved with foreign firms about building Beyer-Garratts. Ten Garratts were built in 1961 by Babcock and Wilcox in Spain(17) and eight by Hunslet Taylor in 1967-68 in South Africa but Beyer, Peacock was not involved.

Notes

1 B.P. Board Minutes No. 1, 21 December 1910, 1 March and 5 May 1911
2 Wiener, op. cit., p. 182
3 ibid, p. 189
4 B.P. Board Minutes No. 2, 26 January 1926
5 ibid, 12 April 1938
6 ibid, 9 September 1947, No. 95
7 B.P. Board Minutes, No. 2, 9 July 1929 and L.G. Marshall, **Steam on the RENFE**(1965), p. 191
8 B.P. Board Minutes, 5 April 1949, No. 54
9 ibid, 1 September 1937, No. 12 and 12 October 1937, No. 10
10 **The Engineer,** Vol. 154, 11 November 1932, p. 480
11 B.P. Board Minutes, 8 March 1938, No. 13
12 B.P. Company Minutes No. 2, 26 July 1936 and **The Engineer,** Vol. 163, 9 April 1937, p. 426
13 B.P. Board Minutes, 11 October 1938, No. 111
14 ibid, 17 September 1952, No. 135
15 ibid, 10 October 1950, No. 146
16 ibid, 12 June 1956, No. 95
17 Marshall, op. cit., p. 195

[Below] The 4-8-2 + 4-8-2 Beyer-Garratts for the Great Western Railway of Brazil were finally built in Germany by Henschel as one of the Standard Light Garratt designs.

Appendix VII

Metropolitan-Vickers, Beyer, Peacock Limited, 1949-1960

In May 1947, the proposal was put to the Board of Beyer, Peacock that it collaborate with Metropolitan-Vickers Ltd. "for the purpose of designing, manufacturing and selling Electric, Diesel-Electric and Gas Turbo-Electric Locomotives (excluding Steam Locomotives)".(1) It was suggested that Scotswood Works at Newcastle-upon-Tyne might be used. Negotiations continued throughout the rest of 1947 and through the whole of 1948 and it was not until January 1949 that the terms of the agreement, which had been approved by the Met.-Vick. Board were put before its parent company, Associated Electrical Industries.(2) Further discussions took place so it was not until November 1949(3) that the jointly owned subsidiary company was formed with a factory, Bowesfield Works, at Stockton-on-Tees, which was extended and equipped to build 'Locomotives other than Steam'.

The Traction Division of Met.-Vick. had long been in the forefront of the electric locomotive field, but did not have facilities allocated at Trafford Park for building mechanical parts which were sub-contracted. Moreover, it planned to extend its operations to include diesel-electric locomotives, in which field it would have competed against its usual sub-contractors. Beyer, Peacock wished to have some share in such business with an eye to future developments, although at that date its business in steam locomotives was booming with full production booked far ahead.

The share capital for the new company was provided jointly by Met.-Vick. and Beyer, Peacock. Met.-Vick. subscribed £15,000 towards 6 per cent. Cumulative Preference shares, but the interest was not to become cumulative until after 1954. Both companies subscribed £50,000 in Ordinary shares. The initial capital investment to set up the works was allocated up to the end of November 1950 as follows:-

1. Machine tools and works transport, £124,514
2. Building and construction work at Bowesfield 42,050
3. Building and construction at Bowesfield by North East Trading Estates Ltd. 13,496

£180,060
(4)

Some of the machine tools were supplied second-hand by the parent companies while others were acquired from war surplus stocks. Over the years, further additions were made to the machine tools to enable a wider variety of production to be undertaken.

[Below] The first locomotive for the Rede de Mineira de Viacao being built in Bowesfield Works.

The key personnel required initially to organise and manage the works was recruited from Beyer, Peacock, with James Hadfield as Managing Director (later Chairman for a period), and the Board of Directors comprised executives of both companies with initially Mr. E.W. Steele of Met.-Vick. as Chairman. During the first three years, all the drawings were produced by the parent companies and were all for contracts secured by Met.-Vick. who was responsible for the overall designs and specifications, while the drawings of the mechanical parts were prepared in a section of Beyer, Peacock's Drawing Office. Beyer, Peacock also manufactured many of the wheel and axle sets, steel castings, forgings and initially some of the heavy fabrications.

[Left] The first engine built at Bowesfield Works leaving for the Rede de Mineira de Viacao.

The post-war years saw many restrictions in the supply of raw materials to manufacturing industries. The supply of steel was one difficulty which affected the production at Bowesfield and in addition suppliers of elctrical and other equipment were often late in their deliveries. This affected both recruitment of labour and the profits, which are shown in the following tables.

Labour

Date		Non-prod Labour	Prod Labour	Total
Jan	1952	-	-	258
May	1952	-	-	291
Dec	1953	72	178	250
Jul	1954	74	208	282
Dec	1954	79	256	335
Apr	1955	79	286	365
Oct	1955	79	257	336
Jan	1956	-	262	-
Dec	1956	-	304	-
-	1957	No figures found		
Jan	1958	-	-	300
Dec	1958	-	-	470
Feb	1959	-	-	620
Aug	1959	-	-	650
Apr	1960	144	421	513

[5]

Sales and Profits

Year	Sales Locomotives £	Sales Sundries £	Sales Total £	Net Profits After Tax £	Dividends 6% Cum Pref. £	Ord Shares % £
1950	NA	NA	13,238	1,814 [loss]	none	- none
1951	NA	NA	94,560	2,302 [loss]	none	- none
1952	No figures found			19,334	none	- none
1953	127,925	1,197	129,222	7,423	2,475 ★	- none
1954	482,346	1,250	483,596	21,933	5,175	- none
1955	541,676	2,067	543,743	23,207	5,175	- none
1956	881,084	16,766	895,850	22,510	5,175	- none
1957	609,176	123,248	732,424	26,513	5,175	5 3,450
1958	422,656	141,271	563,927	2,838	none	- none
1959	1,476,575	52,579	1,529,154	11,439	11,025 †	6 4,410
1960	1,438,183	134,238	1,562,421	19,662 *	5,512	6 4,410

[6]

Notes ★ Half year only
      † Payment for 2 years
      * Before tax was deducted

The early years while production was building up were, of course, run at a loss, but by the end of 1952, there was a profit of £19,334. However, by the time two sums had been set aside for reserves, there was a final credit balance of £1,538, so no dividend was paid. In the following years, the dividend on the Cumulative Preference Shares was met and dividends paid on the Ordinary Shares in three years.

[Below] The electric locomotives for the Rede de V. Parana - Santa Catarina in Brazil were the same design as those for the Rede de Mineira de Viacao.

As it turned out, all the orders for locomotives were for contracts obtained by Met.-Vick. From 1953 onwards, all the drawings were produced at Trafford Park and in an office created at Bowesfield Works. The following locomotives were built:-

Rede Mineira de Viacao, Brazil, 14 electric locomotives, built 1949.

Rede de V. Parana - Santa Catarina, Brazil, 10 electric locomotives built 1950-51.

Horsepower	1,072
Wheel arrangement	Bo-Bo
Gauge	Metre
Line voltage	3,000v dc
Weight	49.5 tons

The under-frame, bogies and superstructure were of all-welded construction and a special feature of interest was the Met.-Vick. patent side link suspension, in which the complete superstructure was suspended from the bogies on four links (two per bogie), fitted with special "Metalastik" bushes permitting lateral and rotational movement of the bogies. Traction forces were transmitted through a linkage system to each bogie.

[Below] The first of fourteen electric locomotives for the Rede de Mineira de Viacao in Brazil.

Western Australian Government Railways, 48 diesel-electric locomotives, built 1953-55.

Horsepower 1,105
Wheel arrangement 2-Do-2
Gauge 3ft. 6in.
Weight 77 tons

The design evolved by Met.-Vick. was unusual among diesel-electric locomotives in having a long rigid plate frame with the motored axles closely grouped in the centre, a long overhang beyond the rigid wheel-base, and four-wheeled carrying bogies fitted with radial arms. The frame and superstructure were of all-welded construction. The power unit selected by Met.-Vick. was a Crossley 2-stroke loop-scavenge diesel engine not previously used for main-line rail traction work and delays in delivery were experienced. It unfortunately developed troubles in service which ultimately led to replacement by another make of engine.

New South Wales Government Railways, 40 electric locomotives, built 1954-55.

Horsepower 3,820
Wheel arrangement Co-Co
Gauge 4ft. 8½in.
Line voltage 1,500v dc
Weight 108 tons

The design of these locomotives was based on that of a prototype built by the railway company. The bogie frames were one-piece steel castings of robust design, cast and machined by the General Steel Castings Corporation of the U.S.A. They carried the buffers and draw-gear at the outer ends and were coupled together at the inner ends, thus taking all the traction and buffing forces. A combination of riveting and welding was used for the frame and super-structure. Constructional delays were experienced through late delivery of the steel bogie castings, but then production proceeded smoothly.

British Railways, 20 diesel-electric locomotives, built 1955-56.

Horsepower 1,200
Wheel arrangement Co-Bo
Gauge 4ft. 8½in.
Weight 97 tons

This was Met.-Vick.'s contribution when batches of Type 2 locomotives were ordered from various builders to their individual designs, the intention being to compare their design and performance before deciding which type or types should form the basis for future bulk orders. The power unit was again the Crossley 2-stroke loop-scavenge engine, now rated at 1,200hp, and in order to keep within the permitted axle-load while using this relatively heavy engine, the most unusual Co-Bo wheel arrangement was adopted, involving two different designs of bogies. The bogies were of "Commonwealth" cast steel type supplied by General Steel Castings Corporation of the U.S.A. This version of the Type 2 locomotive was not perpetuated by British Railways and these were the last diesel-electrics built at Stockton.

National Coal Board, 10 flame-proof battery locomotives, built 1957-58.

Horsepower 90
Wheel arrangement 2-axle
Gauge Narrow
Weight 14 tons

These were designed for underground operation.

South African Railways, 5 E.1 class, 100 electric locomotives, built 1958-60.

Horsepower 2,280
Wheel arrangement Bo-Bo
Gauge 3ft. 6in.
Line voltage 3,000v dc
Weight 84 tons

This modern design, generally similar to those already built of the same class, was the final batch of locomotives built at Bowesfield Works. The last ones were shipped in February 1961.

In 1957, the Met.-Vick. Gas Turbine locomotive was converted at Bowesfield Works to an A.C. Electric locomotive. It had been the original intention that these works should concentrate solely on building electric or diesel-electric locomotives for the parent companies, but it became increasingly obvious that additional work had to be found to even out the fluctuations on the locomotive orders so that the labour force could be kept fully employed. Difficulty had been experienced in recruiting labour in an area of well-established heavy industry, and men once made redundant would not have been likely to reapply for work again. Therefore, starting at the end of 1955, other jobs, such as machining and building parts for pantagraphs and armatures was undertaken to even out the work load. The effect of this can be seen in the sales of sundries.

No orders were in sight after that for South Africa partly because Met.-Vick. and the A.E.I. Group had acquired capacity for building locomotives elsewhere. Then Gorton Foundry itself was struggling for survival and was desperately looking for orders in the diesel or electric locomotive fields. So an Extraordinary General Meeting of the shareholders was called on 2 February 1961 at which it was agreed to place the company in voluntary liquidation. In the eleven years of its existence, it had built a total of 242 locomotives plus other sub-contract work of various kinds.

Notes

1 B.P. Board Minutes, 6 May 1947, No. 52
2 ibid, see 6 July 1948, No. 99, 9 November 1948, No. 148 and 24 January 1949, No. 24.
3 ibid, 6 September 1949, No. 121 and 8 November 1949, No. 159.
4 Met.-Vick. B.P. Board Minutes, 1950-57, December 1950.
5 ibid, collated from graphs and other figures and B.P. Group Annual Reports.
6 ibid, also Met.-Vick. B.P. Proceedings at the A.G.M., 1951-53 and B.P. Group Annual Reports.

[Below] 2-Do-2 diesel electric locomotive for the Western Australian Government bound for the docks.

Bibliography

Archive Material

The North Western Museum of Science & Industry in Manchester houses the Beyer, Peacock Archives. These consist of official company records, such as Minute Books, account and wages books (incomplete runs), records from the Drawing Office such as the Order Books, draughtsmen's Note Books, catalogues, drawings, schemes drawings, photographs, etc. There is also the Centenary History prepared in 1954 and the papers on which it was based.

The Robertson Collection in the National Library of Wales contains many papers and letters relating to Beyer, Peacock & Co.

The Sharp Stewart Collection at the Science Museum, London, has the Order Books and some drawings of Sharp Roberts, Sharp Bros., and Sharp Stewart connected with C.F. Beyer.

Mrs. M. Mumford granted access to the papers of her father, H.W. Garratt.

Periodicals

The following periodicals have been consulted where appropriate:-
Beyer, Peacock Quarterly Review
The Engineer
Engineering
Journal of the Institution of Locomotive Engineers
The Locomotive
Transactions of the Newcomen Society
Proceedings of the Institution of Civil Engineers
Proceedings of the Institution of Mechanical Engineers
The Railway Gazette
The Railway Magazine

Books

Abbott, R.A.S.,
   The Fairlie Locomotive. (David & Charles, Newton Abbot, 1970)
Ahrons, E.L.,
   The British Steam Railway Locomotive, Vol. I, 1825-1925. (Loco. Pub. Co., London, 1927)
   The Development of British Locomotive Design, (Loco. Pub. Co., London, 1914)
Beyer, Peacock & Co.,
   Beyer-Garratt Articulated Locomotives, (Private Pub., London, 1947)
   The Second World War, (Private Pub., London, 1945)
Bennett, A.R..,
   The Chronicles of Boulton's Sidings, (Loco. Pub.Co., London, 1927)
Birch, A.,
   The Economic History of the British Iron & Steel Industry, (London, 1967)
Bourne, J.,
   A Catechism of the Steam Engine, (Longmans Green, London, new ed. 1876)
   Recent Improvements in the Steam-Engine, (Longmans Green, London, new ed. 1880)

Boyd, J.I.C.,
   The Festiniog Railway, (Oakwood, South Godstone, Vol. I, 1960, Vol. II, 1959)
   Narrow Gauge Rails in Mid-Wales, (Oakwood, South Godstone, 1952)
Carling, D.R.,
   4-8-0 Tender Locomotives, (David & Charles, Newton Abbot, 1971)
Clark, D.K.,
   The Exhibited Machinery of 1862, (Day & Son, London, 1864)
   Railway Locomotives, (Blackie, Glasgow, 1860)
   The Steam Engine: A Treatise on Steam Engines and Boilers, (Blackie, London, 1890)
Clark, R.H.,
   The Development of the English Steam Wagon, (Goose, Norwich, 1963)
   Midland and Great Northern Joint Railway, (Goose, Norwich, 1967)
Clarke, J.F.,
   Power on Land & Sea, A History of R.&W. Hawthorn Leslie, (Private Pub. Newcastle, 1978)
Colburn, Z.,
   Locomotive Engineering and the Mechanism of Railways, (Collins, London, 1871)
Court, J.H.,
   North British Steam Locomotives built 1833-1948 for railways in Britain, (Bradford Barton, Truro, 1979)

Dempsey, G.C. and Clark, D.K.,
   Rudimentary Treatise of the Locomotive Engine, (Crosby Lockwood, London, 1879)
Dow, G.,
   The Great Central, (Ian Allan, London, Vol. I, 1959, Vol. II, 1962)
Dunn, J.M.,
   The Wrexham, Mold & Connah's Quay Railway, (Oakwood, Lingfield, 1957)
Durrant, A.E.,
   Australian Steam, (David & Charles, Newton Abbot, 1978)
   The Garratt Locomotive, (David & Charles, Newton Abbot, 1969)
   The Mallet Locomotive, (David & Charles, Newton Abbot, 1974)

Fawcett, B.,
   Railway of the Andes, (London, 1963)
Fayle, H.,
   The Narrow Gauge Railways of Ireland, (Greenlake, London, 1946)
Glover, G.,
   British Locomotive Design, 1825-1960, (Allen & Unwin, London, 1967)
Highet, C.,
   Scottish Locomotive History, 1831-1923, (Allen & Unwin, London, 1970)
Holland, D.F.,
   Steam Locomotives of the South African Railways, (David & Charles, Newton Abbot, Vol. I, 1971, Vol. II, 1972)
Hyde, W.G.S.,
   The Manchester Bury Rochdale and Oldham Steam Tramway, (Transport Pub. Co., Glossop, 1980)
Johnson, W.,
   Imperial Cyclopaedia of Machinery, (Mackenzie, Glasgow, 1854)
Kitson Clark, E.,
   Kitsons of Leeds, (Loco. Pub. Co., London, 1937)

Kyle, I.,
   Steam from Lowca, A History of the Rise and Fall of Locomotive Building at Lowca Foundry, 1840-1921, (Kyle, Moresby, 1974)
Lane, M.R.,
   The Story of the Steam Plough Works, Fowlers of Leeds, (Northgate Pub. Co., London, 1980)
Lerry, G.G.,
   Collieries of Denbighshire, (Wrexham, 1968)
   Henry Robertson, Pioneer of Railways into Wales, (Oswestry, 1949)
   [Locomotive Engineers Pocket Book, (Loco. Pub. Co., London, 1929 et al.)
   Locomotive Manufacturers Association, Handbook, (L.M.A. London, 1949)
Lowe, J.W.,
   British Steam Locomotive Builders, (Goose, Cambridge, 1975)
   Building Britain's Locomotives, (Moorland Pub., Ashbourne, 1979)
McClare, E.J.,
   The New Zealand Garratt Story, (New Zealand Railway & Loco. Soc., Wellington, 1978)
Marshall, L.G.,
   Steam on the RENFE, The Steam Locomotive Stock of the Spanish National Railways, (MacMillan, London, 1965)
Mason, E.,
   The Lancashire & Yorkshire Railway, (Ian Allan, London, 1954)
Moir, S.M.,
   Twenty-four Inches Apart, the two-foot Gauge Railways of the Cape of Good Hope, (Oakwood, South Godstone, 1963)
Nock, O.S.,
   The British Steam Railway Locomotive, 1925-1965, (Ian Allan, London, 1966)
   British Steam Railways, (Ian Allan, London, 1961)
   Historic Railway Disasters, (Ian Allan, London, 1966)
   The Locomotives of Sir Nigel Gresley, (Railway Pub. Co., London, 1946)
   The Premier Line, (London, 1952)
   William Stanier, (Ian Allan, London, 1964)
A History of the North British Locomotive Co., (Privately Pub., Glasgow, 1953)
Parsons, R.H.,
   History of the Institution of Mechanical Engineers, 1847-1947, Privately Pub., London, 1947)
Ramaer, R.,
   Steam Locomotives of the East African Railways, (David & Charles, Newton Abbot, 1974)
Record of the International Exhibition, (London, 1862)
Redman, R.N.,
   The Railway Foundry Leeds, 1839-1969, E.B. Wilson-Hudswell Clarke & Co. Ltd., (Goose, Norwich, 1972)
Reed, B.,
   Diesel Hydraulic Locomotives of the Western Region, (David & Charles, Newton Abbot, 1974)
   Locomotives in Profile, Vol. I, (Profile Pub., Windsor, 1971)
   A Source Book of Locomotives, (Ward Lock, London, 1970)
Rivington,
   My Life with Locomotives, (Ian Allan, London, 1962)

Rolt, L.T.C.,
   A Hunslet Hundred, (David & Charles, Dawlish, 1964)
   The Mechanicals, the Progress of a Profession, (Privately Pub., London, 1967)
Singleton, C.C. and Burke, D.,
   Railways of Australia, (Angus & Robertson, Sydney, 1963)
Smith, J.H. Ed.,
   The Great Human Exploit, Historic Industries of the North-West, (Phillimore, London, 1973)
Snell, J.B.,
   Early Railways, (Weidenfeld & Nicolson, London, 1964)
   Mechanical Engineering: Railways, (Longman, London, 1971)
Stretton, C.E.,
   The Locomotive and its Development, 1803-1895, (Crosby Lockwood, London, 1896)
Swift, M.,
   The Darjeeling-Hymalayan Railway Garratt, Narrow Gauge No. 79, (Spring 1978)
Thomas, J.,
   The Springburn Story, the history of the Scottish Railway Metropolis, (David & Charles, Newton Abbot, 1964)
Toms, G.,
   Brush Diesel Locomotives, 1940-78, (Transport Pub., Co., Glossop, 1978)
Tredgold, T.,
   The Steam Engine, its Invention, etc., (Weale, London, 1838)
Vulcan Heritage, a brief history of the Vulcan Site, produced by Ruston Diesels Limited, (Newton Le Willows, 1978)
The Vulcan Locomotive Works, 1830-1930, (Loco. Pub., Co., London, 1930)
Warren, J.G.H.,
   A Century of Locomotive Building by Robert Stephenson & Co., 1823-1923, (Reid & Co., 1923)
Webb, B.,
   The British Internal-Combustion Locomotive, 1894-1940, (David & Charles, Newton Abbot, 1973)
Webster, N.W.,
   Joseph Locke, Railway Revolutionary, (Allen & Unwin, London, 1970)
Westcott, G.F.,
   The British Railway Locomotive, A Brief Pictorial History of the First Fifty Years of the British Steam Railway Locomotive, 1803-1853, (H.M.S.O., London, 1958)
Whitehead, R.A.,
   Garretts of Leiston, (Percival Marshall, London, 1964)
   Garrett 200, a Bicentenary History of Garretts of Leiston, 1778-1978, (Transport Bookman Publications, 1978)
Whitehouse, P.B.,
   Narrow Gauge Album, (Ian Allan, London, 1957)
Wiener, L.,
   Articulated Locomotives, (Constable, London, 1930)
Wilson, R.B.,
   Sir Daniel Gooch, Memoirs & Diary, (David & Charles, Newton Abbot, 1972)
Winton, J.G.,
   Modern Steam Practice and Engineering, (Blackie, London, 1885)

Index

U

V

W

Y

Z

ADDENDUM AND ERRATUM

The Author and Publishers would like to take this opportunity to correct some errors which appeared in the original edition, and, where appropriate to add to the information then published.

Note; The figures for Tractive Effort are quoted at 85% Boiler Pressure unless stated otherwise.

---

7   Lft., l. 5 up, Kreishauptmann.

9   Caption, "Flora" was built by Sharp Brothers in 1849 for the Manchester, Sheffield & Lincolnshire Railway and worked on the Manchester South Junction & Altrincham line.

11 Lft., l. 24, and Rt. l. 1, Sheffield, Ashton-under-Lyne & Manchester Railway not Manchester Sheffield.

19 Lft., l. 32, 1831.

22 Rt., l. 4, industry

25 Lft., l. 12, in 1945.

30 Lft., l. 22, Oppeln

38 Lft., No 7, Peto

60 Rt., l. 6, 6166

61 Caption, [Right] The first of 35 'W' class 2-6-0 tender engines for the South Australian Railway 3 ft. 6 in. gauge [3591 of 1887].

65 Rt., l. 5 up, between

76 Caption, Mersey Railway... to force water into the boiler.

86 Lft., l. 3, Stirling

87 Lft., l. 12, The 2-8-0 type for New South Wales eventually totalled 151 built by Beyer, Peacock up to 1911.

98 Lft., bottom, Manchester, Bury, Rochdale steam tram now being restored... Most of this seems to have been scrapped!

106 Caption, [Below] View of the yard around 1900...

116 Lft., l. 31, Cambrian Railways

118 Rt., l. 13, Havana.

123 Rt., l. 11, horn-blocks

124 Lft., l. 11 up, South

129 Caption, [Below] [0200] delivered to the Central Argentine Railway.

130 Rt., bottom, Railway Operating Division

138 Lft., l. 30, movement, es-

154 Rt. in Table, l. 5, 22 ft. 0 in.

157 Lft., l. 11, East

158 Lft., l. 2, built

161 Lft., l. 28, Whitelegg was Locomotive, Carriage, Wagon & Marine Superintendent of the London, Tilbury & Southend Railway.

162 Lft., l. 10 up, house

167 Caption, [Above] 02160

168 Caption, [Below] 2nd. photo, 2-8-2 supplied to Central Argentine Railway

170 Top caption, Oroya

175 Lft., l. 31, all right

178 Lft., l. 3, most powerful loco for metre gauge, There was an Argentine State Rly. 2-10-2 slightly more powerful.

179 Lft. l. 9, Colombia
179 Golwe caption, The "Golwe" locomotive built by Haine-St.-Pierre in 1927 for the Ivory Coast Railway.

179 Rt. l. 14 up, 02437 not 111

180 Top caption, 02437

ADDENDUM AND ERRATUM

continued

---

195 Lft., l. 8, two types

196 Caption, [Above] Boilers for the Buenos Ayres & Pacific Railway tender locomotives [1518] leaving Gorton in 1929.

197 Caption, [Above] The Cordoba Central Railway.

200 Top caption, [Above] The oil-fired... any main line standard gauge railway in the Galera tunnel at 15,643 ft....

201 Lft., l. 3, three (not two)
   Lft., l. 6, through the Galera tunnel at

205 Lft., l. 14, Garratts.

213 Top caption, 1186

220 Bottom Caption, where

223 Lft., l. 7/6 up, powerful passenger locomotives

227 Bottom caption, Bengal Assam Railway (not K. & U.R.)

237 Caption, [Below] Nanyuki

243 Top caption, 11115 (not 51)

247 Rt., l. 10, "1.E."

249 Lft., l. 8 f. Order 1425 for Belfast & County Down Rly. was delivered in 1945 and not 1951.

249 Caption top right, built in 1945

250 Top caption, Silverton Tramway
   Lft., l. 7, Silverton Tramway

251 Caption, [Foot] Oroya

263 Lft., Table, l. 8, 1954 R Stephenson

275 Rt., l. 5, Taylor Proprietary (not & Co.)

276 Rt., l. 31, cash

286 Further locomotives based on this design were Order 170 in 1857 for G. Thomson and for the Swedish Government Railways Order 2034 in 1867 and in 1876 Orders 3216 and 3456.

289 Rt., l. 10 up, Euskalduna

290 Rt. l. 16, 142 tons

296 Lft., l. 17, The late Mrs. Mumford...
   Rt., l. 33, Dow... Great Central

297 Lft., l. 12, Locomotive Engineers..., delete [and move to left.
   Lft., l. 14, Locomotive Manufacturers... move to left.
   Lft., l. 17 up, (Privately

INDEX